COPYRIGHT

DISCLAIMER

TRADEMARK

LEED® is a registered trademark of the U.S. Green Building Council, Inc.

LEED Reference Guide for Green Neighborhood Development

Based on the rating system created in collaboration with the Congress for the New Urbanism and the Natural Resources Defense Council.

2009 Edition

ISBN 978-1-932444-30-8

TABLE OF CONTENTS

Green Infrastructure and Buildings (GIB) — 293

Innovation and Design Process (IDP) — 451

Regional Priority Credit (RPC) — 459

Appendix. Diverse Uses — 461

Glossary — 463

PREFACE FROM USGBC

The built environment has a profound impact on our natural environment, economy, health, and productivity. Through its Leadership in Environmental and Energy Design (LEED®) certification programs, the U.S. Green Building Council (USGBC) is transforming the built environment. The green building movement offers an unprecedented opportunity to respond to the most important challenges of our time, including global climate change, dependence on unsustainable and expensive sources of energy, and threats to human health. The work of innovative building planning professionals is a fundamental driving force in the green development movement. Such leadership is a critical component to achieving USGBC's mission of a sustainable built environment for all within a generation.

USGBC MEMBERSHIP

USGBC's greatest strength is the diversity of our membership. USGBC is a balanced, consensus-based nonprofit with more than 20,000 member companies and organizations representing the entire building industry. Since its inception in 1993, USGBC has played a vital role in providing a leadership forum and a unique, integrating force for the building industry. USGBC's programs have three distinguishing characteristics:

Committee-based
The heart of this effective coalition is our committee structure, in which volunteer members design strategies that are implemented by staff and expert consultants. Our committees provide a forum for members to resolve differences, build alliances, and forge cooperative solutions for influencing change in all sectors of the building industry.

Member-driven
Membership is open and balanced and provides a comprehensive platform for carrying out important programs and activities. We target the issues identified by our members as the highest priority. We conduct an annual review that allows us to set policy, revise strategies, and devise work plans based on members' needs.

Consensus-focused
We work together to promote green buildings and neighborhoods, and in doing so, we help foster greater economic vitality and environmental health at lower costs. We work to bridge ideological gaps between industry segments and develop balanced policies that benefit the entire industry.

PARTNERSHIP

The Congress for the New Urbanism and the Natural Resources Defense Council collaborated with the U.S. Green Building Council in creating the LEED for Neighborhood Development Rating System. USGBC's consensus-focused approach to rating system development was furthered by these organizations' expertise in New Urbanism and smart growth strategies.

Contact the U.S. Green Building Council:
2101 L Street, NW
Suite 500
Washington, DC 20037
(800) 795-1747 Office
(202) 828-5110 Fax
www.usgbc.org

ACKNOWLEDGMENTS

The LEED 2009 for Neighborhood Development Rating System has been made possible only through the efforts of many dedicated volunteers, staff members from USGBC and the two partner organizations, consultants, and others in the USGBC community. The rating system development work was managed and implemented by USGBC staff and the LEED for Neighborhood Development Core Committee and included review and input by many Technical Advisory Group (TAG) members with oversight by the LEED Steering Committee. We extend our deepest gratitude to all of our LEED committee members who participated in the development of this rating system, and especially the LEED for Neighborhood Development Core Committee, for their tireless volunteer efforts and support of USGBC's mission:

LEED Steering Committee

Scot Horst, Former Chair	U.S. Green Building Council
Joel Ann Todd, Vice-Chair	Joel Ann Todd
Neal Billetdeaux	JJR
Bryna Dunn	Moseley Architects
Stu Carron	JohnsonDiversey, Inc.
Holley Henderson	H2 Ecodesign, LLC
Greg Kats	Good Energies
Malcolm Lewis	CTG Energetics, Inc.
Christine Magar	Greenform
Muscoe Martin	M2 Architecture
Jessica Millman	Agora DC
Sara O'Mara	Choate Construction Company
Kristin Shewfelt	Architectural Energy Corporation
Lynn Simon	Simon and Associates, Inc.
Bob Thompson	U.S. Environmental Protection Agency, Indoor Environments Management Branch
Mark Webster	Simpson Gumpertz & Heger

Energy and Atmosphere TAG

Marcus Sheffer, Chair	Energy Opportunities/7Group
Chris Schaffner	The Green Engineer, LLP
John Adams	U.S. General Services Administration
Lane Burt	Natural Resources Defense Council
Allan Daly	Taylor Engineering
Charles Dorgan	University of Wisconsin–Madison
Jay Enck	Commissioning & Green Building Solutions
Ellen Franconi	Architectural Energy Corporation
Scott Frank	Jaros Baum & Bolles
Nathan Gauthier	Harvard Office for Sustainability
Gail Hampsmire	CTG Energetics, Inc.

John Hogan	City of Seattle
Bion Howard	Building Environmental Science and Technology
Rusty Hodapp	Dallas/Fort Worth Airport Board
Greg Kats	Good Energies
Dan Katzenberger	Engineering, Energy, and the Environment
Richard Lord	Carrier Corporation
Bob Maddox	Sterling Planet
Brenda Morawa	BVM Engineering, Inc.
Erik Ring	LPA, Inc.
Michael Rosenberg	U.S. Department of Energy, Pacific Northwest National Laboratory
Greg San Martin	PG&E
Gordon Shymko	G.F. Shymko & Associates
Mick Schwedler	The Trane Company
Jorge Torres Coto	mbo, Inc.
Tate Walker	Energy Center of Wisconsin
Michael Zimmer	Thompson Hine LLP

Location and Planning TAG

Ted Bardacke, Chair	Global Green USA
Justin Horner, Vice-Chair	Natural Resources Defense Council
Laurence (LJ) Aurbach	Office of Laurence Aurbach
Uwe Brandes	Urban Land Institute
Fred Dock	City of Pasadena
Bruce Donnelly	Auricity
Reid Ewing	University of Utah
Lois Fisher	Fisher Town Design, Inc.
Tim Frank	Sierra Club
Norman Garrick	University of Connecticut
Ron Kilcoyne	Greater Bridgeport Transit
Dana Little	Treasure Coast Regional Planning Council
Steve Mouzon	New Urban Guild
Lucy Rowland	Athens-Clarke Co. Planning Commission
Harrison Rue	ICF International
Tony Sease	Civitech, Inc
Laurie Volk	Zimmerman/Volk Associates

Materials and Resources TAG

Steven Baer, Chair	Five Winds International
Lee Gros, Vice-Chair	Lee Gros Architect and Artisan, Inc.
Paul Bertram	Kingspan
Paul Bierman-Lytle	Renomics Corporation
Steve Brauneis	Rocky Mountain Institute
Amy Costello	Armstrong World Industries
Chris Dixon	NBBJ
Ann Edminster	Design AVEnues
Chris Geiger	San Francisco Department of the Environment
Avi Golen	Construction Waste Management
Brad Guy	Building Materials Reuse Association
Rick Levin	Kahler Slater, Inc.
Nadav Malin	BuildingGreen, LLC

Nancy Malone — Siegel & Strain Architects
Joep Meijer — The Right Environment Ltd. Co.
Kriten Ritchie — Gensler
Raymond Smith — U.S. Environmental Protection Agency
Wayne Trusty — Athena Sustainable Materials Institute
Denise Van Valkenburg — MASCO Retail Cabinet Group
Mark Webster — Simpson Gumpertz & Heger
Gabe Wing — Herman Miller, Inc

Sustainable Sites TAG

Steven Benz, Chair — Sasaki Associates
Alfred Vick, Vice-Chair — University of Georgia
Michele Adams — Meliora Environmental Design
Neal Billetdeaux — JJR
Gina Bocra — Burt Hill
Mark Brumbaugh — Brumbaugh & Associates
Joby Carlson — Global Institute of Sustainability, Arizona State University
Jenny Carney — YRG Sustainability
Laura Case — BMV-Engineering, Inc.
Stewart Comstock — Maryland Department of the Environment
Stephen Cook — Brickman
Bryna Dunn — Moseley Architects
Jay Enck — Commissioning & Green Building Solutions
Ron Hand — E/FECT. Sustainable Design Solutions
Richard Heinisch — Acuity Lighting Group
Heather Holdridge — Lake Flato Architects
Jason King — Greenworks, PC
Michael Lane — Lighting Design Lab
Marita Roos — HNTB Corporation
Katrina Rosa — Eco>Logic Studio
Zolna Russell — Hord Coplan Macht, Inc.
Kyle Thomas — Natural Systems Engineering

Water Efficiency TAG

Neal Billetdeaux, Chair — JJR
John Koeller, Vice-Chair — Koeller and Company
Damann Anderson — Hazen & Sawyer, P.C.
Gunnar Baldwin — TOTO USA, INC
Robert Benazzi — Jaros Baum & Bolles
Doug Bennett — Southern Nevada Water Authority
David Bracciano — Tampa Bay Water
David Carlson — Columbia University
Ron Hand — E/FECT. Sustainable Design Solutions
Bill Hoffman — H.W. Hoffman and Associates
Winston Huff — SSR Engineers
Joanna Kind — Eastern Research Group, inc.
Heather Kinkade — ARCADIS
Don Mills — Clivus Multrum, Inc.
Geoff Nara — Civil & Environmental Consultants, Inc
Karen Poff — Austin Energy
Shabbir Rawalpindiwala — Kohler Co.

Neil Rosen	North Shore LIJ Health System
Robert Rubin	McKim and Creed
Stephanie Tanner	U.S. Environmental Protection Agency
Bill Wall	Clivus New England, Inc.
Daniel Yeh	University of South Florida

LEED for Neighborhood Development Core Committee

The LEED 2009 for Neighborhood Development Rating System is the work of members of the LEED for Neighborhood Development Core Committee, both those who have worked on this version and those who helped create previous versions.

Current Members

Jessica Millman, Chair	Agora DC
Bert Gregory, Vice-Chair	Mithun
Susan Mudd, Vice-Chair	The Congress for the New Urbanism
Ted Bardacke	Global Green USA
Constance Beaumont	Oregon Department of Land Conservation and Development
Kaid Benfield	Natural Resources Defense Council
John Dalzell	Boston Redevelopment Authority
Victor Dover	Dover, Kohl & Partners
Lee Epstein	Chesapeake Bay Foundation
Doug Farr	Farr Associates
Tim Frank	Sierra Club
Daniel Hernandez	Jonathan Rose Companies
Bruce Knight	City of Champaign, IL
John Norquist	The Congress for the New Urbanism
Ken Potts	McGough Companies

Former Members

Eliot Allen	Criterion Planners
Dana Beach	Coastal Conservation League
Bill Browning	Terrapin Bright Green
Sharon Feigon	I-Go Car Sharing
Rebecca Flora	U.S. Green Building Council
Justin Horner	Natural Resources Defense Council
Melissa Knott	Forest City Enterprises
Megan Lewis	JF New
Michael Pawlukiewicz	Urban Land Institute
Shelley Poticha	U.S. Department of Housing and Urban Development
Tom Richman	Office of Tom Richman
Elizabeth Schilling	Smart Growth Leadership Institute
Laura Watchman	Watchman Consulting
Sandy Wiggins	Conscilience, LLC

A special thanks to USGBC staff for their invaluable efforts in developing this LEED Reference Guide, especially Dara Zycherman for her extraordinary commitment, management, and attention to detail, Meghan Bogaerts for her hard work and eye for consistency, and Sophie Lambert for technical expertise and guidance. In addition, staff acknowledges Criterion Planners and its team of Raimi & Associates and Watchman Consulting for technical assistance in preparing the reference guide and the graphic contributors Criterion Planners, AECOM, Dover, Kohl & Partners, Mithun, and Urban Advantage.

INTRODUCTION

I. THE CASE FOR GREEN NEIGHBORHOOD DEVELOPMENTS

As the U.S. population continues to expand rapidly, consumption of land grows exponentially—currently, at three times the rate of population growth. At this breathtaking pace, two-thirds of the development on the ground in 2050 will be built between now and then.[1] The way we grow—especially how and where we grow—will have a profound effect on our planet and on us.

Land use and neighborhood design patterns create a particular physical reality and compel behaviors that have a significant effect on the environmental performance of a given place. Segregated land uses accessed by high-speed roadways that necessitate the use of cars have been the predominant development pattern over the past 50 years. In the United States, transportation accounts for roughly one-third of greenhouse gas emissions, a large portion of which can be attributed to personal automobile use.[2] Burning fossil fuels for transportation increases air pollution and related respiratory diseases. Automobile-oriented neighborhoods tend to be hostile to pedestrians and unsupportive of traditional mixed-use neighborhood centers. Sprawling development patterns fragment habitat, endanger sensitive land and water bodies, destroy precious farmland, and increase the burden on municipal infrastructure.

In contrast, by placing residences and jobs proximate to each other, thoughtful neighborhood planning and development can limit automobile trips and the associated greenhouse gas emissions. Mixed-use development and walkable streets encourage walking, bicycling, and public transportation for daily errands and commuting. Environmentally responsible buildings and infrastructure are an important component of any green neighborhood, further reducing greenhouse gas emissions by decreasing energy consumption. Green buildings and infrastructure also lessen negative consequences for water resources, air quality, and natural resource consumption.

Green neighborhood developments are beneficial to the community and the individual as well as the environment. The character of a neighborhood, including its streets, homes, workplaces, shops, and public spaces, significantly affects the quality of life. Green neighborhood developments enable a wide variety of residents to be part of the community by including housing of varying types and price ranges. Green developments respect historical resources and the existing community fabric; they preserve open space and encourage access to parks. Green buildings, community gardens, and streets and public spaces that encourage physical activity are beneficial for public health. Combine the substantial environmental and social benefits and the case for green neighborhoods makes itself.

II. LEED® RATING SYSTEMS

Background on LEED®

Following the formation of the U.S. Green Building Council (USGBC) in 1993, the organization's members quickly realized that the sustainable building industry needed a system to define and measure "green buildings." USGBC began to research existing green building metrics and rating systems. Less than a year after formation, the members acted on the initial findings by establishing a committee to focus solely on this topic. The composition of the committee was diverse; it

---

1 Reid Ewing, Keith Bartholomew, Steve Winkelman, Jerry Walters, and Don Chen, Growing Cooler: *The Evidence on Urban Development and Climate Change* (Washington, D.C.: Urban Land Institute, 2008).
2 "Greenhouse Gases, Climate Change, and Energy" (Energy Information Administration, May 2008).

included architects, real estate agents, a building owner, a lawyer, an environmentalist, and industry representatives. This cross section of people and professions added a richness and depth both to the process and to the ultimate product, the Leadership in Energy and Environmental Design (LEED) certification system.

The first LEED Pilot Project Program, also referred to as LEED Version 1.0, was launched at the USGBC Membership Summit in August 1998. After extensive modifications, LEED Green Building Rating System Version 2.0 was released in March 2000, with LEED Version 2.1 following in 2002 and LEED Version 2.2 following in 2005.

As LEED has evolved and matured, the program has undertaken new initiatives. In addition to a rating system specifically devoted to building operational and maintenance issues (LEED for Existing Buildings: Operations & Maintenance), LEED addresses the different project development and delivery processes that exist in the U.S. building design and construction market, through rating systems for specific building typologies, sectors, and project scopes: LEED for Core & Shell, LEED for New Construction, LEED for Schools, LEED for Retail, LEED for Healthcare, LEED for Homes, and LEED for Commercial Interiors. LEED for Neighborhood Development is the latest LEED certification system to be released.

Project teams interact with the Green Building Certification Institute (GBCI) for project registration and certification. GBCI was established in 2008 as a separately incorporated entity with the support of the U.S. Green Building Council. GBCI administers credentialing and certification programs related to green building practice. These programs support the application of proven strategies for increasing and measuring the performance of buildings and communities as defined by industry systems such as LEED.

The green building and neighborhood development field is growing and changing daily. New technologies and products are being introduced into the marketplace, and innovative designs and practices are proving their effectiveness. The LEED rating systems and reference guides will evolve as well. Project teams must comply with the version of the rating system that is current at the time of their registration. USGBC will highlight new developments on its website on a continual basis, at www.usgbc.org.

Background on LEED for Neighborhood Development

The U.S. Green Building Council (USGBC), the Congress for the New Urbanism (CNU), and the Natural Resources Defense Council (NRDC)—organizations that represent leading design professionals, progressive builders and developers, and the environmental community—have come together to develop a rating system for neighborhood planning and development based on the combined principles of smart growth, New Urbanism, and green infrastructure and building. The goal of this partnership is to establish a national leadership standard for assessing and rewarding environmentally superior green neighborhood development practices within the framework of the LEED® Green Building Rating System™.

Unlike other LEED rating systems, which focus primarily on green building practices and offer only a few credits for site selection and design, LEED for Neighborhood Development places emphasis on the site selection, design, and construction elements that bring buildings and infrastructure together into a neighborhood and relate the neighborhood to its landscape as well as its local and regional context. The work of the LEED-ND core committee, made up of representatives from all three partner organizations, has been guided by sources such as the Smart Growth Network's ten principles of smart growth, the charter of the Congress for the New Urbanism, and other LEED rating systems. LEED for Neighborhood Development creates a label, as well as guidelines for both decision making and development, to provide an incentive for better location, design, and construction of new residential, commercial, and mixed-use developments.

Whereas the other LEED rating systems have five environmental categories, LEED for Neighborhood Development has three: Smart Location and Linkage, Neighborhood Pattern and Design, and Green Infrastructure and Buildings. An additional category, Innovation and Design Process, addresses sustainable design and construction issues and measures not covered under the three categories. Regional bonus credits are another feature of LEED-ND. These credits acknowledge the importance of local conditions in determining best environmental design and construction practices as well as social and health practices.

The LEED 2009 minimum program requirements define the minimum characteristics that a project must possess to be eligible for certification under LEED 2009. *These requirements do not apply to LEED for Neighborhood Development projects.*

LEED Credit Weightings

In LEED 2009, the allocation of points among credits is based on the potential environmental impacts and human benefits of each credit with respect to a set of impact categories. The impacts are defined as the environmental or human effect of the design, construction, operation, and maintenance of the building, such as greenhouse gas emissions, fossil fuel use, toxins and carcinogens, air and water pollutants, and indoor environmental conditions. In the LEED for Neighborhood Development Rating System, social and public health benefits were added to the impact categories, and the impact categories were then applied at the neighborhood scale. A combination of approaches, including energy modeling, life-cycle assessment, and transportation analysis, is used to quantify each type of impact. The resulting allocation of points among credits is called credit weighting.

LEED 2009 uses the U.S. Environmental Protection Agency's TRACI[3] environmental impact categories as the basis for weighting each credit. TRACI was developed to assist with impact evaluation for life-cycle assessment, industrial ecology, process design, and pollution prevention. LEED 2009 also takes into consideration the weightings developed by the National Institute of Standards and Technology (NIST); these compare impact categories with one another and assign a relative weight to each. Together, the two approaches provide a solid foundation for determining the point value of each credit in LEED 2009.

The LEED 2009 credit weightings process is based on the following parameters, which maintain consistency and usability across rating systems:

- All LEED credits are worth a minimum of 1 point.

- All LEED credits are positive, whole numbers; there are no fractions or negative values.

- All LEED credits receive a single, static weight in each rating system; there are no individualized scorecards based on project location.

- All LEED rating systems have 100 base points; Innovation and Design Process and Regional Priority credits provide opportunities for up to 10 bonus points.

Given the above criteria, the LEED 2009 credit weightings process involves three steps for LEED for Neighborhood Development:

1. A reference neighborhood is used to estimate the environmental impacts in 15 categories associated with a typical neighborhood development pursuing LEED certification.

---

3 Tools for the Reduction and Assessment of Chemical and Other Environmental Impacts (TRACI) (U.S. Environmental Protection Agency, Office of Research and Development, www.epa.gov/nrmrl/std/sab/traci/).

2. The relative importance of neighborhood impacts in each category is set to reflect values based on the NIST weightings.[4]

3. Data that quantify neighborhood impacts on environmental and human health are used to assign points to individual credits.

Each credit is allocated points based on the relative importance of the neighborhood-related impacts that it addresses. The result is a weighted average that combines neighborhood impacts and the relative value of the impact categories. Credits that most directly address the most important impacts are given the greatest weight, subject to the system design parameters described above. Credit weights also reflect a decision by LEED to recognize the market implications of point allocation.

The details of the weightings process vary slightly among individual rating systems. For example, LEED for Neighborhood Development includes credits related to infill development but LEED for New Construction does not. This results in a difference in the portion of the environmental footprint addressed by each rating system and the relative allocation of points.

The weightings process for each rating system is fully documented in a weightings workbook. The credit weightings process will be reevaluated over time to incorporate changes in values ascribed to different neighborhood impacts and neighborhood types, based on both market reality and evolving knowledge related to buildings and neighborhood design. A complete explanation of the LEED credit weightings system is available on the USGBC website, at www.usgbc.org.

III. OVERVIEW AND PROCESS

When to Use LEED for Neighborhood Development

The LEED for Neighborhood Development Rating System responds to land use and environmental considerations in the United States. It is designed to certify exemplary development projects that perform well in terms of smart growth, urbanism, and green building. Projects may constitute whole neighborhoods, portions of neighborhoods, or multiple neighborhoods. There is no minimum or maximum size for a LEED-ND project, but the core committee's research has determined that a reasonable minimum size is at least two habitable buildings and that the maximum area that can appropriately be considered a neighborhood is 320 acres, or half a square mile. A project larger than 320 acres is eligible but may find documenting certain credits difficult and may want to consider dividing the area into separate LEED-ND projects, each smaller than 320 acres. Although projects may contain only a single use, typically a mix of uses will provide the most amenities to residents and workers and enable people to drive less and safely walk or bicycle more. Small infill projects that are single use but complement existing neighboring uses, such as a new affordable-housing infill development in a neighborhood that is already well served by retail and commercial uses, are also good candidates for certification.

This rating system is designed primarily for the planning and development of new green neighborhoods, whether infill sites or new developments proximate to diverse uses or adjacent to connected and previously developed land. Many infill projects or projects near transit will be in urban areas, which helps direct growth into places with existing infrastructure and amenities. LEED-ND also promotes the redevelopment of aging brownfield sites into revitalized neighborhoods by rewarding connections beyond the site, walkable streets within the site, and the integration of any historic buildings and structures that will give the new neighborhood development a unique sense of place.

4   Relative impact category weights based on an exercise undertaken by NIST (National Institute of Standards and Technology) for the BEES program, www.bfrl.nist.gov/oae/software/bees/.

Existing neighborhoods can also use the rating system, and its application in this context could be especially beneficial in urban areas and historic districts. It is, however, important to point out that the owner or owners applying for certification should already own, have title to, or have significant control over a majority of the land within the project boundary and the plan for new construction or major renovation for the majority of the project's square footage. The new construction could take place on vacant land within the boundary, and the major renovations could involve existing buildings, recent or historic, within the project. In addition to guiding infill development opportunities, LEED-ND has additional relevance for existing neighborhoods, as a tool to set performance levels for a group of owners wanting to retrofit their homes, offices, or shops, and finally for shaping new green infrastructure, such as sidewalks, alleys, and public spaces. Many prerequisites or credits have a specific compliance path for existing buildings; this is highlighted in the rating system, and more detail is provided in the reference guide.

LEED-ND can also be used in suburban locations. There are tremendous opportunities to retrofit the suburbs, whether this involves reviving old shopping centers and their surrounding parking lots or adding new units and vibrant walkable town centers to existing subdivisions. Increasingly, many suburbs are well served by transit and thus should be considered good candidates for creating mixed-use, walkable developments with the potential to decrease residents' and workers' dependence on personal automobiles.

LEED for Neighborhood Development was not designed as a rating system for existing campuses, such as colleges, universities, and military bases. Many campuses have circulation patterns and building forms and placement that differ from the strategies outlined in LEED-ND. As a result, the rating system may not be appropriate for such facilities, but it could be applied in certain situations. For example, LEED-ND could be used for a civilian-style development on or adjacent to a military base, especially now that there is increased interest in developing mixed-use main streets as a focal point for new residential development in military bases. In addition, with many installations facing closure under the Base Realignment and Closure Act, LEED-ND could be used to guide the redevelopment of a base as it finds a new use. For colleges and universities, the program best lends itself to campuses that are expanding or undergoing major redevelopment. Increasingly, many universities are creating mixed-use development projects, often with local partners, to serve as catalytic projects in their communities, and LEED-ND could be a good framework and certification tool. Some universities are looking to their own campus lands for new development opportunities, particularly for housing that is affordable to faculty and staff but also walkable to campus and other amenities, and LEED-ND may be appropriate.

LEED for Neighborhood Development is not meant to be a national standard that replaces zoning codes or comprehensive plans, nor has it been designed to certify sector plans or other policy tools. Local development patterns and performance levels vary greatly across the country because land regulation is largely controlled by local governments. One city may be a leader in stormwater management, and another an innovator in traffic calming, but neither may be advanced in all areas covered by LEED-ND. The rating system should therefore not be considered a one-size-fits-all policy tool. Instead, LEED-ND is a voluntary leadership standard, and local governments should consider promoting its use by the development community or public-private partnerships. In addition, LEED-ND can be used to analyze whether existing development regulations, such as zoning codes, development standards, landscape requirements, building codes, or comprehensive plans, are "friendly" to sustainable developments. By comparing a locality's development practices with the rating system, public officials and the planning department can better identify code barriers that make it onerous, costly, or even impossible to undertake some aspects of sustainable development. Finally, public sector projects (e.g., those sponsored by housing authorities, redevelopment agencies, or specialized development authorities) are eligible to use the rating system. Please visit the LEED for Neighborhood Development web page at www.usgbc.org for LEED-ND policy guidance for state and local governments.

"Neighborhood Development," Defined

Based on research on the origins of neighborhood design and current best practices for locating and designing new development, the LEED for Neighborhood Development core committee has developed a rating system for smart, healthy, and green neighborhood development. Although LEED-ND does not strictly define what constitutes a neighborhood, the prerequisites and credits are written to encourage a type of development that recalls the siting and design of traditional neighborhoods and promotes best practices in new neighborhood development today.

Since ancient times, cities around the world have been spatially divided into districts or neighborhoods. Excavations of some of the earliest cities reveal evidence of social neighborhoods. Urban scholar Lewis Mumford noted that "neighborhoods, in some primitive, inchoate fashion exist wherever human beings congregate, in permanent family dwellings; and many of the functions of the city tend to be distributed naturally—that is, without any theoretical preoccupation or political direction—into neighborhoods."[5] In basic terms, a neighborhood is an area of dwellings, workplaces, shops, and civic places and their immediate environment that residents and/or employees identify with in terms of social and economic attitudes, lifestyles, and institutions.

Figure 1. Clarence Perry's Neighborhood Unit, 1929. Source: Regional Plan Association

Figure 2. A "sustainable" update of Perry's neighborhood unit. Source: Douglas Farr, *Sustainable Urbanism*

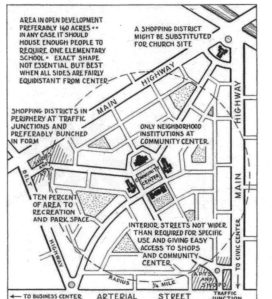

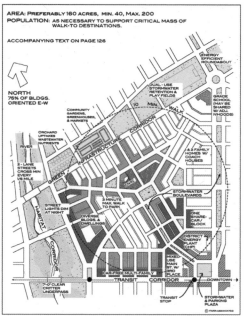

A neighborhood can be considered the planning unit of a town. The charter of the Congress for the New Urbanism characterizes this unit as "compact, pedestrian-friendly, and mixed-use."[6] By itself the neighborhood is a village, but combined with other neighborhoods it becomes a town or a city. Similarly, several neighborhoods with their centers at transit stops can constitute a transit corridor. The neighborhood, as laid out in LEED-ND, is in contrast to sprawl development patterns, which create podlike clusters that are disconnected from surrounding areas. Existing and

5   Lewis Mumford, "The Neighbourhood and the Neighbourhood Unit," Town Planning Review 24 (1954): 256-270, p. 258.
6   Charter of the Congress for the New Urbanism, www.cnu.org/charter, 1996.

new traditional neighborhoods provide an alternative to development patterns that characterize sprawl, such as the single-zoned, automobile-dominated land uses that have been predominant in suburban areas since the 1950s. Instead, traditional neighborhoods meet all those same needs—for housing, employment, shopping, civic functions, and more—but in formats that are compact, complete, and connected, and ultimately more sustainable and diverse.[7] The metrics of a neighborhood vary in density, population, mix of uses, and dwelling types and by regional customs, economies, climates, and site conditions. In general, they include size, identifiable centers and edges, connectedness with the surroundings, walkable streets, and sites for civic uses and social interaction.

Size is a defining feature of a neighborhood and is typically based on a comfortable distance for walking from the center of the neighborhood to its edge; that suggests an area of 40 to 160 acres. In the 1929 *Regional Plan of New York and Environs*, urban planner Clarence Perry outlined a neighborhood center surrounded by civic uses, parks, residential uses, a school, and retail at the edge, all within one-quarter mile—about a five-minute walk. This amounts to an area or pedestrian "shed" of 125 acres, or if the land area is a square, 160 acres. Although Perry's diagram does not address many of the sustainable features of LEED-ND, such as access to multimodal transportation options, location of infrastructure, and building form, it serves as a reference point for the mix of uses and walkable scale of neighborhood development encouraged in the rating system. Most people will walk approximately one-quarter mile (1,320 feet) to run daily errands; beyond that, many will take a bicycle or car. Additional research shows that people will walk as far as a half-mile (2,640 feet) to reach heavy rail transit systems or more specialized shops or civic uses.[8] Since half a square mile contains 320 acres, the core committee has decided that this size should serve as guidance for the upper limit of a LEED-ND project.

A neighborhood should have places where the public feels welcome and encouraged to congregate, recognizable as the heart of the community. A proper center has at least one outdoor public space for this purpose, designed with pedestrians in mind; this is the most well-defined outdoor "room" in the neighborhood. The best centers are within walking distance of the primarily residential areas, and typically some gradient in density is discernible from center to edge. The "center" need not be in the geographic center of the neighborhood; it can be along the edge, on an arterial or transit line. It is important for a neighborhood to have boundaries as well as a defined center, and this characteristic is often achieved through identifiable edges, either man-made or natural, such as adjacent farmland, parks, greenways, schools, major rights-of-way, or other uses.

When a neighborhood has a robust network of internal streets and good connections to surrounding communities, pedestrians, bicyclists, and drivers can move more efficiently and more safely. Multiple intersections and short blocks also give pedestrians a more interesting environment. The maximum average block perimeter to achieve an integrated network is 1,500 feet, with a maximum uninterrupted block face of ideally no more than 450 feet; intersecting streets are placed at intervals of 500 to 600 feet, and no greater than 800 feet apart along any single stretch.

The morphology of a sustainable neighborhood—the design of its blocks, streets, and buildings—can serve as the foundation of a walkable environment. Walkable streets have many features, and those elements deemed most important by the core committee are encouraged by the LEED-ND Rating System. These features, such as human-scaled buildings and street widths, wide sidewalks, buildings that are pulled up to the sidewalk to create a continuous street wall, retail storefronts and other uses, and interesting street furniture and trees, are meant to create a safe, inviting, and well-used public realm with visual interest. To keep loading docks, garage openings, and utilities away from sidewalks, neighborhoods with walkable streets often feature alleys.

7 Ibid.
8 H. Dittmar and G. Ohland, eds., The New Transit Town: Best Practices in Transit-Oriented Development (Washington, D.C.: Island Press, 2004), p. 120.

Figure 3. Examples of neighborhood morphology. Source: Douglas Farr, *Sustainable Urbanism*

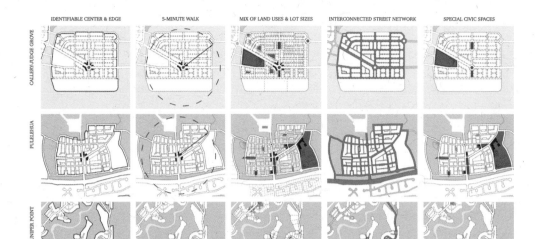

A mix of uses is often integral to the vitality of a neighborhood; the mix can include not only residential and commercial but also a variety of retail establishments, services, community facilities, and other kinds of "diverse uses," whether available within the neighborhood or adjacent. Urban theorist Ray Oldenburg would classify diverse uses as "Third Places"—small neighborhood grocers, coffee shops, pubs, or post offices that allow residents and workers to mingle and have social interactions. A mix of active and diverse retail uses on a walkable street can create a place that is alive day and night, and not closed down at 6 p.m.

Existing neighborhoods have the added benefit of historic buildings and events with cultural significance. Jane Jacobs argued that every neighborhood needed a mixture of newer and older buildings to allow for a variety of uses, income levels, and even ideas within the neighborhood.[9] New neighborhoods can introduce some of the architectural diversity found in existing neighborhoods by including a mix of uses and housing types, each of which might need a different building type and design, thus generating visual interest. Finally, placing important civic buildings, such as churches, libraries, schools, or local government buildings at the termination of a street can create civic pride and also an interesting vista for pedestrians. With a focus on civic buildings and gathering places and the pedestrian experience in general, it is no surprise that walkable neighborhoods are often defined by the social interaction among people living and working near one another.

In conclusion, LEED for Neighborhood Development emphasizes the creation of compact, walkable, vibrant, mixed-use neighborhoods with good connections to nearby communities. In addition to neighborhood morphology, pedestrian scale, and mix of uses, the rating system also emphasizes the location of the neighborhood and the performance of the infrastructure and buildings within it. The sustainable benefits of a neighborhood increase when it offers proximity to transit and when residents and workers can safely travel by foot or bicycle to jobs, amenities, and services. This can create a neighborhood with a high quality of life and healthy inhabitants. Likewise, green buildings can reduce energy and water use, and green infrastructure, such as

9   Jane Jacobs, *The Death and Life of Great American Cities* (New York: Random House, 1961), p. 187.

landscaping and best practices to reduce stormwater runoff, can protect natural resources. Together, well-located and well-designed green neighborhood developments will play an integral role in reducing greenhouse gas emissions and improving quality of life.

Registration

Project teams interested in earning LEED-ND certification must first register the project with the Green Building Certification Institute. Projects can be registered on the GBCI website, at www. gbci.org. Registration is an important step that establishes contact with GBCI and provides access to software tools, errata, critical communications, and other essential information. Projects must comply with the version of the rating system that is current at the time of project registration.

Documentation Process

The documentation process for LEED-ND will be outlined on GBCI's website. Resources will be available to help project teams manage project details, complete documentation requirements for LEED-ND prerequisites and credits, upload supporting files, submit applications for review, receive reviewer feedback, and ultimately earn LEED-ND certification. All project teams pursuing LEED-ND certification are required to use the submittal documentation paths as outlined on GBCI's website.

Credit Interpretation Requests and Rulings

In some cases, a LEED project team may encounter challenges when interpreting the requirements of a prerequisite or credit for the project, perhaps because the reference guide does not sufficiently address a specific issue or a conflict requires resolution. To address such issues, a credit interpretation ruling process has been established for each LEED rating system. See the GBCI website for more information, at www.gbci.org.

When submitting a credit interpretation request, provide a brief but clear description of the challenge encountered, refer to the prerequisite or credit information found in the rating system and reference guide, and emphasize the intent of the prerequisite or credit. If possible, the project team should offer potential solutions to the problem or a proposed interpretation.

Communications related to credit interpretation requests will be in electronic format.

Fees

Information on certification fees can be found on the GBCI website. GBCI will acknowledge receipt of the application and proceed with application review when all project documentation and payments have been received and processed. Registration fees, appeal review fees, and any additional fees required to expedite LEED certification are not refundable.

Updates and Addenda

This is the first edition of the LEED Reference Guide for Green Neighborhood Development, 2009. As materials and technology continue to improve and evolve, updates and addenda will be made available. USGBC cannot be held liable for any criteria set forth herein that may not be applicable to later versions of LEED rating systems, and GBCI reserves the right to modify its policies from time to time. Updates and addenda will be accumulated between revisions and will be formally incorporated in major revisions. In the interim, between major revisions, USGBC may issue updates or addenda to clarify criteria. The prerequisites, credits, amendments, and addenda current at the time of project registration will continue to guide the project throughout its certification process.

Information Privacy and Policy Guidelines

For more information on the privacy policy of the U.S. Green Building Council, refer to the Policies and Guidelines section of the USGBC website, at www.usgbc.org. With the support of its members, volunteers, and other stakeholders, USGBC is the developer of the LEED rating systems.

The Green Building Certification Institute implements the LEED rating systems and carries out credentialing programs relating to LEED. For more information on the privacy policy of GBCI, including the privacy policy on documentation submitted for LEED-ND projects, refer to the Policies and Guidelines section of the GBCI website, at www.gbci.org. Projects whose information should be treated as confidential may select this option during registration; project confidentiality status may be changed at any time. Please review the GBCI privacy policy for further details.

IV. DOCUMENTATION REQUIREMENTS

Certification applications must include general documentation and documentation for all prerequisites and for all pursued credits. General documentation consists of the basic details pertaining to project site conditions, construction scope and timeline, occupant and usage data, and project team identification. Project teams must address all the elements in the general documentation requirements, providing details and clarifications where appropriate, and they may include any optional elements that are helpful in describing the project. Documentation for prerequisites and credits is detailed on GBCI's website.

V. CERTIFICATION APPLICATION

Stages of Certification

LEED for Neighborhood Development involves projects that may have significantly longer construction periods than single buildings, and as a result the standard LEED certification process has been modified. To provide developers of certifiable projects with conditional approval at an early stage, LEED 2009 for Neighborhood Development certification is divided into a three-stage process. A land-use entitlement, referred to below, is the existing or granted right to use property for specific types and quantities of residential and nonresidential land uses.

Stage 1. Conditional Approval of a LEED-ND Plan. This stage is optional for projects at any point before the entitlement process begins, or when no more than 50% of a project's total new and/or renovated building square footage has land-use entitlements to use property for the specific types and quantities of residential and nonresidential land uses proposed, either by right or through a local government regulatory change process. Projects with more than 50% of new and/or renovated square footage already entitled must complete the local entitlement process for 100% of new and/or renovated square footage and apply under Stage 2. If conditional approval of the plan is achieved, a letter will be issued stating that if the project is built as proposed, it will be eligible to achieve LEED for Neighborhood Development certification. The purpose of this letter is to help the developer build a case for entitlement among land-use planning authorities, as well as attract financing and occupant commitments.

Stage 2. Pre-Certified LEED-ND Plan. This stage is available after 100% of the project's total new and/or renovated building square footage has been fully entitled by public authorities with jurisdiction over the project. The project can also be under construction or partially completed, but no more than 75% of the total square footage can be constructed; projects that are more than 75% constructed must finish and use Stage 3. Any changes to the conditionally approved plan that could affect prerequisite or credit achievement must be communicated as part of this submission. If precertification of the plan is achieved, a certificate will be issued stating that the plan is a Pre-

Certified LEED for Neighborhood Development Plan and it will be listed as such on the USGBC website.

Stage 3. LEED-ND Certified Neighborhood Development. This final step takes place when the project can submit documentation for all prerequisites and attempted credits, and when certificates of occupancy for buildings and acceptance of infrastructure have been issued by public authorities with jurisdiction over the project. Any changes to the Pre-Certified LEED-ND Plan that could affect prerequisite or credit achievement must be communicated as part of this submission. If certification of the completed neighborhood development is achieved, a plaque or similar award for public display at the project site will be isssued and it will be listed as certified on the USGBC website.

Preliminary and Final Reviews

For each of the three stages, a project submits all required documentation for all prerequisites and attempted credits. GBCI conducts a preliminary review and marks the prerequisites and credits "anticipated," "pending," or "denied." After the project resubmits its application, with any additional information that is requested, a final review is issued with prerequisites and credits marked "awarded" or "denied" and the final point tally indicating the certification level.

Smart Location and Linkage Prerequisite Review

Since the location of a project cannot be changed, whereas its design and technologies can, GBCI offers to review a project's compliance with the Smart Location and Linkage (SLL) prerequisites and inform the team whether the location qualifies. If it does, a project team can proceed; if it doesn't, the team can end its participation in the program before investing more time. This optional review of the SLL prerequisites is available to projects in advance of a Stage 1, Stage 2, or Stage 3 application. The advance review of SLL prerequisites is available to each project only one time, however. Once a project team has undergone an SLL prerequisite review, the submission for any subsequent stage must include all required documentation for all prerequisites and attempted credits.

The documentation requirements for the optional SLL prerequisite review are listed on GBCI's website. The process involves a preliminary and a final review. During the final review, GBCI formally rules on the SLL prerequisite review application by designating each prerequisite as either "anticipated" or "denied."

Participating in an SLL prerequisite review and receiving "anticipated" ratings does not guarantee award of any prerequisite and will not result in achievement of the attempted stage. SLL prerequisites that were designated as "anticipated" are awarded only during the full certification review, provided the circumstances have not changed since the prerequisite review.

If the project's compliance with the SLL prerequisites is anticipated, the project team prepares documentation for the remaining prerequisites and credits for the first stage it is eligible to submit. If any of the anticipated SLL prerequisites change, additional documentation must be submitted to substantiate continued compliance with the requirements.

LEED Ratings

The LEED-ND project must satisfy all the prerequisites and qualify for a minimum number of points to attain the desired project rating. Having satisfied the basic prerequisites of the program, applicant projects are then rated according to their degree of compliance within the rating system.

All stages are awarded according to the following scale:

Certified	40–49 points
Silver	50–59 points
Gold	60–79 points
Platinum	80 points and above

Appeals

Appeals may be filed after the SLL prerequisite review or the full application review. Please see the GBCI website for more information on appeals.

VI. CERTIFICATION STRATEGY

After registration, the project design team should begin to collect information and perform calculations to satisfy prerequisite and credit documentation requirements. Because a variety of maps will be required, it is helpful to designate a LEED team leader who will create a base map for others to use and be responsible for managing the entire submittal compilation.

Timeline and Project Design Phases

Project teams should study the goals and objectives of LEED for Neighborhood Development as early in the site selection and conceptual project planning process as possible. The process phases mentioned throughout this reference guide correspond to the planning and development steps commonly used in the land development industry:

1. **Site analysis and programming.** Property selection, stakeholder identification and outreach, information gathering, environmental review, conceptual planning, and development programming.

2. **Preliminary planning.** Initial planning of land uses, transportation networks, and major facilities; public outreach and refinement of plans.

3. **Final design.** Continued public outreach; preparation of final site plan, infrastructure design, and building designs; acquisition of construction permits.

4. **Construction.** Construction of infrastructure and buildings.

5. **Completion and occupancy.** Acceptance of infrastructure by local jurisdiction, and issuance of occupancy certificates by building department.

Figure 4. Integrating LEED-ND Into the Land Development Process

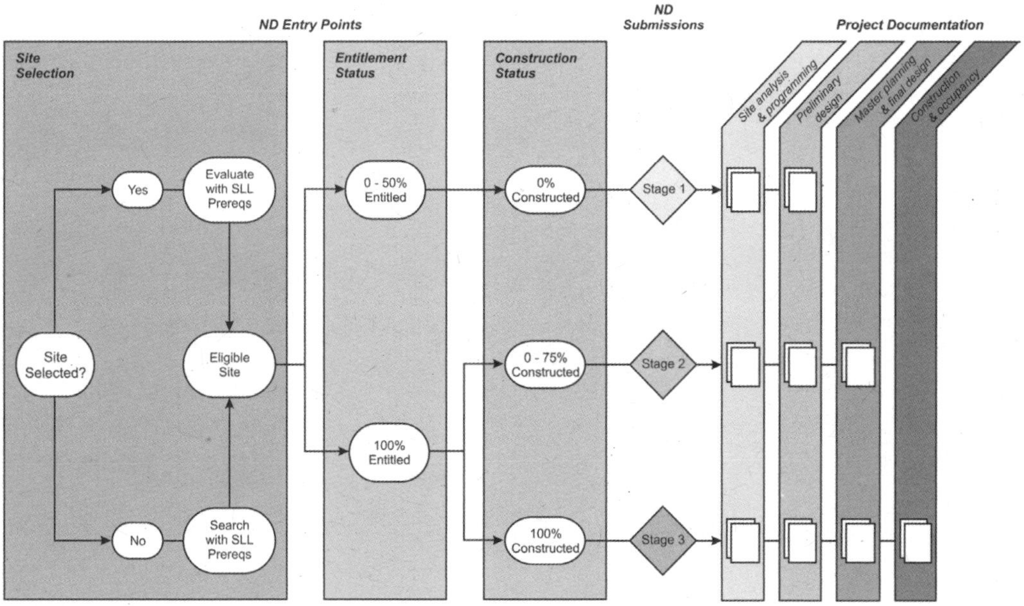

Related Credits

When pursuing LEED certification, it is important to consider how credits are interconnected and how their synergies and trade-offs will ultimately affect both the project and the other credits the team may consider pursuing. Consult the Related Credits section of each prerequisite and credit to help inform design and construction decisions leading to certification.

Consistent Documentation across Credits

Several kinds of project information are required for consistent LEED documentation across various credits. Pay special attention to overlapping project data; doing so will help the application and review process go smoothly.

VII. EXEMPLARY PERFORMANCE

Exemplary performance strategies result in performance that greatly exceeds the performance level or expands the scope required by an existing credit. The credits for which exemplary performance points are available through expanded performance are noted throughout this reference guide.

See the Innovation and Design Process chapter for further details.

The credits for which exemplary performance points are available through expanded performance are noted throughout this reference guide by the logo shown below.

The list for exemplary performance points available is as follows:

Smart Location and Linkage

SLL Credit 1	Preferred Locations
SLL Credit 3	Locations with Reduced Automobile Dependence
SLL Credit 8	Restoration of Habitat or Wetlands and Water Bodies

Neighborhood Pattern and Design

NPD Credit 1	Walkable Streets
NPD Credit 3	Mixed-Use Neighborhood Centers
NPD Credit 4	Mixed-Income Diverse Communities
NPD Credit 11	Visitability and Universal Design
NPD Credit 13	Local Food Production
NPD Credit 14	Tree-Lined and Shaded Streets

Green Infrastructure and Buildings

GIB Credit 1	Certified Green Buildings
GIB Credit 2	Building Energy Efficiency
GIB Credit 3	Building Water Efficiency
GIB Credit 4	Water-Efficient Landscaping
GIB Credit 5	Existing Building Reuse
GIB Credit 6	Historic Resource Preservation and Adaptive Use
GIB Credit 8	Stormwater Management
GIB Credit 9	Heat Island Reduction
GIB Credit 10	Solar Orientation
GIB Credit 11	On-Site Renewable Energy Sources
GIB Credit 12	District Heating and Cooling
GIB Credit 13	Infrastructure Energy Efficiency
GIB Credit 14	Wastewater Management
GIB Credit 15	Recycled Content in Infrastructure

VIII. REGIONAL PRIORITY

To provide incentive to address geographically specific environmental issues, USGBC regional councils and chapters, CNU chapters, and representatives of Smart Growth America's State and Local Caucus have identified six credits per rating system that are of particular importance to specific areas. Each Regional Priority credit is worth an additional 1 point, and a total of 4 additional points may be earned by achieving Regional Priority credits, with 1 point earned per credit. If the project achieves more than four Regional Priority credits, the team can choose the credits for which these points will apply. The USGBC website contains a searchable database of Regional Priority credits.

IX. TOOLS FOR REGISTERED PROJECTS

LEED offers additional resources for LEED project teams on the USGBC website, at www.usgbc.org/projecttools. The Registered Projects Tools website provides resources for starting the project and includes rating system errata, documentation requirements, and referenced industry standards.

X. HOW TO USE THIS REFERENCE GUIDE

The LEED Reference Guide for Green Neighborhood Development is a supporting document to the LEED 2009 for Neighborhood Development Rating System. The guide helps teams understand the criteria, the reasons behind them, strategies for implementation, and documentation requirements. It includes calculations, examples of their use, and additional resources. It does not provide an exhaustive list of strategies for meeting the criteria or all the information that a project team needs to determine the applicability of a credit to the project.

The rating system, published in its entirety on the USGBC website, is embedded in this reference guide. Each prerequisite and credit discussion begins with a gray page that repeats the rating system's intent and requirements.

Each prerequisite or credit is organized in a standardized format for simplicity and quick reference. The first section summarizes the main points regarding the green measure and includes the intent, requirements, and a summary of any referenced industry standards. Subsequent sections provide supporting information to help interpret the measure and offer links to resources and examples. The sections for each credit are described in the following paragraphs.

Intent identifies the main sustainability goal or benefit of the prerequisite or credit.

Requirements specifies the criteria that satisfy the prerequisite or credit and the number of points available. The prerequisites must be achieved; the credits are optional, but each contributes to the overall project score. Some credits have two or more paths with cumulative points. Other credits have several options from which the project team must choose.

Benefits and Issues to Consider addresses the environmental and social benefits of the activity encouraged by the prerequisite or credit and then summarizes economic considerations related to first costs, life-cycle costs, and estimated savings.

Related Credits acknowledges the trade-offs and synergies within the LEED rating system credit categories. Achieving a particular credit may make it worthwhile and comparatively easy to pursue related credits; the converse is also possible.

The **Summary of Referenced Standards**, where applicable, introduces the standards used to measure achievement of the credit intent. Teams are strongly encouraged to review the full standard and not rely on the summary.

Implementation discusses specific methods or assemblies that facilitate achievement of the requirements.

Timeline and Team guides the project team by identifying who should lead an effort and when the tasks should begin.

Calculations offers formulas and computations for determining achievement of a particular prerequisite or credit.

The **Documentation Guidance** section lists the first steps in preparing to complete the LEED-ND documentation requirements.

Examples illustrates strategies for credit achievement.

Exemplary Performance, if applicable, details the level of performance needed for the award of points in addition to those for credit achievement.

Regional Variations outlines concerns specific to the geographic location of the project.

Resources offers suggestions for further research, detailed technical information, and other relevant information. The resources include websites, on-line materials, and printed books and articles that can be obtained directly from organizations listed.

Definitions clarifies the meaning of certain terms used in the prerequisite or credit. These may be general terms or terms specific to LEED for Neighborhood Development. A complete glossary is found at the end of this reference guide. Projects teams should read all the definitions so that members fully understand the meaning of the prerequisites and credits.

GETTING STARTED

INTRODUCTION

To help the project team begin preparing a LEED for Neighborhood Development certification submittal, this chapter of the reference guide addresses the following elements, which are basic to the rating system and reappear frequently across prerequisites and credits. Becoming familiar with these at the outset will help teams assemble successful submissions more efficiently.

- **Project team.** In addition to developing the project, the project team documents and calculates a project's achievements and compliance with the rating system requirements; in some cases the team may call on the resources of local partners.

- **Related credits.** An important aspect of selecting credits for a project is their interconnection. Many credits are related to others, and earning one may help achieve several others.

- **Project site.** The location and characteristics of the project site are fundamental to a project's certification submittal because they determine eligibility for certain rating system provisions. Based on its boundary, a project may fall into one or more categories of site types, and its land most likely consists of buildable and nonbuildable portions.

- **Development program.** The amount and type of development are also fundamental to the submission. This is expressed by the number of buildings, whether planned or existing, and their square footage in residential and nonresidential categories. A project's transportation features, including walking, bicycling, and transit facilities, can play a major role, too.

- **Mapping.** Because of the neighborhood scale of LEED-ND projects, mapping is an important part of a submission, used to show relationships among buildings and between the project and its vicinity.

- **Base calculations.** Several calculations, such as land-use density and street connectivity, appear in multiple credits. These calculations must remain consistent throughout.

- **Definitions.** Several terms are commonly used throughout the rating system, and knowing their specific LEED meanings will help during submission preparation.

Each of those elements is discussed below and should be reviewed in concert with LEED-ND documentation requirements. Becoming familiar with them at the outset will help teams assemble successful submissions more efficiently.

PROJECT TEAM

For the purposes of LEED-ND, the project team has three major components: its leadership, a multidisciplinary group of professionals, and local supporting partners.

The applicant is often the person who makes the decision to certify a project under LEED-ND—an owner or developer or a partner working with a group of owners or developers. The owner or developer, whether an individual, a group of individuals, or a corporation or a partnership, should control a majority of the area within a project boundary, either through ownership and/or options to purchase. The owner or developer can join with any combination of the following as joint applicants: another landowner or developer, a building owner, a nonprofit developer or community development corporation, a homeowners' association, or a public or quasi-public agency, such as a housing authority, redevelopment authority, business improvement district, or main street program. LEED-ND is suitable as a certification tool for a municipal or neighborhood land-use plan only if the plan has an associated developer proposing to construct it.

Two LEED-ND definitions are relevant here:

applicant the entity that prepares the LEED-ND project submission and is responsible for project implementation. An applicant may be the developer or another cooperating entity.

developer a public and/or private entity that controls a majority of the project's buildable land and is committed to making a majority of the investments required for the project implementation described in the LEED-ND submission.

Because the rating system integrates smart growth, New Urbanism, and green building practices, a successful LEED for Neighborhood Development submission draws on the diverse skills of a comprehensive team of professionals. The rating system can require expertise in as many as seven professions, depending on project characteristics and credits attempted. Ensuring that a project team has appropriate technical skills is a crucial submission strategy. The owner or developer should consider which of the following kinds of professional expertise need to be represented on the project team:

- Urban planning.
- Architecture.
- Civil engineering.
- Transportation planning.
- Mechanical and electrical engineering.
- Landscape architecture.
- Biology and botany.

In addition to selecting a multidisciplinary project team, consider important local partners—the public agencies and utilities with controlling authority or services that affect certain credits—when starting a submission. The local partners that may be helpful are listed by credit in Table 1. Project teams should identify local partners during credit selection, make them aware of the project, and seek their assistance with planning and documentation where appropriate.

Table 1. Potential local partners for LEED-ND project teams, by credit

	City, county	– Planning, building	– Transportation	– Public works	– Parks	Transit agency	Wildlife, natural resources agency	Housing, community development	School district	Energy utilities	Historic preservation agency	Neighborhood association
Smart Location and Linkage												
Prerequisite 1, Smart Location		●	●	●		●						●
Prerequisite 2, Imperiled Species and Ecological Communities Conservation		●					●					●
Prerequisite 3, Wetland and Water Body Conservation		●					●					●
Prerequisite 4, Agricultural Land Conservation		●										●
Prerequisite 5, Floodplain Avoidance		●		●								●
Credit 1, Preferred Locations		●	●					●				●
Credit 2, Brownfields Redevelopment		●						●				●
Credit 3, Locations with Reduced Automobile Dependence		●	●			●						●
Credit 4, Bicycle Network and Storage		●	●									●
Credit 5, Housing and Jobs Proximity		●										●
Credit 6, Steep Slope Protection		●										●
Credit 7, Site Design for Habitat or Wetland and Water Body Conservation		●					●					●
Credit 8, Restoration of Habitat or Wetlands and Water Bodies		●					●					●
Credit 9, Long-Term Conservation Management of Habitat or Wetlands and Water Bodies		●					●					●
Neighborhood Pattern and Design												
Prerequisite 1, Walkable Streets		●	●								●	●
Prerequisite 2, Compact Development		●				●						●
Prerequisite 3, Connected and Open Community		●	●									●
Credit 1, Walkable Streets		●	●									●
Credit 2, Compact Development		●										●
Credit 3, Mixed-Use Neighborhood Centers		●										●
Credit 4, Mixed-Income Diverse Communities		●						●				●
Credit 5, Reduced Parking Footprint		●	●									●
Credit 6, Street Network		●	●									●
Credit 7, Transit Facilities		●	●			●						●
Credit 8, Transportation Demand Management		●	●			●						●
Credit 9, Access to Civic and Public Space		●			●							●
Credit 10, Access to Recreation Facilities		●			●				●			●

Table 1. Potential local partners for LEED-ND project teams, by credit (continued)

	City, county	– Planning, building	– Transportation	– Public works	– Parks	Transit agency	Wildlife, natural resources agency	Housing, community development	School district	Energy utilities	Historic preservation agency	Neighborhood association
Neighborhood Pattern and Design (continued)												
Credit 11, Visitability and Universal Design	●	●										●
Credit 12, Community Outreach and Involvement	●	●	●	●	●	●	●	●	●	●		●
Credit 13, Local Food Production	●											●
Credit 14, Tree-Lined and Shaded Streets	●											●
Credit 15, Neighborhood Schools	●								●			●
Green Infrastructure and Buildings												
Prerequisite 1, Certified Green Building	●									●		
Prerequisite 2, Minimum Building Energy Efficiency	●									●		
Prerequisite 3, Minimum Building Water Efficiency	●			●								
Prerequisite 4, Construction Activity Pollution Prevention	●											●
Credit 1, Certified Green Buildings	●									●		
Credit 2, Building Energy Efficiency	●									●		
Credit 3, Building Water Efficiency	●			●								
Credit 4, Water-Efficient Landscaping	●											
Credit 5, Existing Building Reuse	●							●			●	●
Credit 6, Historic Resource Preservation and Adaptive Use	●										●	●
Credit 7, Minimized Site Disturbance in Design and Construction	●			●								●
Credit 8, Stormwater Management	●			●								●
Credit 9, Heat Island Reduction	●									●		●
Credit 10, Solar Orientation	●									●		●
Credit 11, On-Site Renewable Energy Sources	●									●		●
Credit 12, District Heating and Cooling	●									●		●
Credit 13, Infrastructure Energy Efficiency										●		●
Credit 14, Wastewater Management				●								
Credit 15, Recycled Content in Infrastructure			●	●								
Credit 16, Solid Waste Management Infrastructure				●								
Credit 17, Light Pollution Reduction	●									●		●

RELATED CREDITS

The project team should begin by confirming the project's compliance with all prerequisites. When selecting credits to attempt, a project team should evaluate the interconnections between them, since earning certain credits may help earn others. To illustrate these relationships, Table 2 shows credits grouped according to shared focus on eight sustainability topics. These relationships are detailed further in Table 3, where each credit's achievement is itemized by the help it may provide toward earning or supporting other credits.

Table 2. Sustainability focus for LEED-ND prerequisites and credits

	Smart location	Sensitive lands protection	Site and transportation design	Public health	Social equity	Energy and climate protection	Water resource efficiency	Infrastructure efficiency
Smart Location and Linkage								
Prerequisite 1, Smart Location	●		●	●	●	●		●
Prerequisite 2, Imperiled Species and Ecological Communities Conservation		●						
Prerequisite 3, Wetland and Water Body Conservation		●					●	
Prerequisite 4, Agricultural Land Conservation		●						
Prerequisite 5, Floodplain Avoidance		●						
Credit 1, Preferred Locations	●			●	●	●		
Credit 2, Brownfields Redevelopment	●				●	●		
Credit 3, Locations With Reduced Automobile Dependence	●		●	●	●	●		
Credit 4, Bicycle Network and Storage	●		●	●	●	●		
Credit 5, Housing and Jobs Proximity	●				●	●		
Credit 6, Steep Slope Protection		●						
Credit 7, Site Design for Habitat or Wetland and Water Body Conservation		●	●				●	
Credit 8, Restoration of Habitat or Wetlands and Water Bodies		●					●	
Credit 9, Long-Term Conservation Management of Habitat or Wetlands and Water Bodies		●					●	
Neighborhood Pattern and Design								
Prerequisite 1, Walkable Streets	●		●	●	●	●		
Prerequisite 2, Compact Development			●	●	●	●		●
Prerequisite 3, Connected and Open Community	●		●	●	●	●		
Credit 1, Walkable Streets			●	●	●	●		
Credit 2, Compact Development			●	●	●	●		●
Credit 3, Mixed-Use Neighborhood Centers			●	●	●	●		●
Credit 4, Mixed-Income Diverse Communities					●			
Credit 5, Reduced Parking Footprint			●			●		
Credit 6, Street Network			●	●	●	●		●

	Smart location	Sensitive lands protection	Site and transportation design	Public health	Social equity	Energy and climate protection	Water resource efficiency	Infrastructure efficiency
Neighborhood Pattern and Design (continued)								
Credit 7, Transit Facilities			●		●	●		
Credit 8, Transportation Demand Management			●			●		
Credit 9, Access to Civic and Public Space			●	●	●	●		
Credit 10, Access to Recreation Facilities			●	●	●	●		
Credit 11, Visitability and Universal Design			●		●			
Credit 12, Community Outreach and Involvement				●	●			
Credit 13, Local Food Production				●	●	●		
Credit 14, Tree-Lined and Shaded Streets			●			●		
Credit 15, Neighborhood Schools			●	●	●			
Green Infrastructure and Buildings								
Prerequisite 1, Certified Green Building						●		
Prerequisite 2, Minimum Building Energy Efficiency						●		
Prerequisite 3, Minimum Building Water Efficiency						●	●	
Prerequisite 3, Connected and Open Community	●	●						●
Credit 1, Certified Green Buildings						●		
Credit 2, Building Energy Efficiency						●		
Credit 2, Building Water Efficiency						●	●	
Credit 4, Water-Efficient Landscaping						●	●	
Credit 5, Existing Building Reuse			●			●		
Credit 6, Historic Resource Preservation and Adaptive Use			●		●			
Credit 7, Minimized Site Disturbance in Design and Construction		●						
Credit 8, Stormwater Management							●	●
Credit 9, Heat Island Reduction						●		
Credit 10, Solar Orientation						●		
Credit 11, On-Site Renewable Energy Sources						●		●
Credit 12, District Heating and Cooling						●		●
Credit 13, Infrastructure Energy Efficiency						●		●
Credit 14, Wastewater Management								●
Credit 15, Recycled Content in Infrastructure						●		●
Credit 16, Solid Waste Management Infrastructure						●		●
Credit 17, Light Pollution Reduction			●					

Table 3. Credit relationship matrix

Achieving these credits →

May help earn these credits ↓

Legend of columns (by category):
- **SMART LOCATION & LINKAGE (S):** p1 Smart Location, p2 Imperiled Species, p3 Wetland and Water, p4 Agricultural Land, p5 Floodplain, c1 Preferred Locations, c2 Brownfields, c3 Reduced Automobile, c4 Bicycle, c5 Housing and Jobs, c6 Steep Slope, c7 Design for Habitat, c8 Restoration of Habitat, c9 Management of Habitat
- **NEIGHBORHOOD PATTERN & DESIGN (N):** p1 Walkable Streets, p2 Compact Development, p3 Connected community, c1 Walkable Streets, c2 Compact Development, c3 Mixed-Use, c4 Mixed-Income, c5 Reduced Parking, c6 Street Network, c7 Transit Facilities, c8 Transportation Management, c9 Access to Public Space, c10 Access to Recreation, c11 Universal Design, c12 Community Outreach, c13 Local Food, c14 Tree-Lined Streets, c15 Neighborhood Schools
- **GREEN INFRASTRUCTURE & BUILDINGS (G):** p1 Certified Green Building, p2 Building Energy Efficiency, p3 Building Water Efficiency, p4 Construction Pollution, c1 Certified Green Buildings, c2 Building Energy Efficiency, c3 Building Water Efficiency, c4 Water Efficient Landscaping, c5 Existing Building Reuse, c6 Historic Preservation, c7 Site Disturbance, c8 Stormwater, c9 Heat Island, c10 Solar Orientation, c11 Renewable Energy, c12 District Heating & Cooling, c13 Infrastructure Energy Efficiency, c14 Wastewater Management, c15 Recycled Content in Infrastructure, c16 Solid Waste Management Infrastructure, c17 Light Pollution Reduction

May help earn ↓ \ Achieving →	S p1	S p2	S p3	S p4	S p5	S c1	S c2	S c3	S c4	S c5	S c6	S c7	S c8	S c9	N p1	N p2	N p3	N c1	N c2	N c3	N c4	N c5	N c6	N c7	N c8	N c9	N c10	N c11	N c12	N c13	N c14	N c15	G p1	G p2	G p3	G p4	G c1	G c2	G c3	G c4	G c5	G c6	G c7	G c8	G c9	G c10	G c11	G c12	G c13	G c14	G c15	G c16	G c17
SMART LOCATION & LINKAGE																																																					
p1: Smart Location				●						●									●			●	●																														
p2: Imperiled Species																																																					
p3: Wetland and Water				●															●			●																															
p4: Agricultural Land																																																					
p5: Floodplain																																																					
c1: Preferred Locations	●			●			●		●											●		●	●			●																											
c2: Brownfields																																																					
c3: Reduced Automobile	●			●	●				●										●			●	●			●	●																										
c4: Bicycle															●							●				●																											
c5: Housing and Jobs	●																			●	●																																
c6: Steep Slope		●	●									●	●	●																													●	●	●								
c7: Design for Habitat		●	●	●	●						●		●	●																													●	●	●								
c8: Restoration of Habitat		●	●								●	●		●																													●	●									
c9: Management of Habitat		●	●								●	●	●																															●									
NEIGHBORHOOD PATTERN & DESIGN																																																					
p1: Walkable Streets																		●																																			
p2: Compact Development			●																●																																		
p3: Connected community																							●																														
c1: Walkable Streets															●	●				●								●			●	●																					
c2: Compact Development		●													●	●		●		●	●	●																							●								
c3: Mixed-Use	●						●		●	●								●	●		●	●			●																												
c4: Mixed-Income																				●																																	
c5: Reduced Parking																		●					●			●	●																		●								
c6: Street Network	●																	●		●			●			●																											
c7: Transit Facilities																		●	●						●																										●			
c8: Transportation Management																		●	●				●	●																													
c9: Access to Public Space																				●							●																										
c10: Access to Recreation																				●				●					●													●											
c11: Universal Design																		●																																			
c12: Community Outreach																																																					
c13: Local Food				●																●																																	
c14: Tree-Lined Streets																				●																									●								
c15: Neighborhood Schools																		●		●					●																									●	●	●	
GREEN INFRASTRUCTURE & BUILDINGS																																																					
p1: Certified Green Building																																					●			●													
p2: Building Energy Efficiency																																						●															
p3: Building Water Efficiency																																							●	●										●			
p4: Construction Pollution																																											●										
c1: Certified Green Buildings																																	●													●							
c2: Building Energy Efficiency																																		●			●									●	●	●	●				
c3: Building Water Efficiency																																			●					●										●			
c4: Water Efficient Landscaping																										●			●										●					●									
c5: Existing Building Reuse																																					●					●											●
c6: Historic Preservation					●																																																●
c7: Site Disturbance		●	●								●	●	●	●		●																												●									
c8: Stormwater Management			●								●	●	●										●																					●	●								
c9: Heat Island																		●		●																								●									
c10: Solar Orientation																																		●				●															
c11: Renewable Energy																																		●				●									●						
c12: District Heating & Cooling																																		●				●										●	●				
c13: Infrastructure Energy Efficiency																																		●				●											●				
c14: Wastewater Management																										●		●											●					●	●								
c15: Recycled Content in Infrastructure																																																					
c16: Solid Waste Management Infrastructure																																																					
c17: Light Pollution Reduction																																																					

PROJECT SITE

A project's site geography is a major element of rating system calculations. Important geographic determinants are a project's boundary, the type of land within and adjacent to the boundary, and the uses of project land for residential and nonresidential development.

Project Boundary

The project boundary defines the land and water area that is reviewed for certification. The term is defined in the rating system as follows:

> **project boundary** the platted property line of the project defining land and water within it. Projects located on publicly owned campuses that do not have internal property lines must delineate a sphere-of-influence line to be used instead. Project site is equivalent to the land and water inside the project boundary. The project must not contain noncontiguous parcels, but parcels can be separated by public rights-of-way. Projects may also have enclaves of nonproject properties that are not subject to the rating system, but such enclaves cannot exceed 2% of the total project area and cannot be described as certified.

The project developer, which can include several property owners, should control a majority of the buildable land within the boundary but does not have to control the entire area. The boundary may include existing uses and buildings, but a majority of the project's total square footage should be planned new construction and/or major renovations.

As noted in the definition, the boundary must be drawn along property lines. This includes public property, such as street rights-of-way. As shown in Figure 1a-c, a boundary may encompass a privately owned parcel, a parcel plus adjacent rights-of-way, or multiple parcels and intervening rights-of-way. If a project team elects to include rights-of-way, the entire width of the rights-of-way must be within the boundary, as shown in the figure.

Figure 1a. Project boundaries encompassing – one block, including public alley

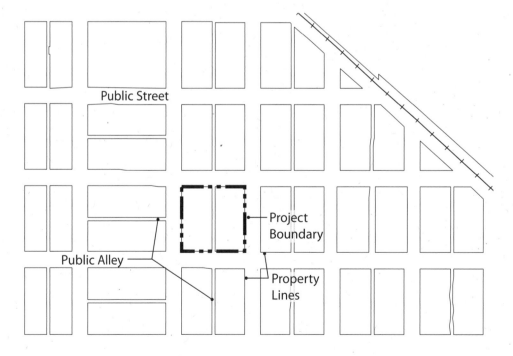

Figure 1b. Project boundaries encompassing – one block and single adjacent street right-of-way

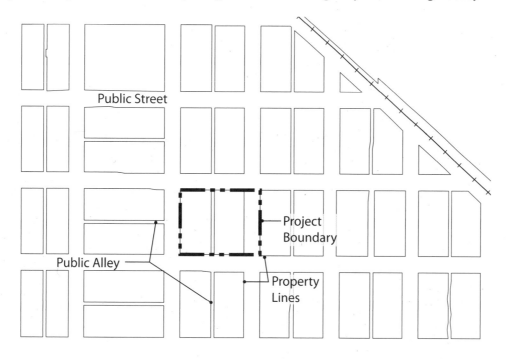

Figure 1c. Project boundaries encompassing – two blocks and intervening street right-of-way

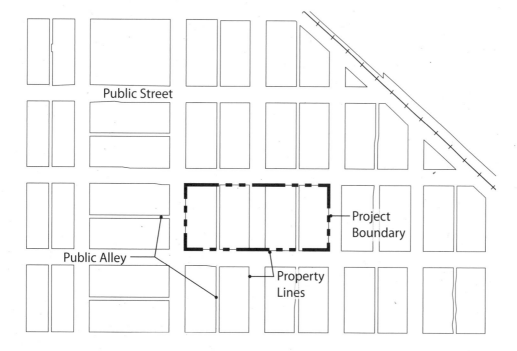

Site Types

A project is categorized by site type depending on where its boundary is set, the status of land inside the boundary, and the status of properties surrounding the boundary. As defined in the rating system, the following site types may apply: previously developed, infill site, and adjacent site.

previously developed altered by paving, construction, and/or land use that would typically have required regulatory permitting to have been initiated (alterations may exist now or in the past). Previously developed land includes a platted lot on which a building was constructed if the lot is no more than 1 acre; previous development on lots larger than 1 acre is defined as the development footprint and land alterations associated with the footprint. Land that is not previously developed and altered landscapes resulting from current or historical clearing or filling, agricultural or forestry use, or preserved natural area use are considered undeveloped land. The date of previous development permit issuance constitutes the date of previous development, but permit issuance in itself does not constitute previous development.

As defined above and illustrated in Figure 2, previously developed land now has (or had in the past) active land uses that require (or would have required) permitting. For residential uses, for example, this would include the development footprint of a single-family unit, attached unit, or multiunit building and its associated landscape alterations, such as walkways, driveways, and landscaped open space. For any lot under 1 acre, the entire lot is considered previously developed, but for parcels larger than 1 acre, any undeveloped land must be identified. Note that the definition considers certain uses, such as land cleared for agriculture, as undeveloped land.

Figure 2. Project site that is minimum 75% previously developed

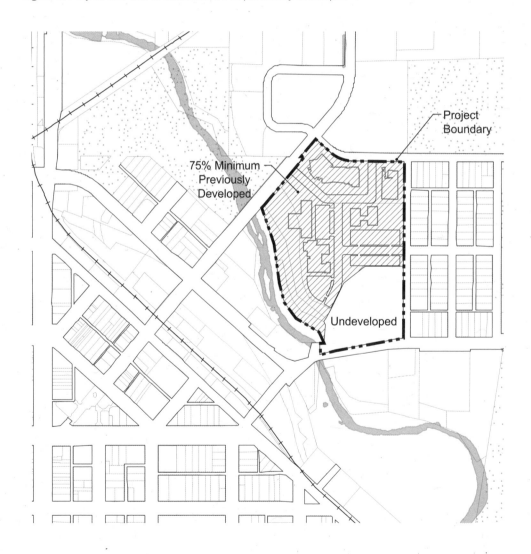

infill site a site that meets any of the following four conditions:

a. At least 75% of its boundary borders parcels that individually are at least 50% previously developed, and that in aggregate are at least 75% previously developed.

b. The site, in combination with bordering parcels, forms an aggregate parcel whose boundary is 75% bounded by parcels that individually are at least 50% previously developed, and that in aggregate are at least 75% previously developed.

c. At least 75% of the land area, exclusive of rights-of-way, within a 1/2-mile distance from the project boundary is previously developed.

d. The lands within a 1/2-mile distance from the project boundary have a preproject connectivity of at least 140 intersections per square mile.

A street does not constitute previously developed land; it is the status of property on the other side of the street that matters. For conditions (a) and (b) above, any fraction of the perimeter that borders waterfront other than a stream is excluded from the calculation.

As defined above and illustrated in the accompanying diagrams, there are four paths by which a LEED-ND project can be considered an infill site. In all instances, the definition looks at the characteristics of the land around the project. The first two conditions look at the parcels bordering the LEED-ND project or close by, and the final two conditions look at the characteristics of the land area within a 1/2-mile distance of the project boundary. For a parcel to qualify as "bordering" the project in the first two conditions, the parcel must share a section of boundary with the project; a "kitty-corner" parcel, which adjoins the project at only a single point, is not considered bordering.

Figure 3. Infill site based on one of these four conditions

(a). Infill project site based on minimum 75% of perimeter adjacent to previously developed parcels

(b). Infill project site based on minimum 75% adjacent to previously developed parcels using project boundary and selected bordering parcels

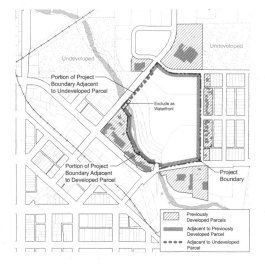
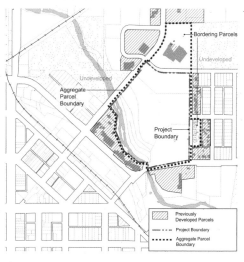

(c). Infill project site based on minimum 75% of land area within 1/2-mile of project boundary being previously developed

(d). Infill project site based on minimum 140 intersections/sq.mi. within 1/2-mile of project boundary

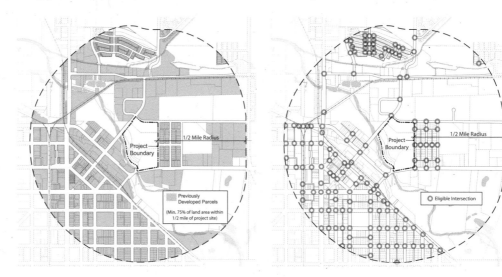

adjacent site a site having at least 25% of its boundary bordering land that has been previously developed. A street does not constitute previously developed land; instead, it is the status of the property on the other side of the street that matters. Any fraction of the boundary that borders waterfront other than a stream is excluded from the calculation. A site is still considered adjacent if the 25% adjacent portion of its boundary is separated from previously developed parcels by undeveloped, permanently protected land averaging no more than 400 feet in width and no more than 500 feet in any one place. The undeveloped land must be permanently preserved as natural area, riparian corridor, park, greenway, agricultural land, or designated cultural landscape. Permanent pedestrian paths connecting the project through the protected parcels to the bordering site may be counted to meet the requirement of SLL Prerequisite 1, Option 2 (that the project be connected to the adjacent parcel by a through-street or nonmotorized right-of-way every 600 feet on average, provided the path or paths traverse the undeveloped land at no more than a 10% grade for walking by persons of all ages and physical abilities).

As defined above and illustrated in Figure 4, to be an adjacent site, the project site needs to border previously developed land along 25% of its border. An adjacent site can be separated from previously developed land by a small greenway or other such undeveloped, permanently protected land. For a project site to qualify as an adjacent site for SLL Prerequisite 1, Smart Location, Option 2, the greenway or other protected open space must allow through connections to the previously developed land.

Figure 4. Adjacent project site based on minimum 25% of perimeter adjacent to previously developed parcels, including allowance for permanently protected land between project boundary and previously developed parcels

When determining infill and adjacent status, if the project site is next to a street or right-of-way, the team must consider the status of property on the other side of the street or right-of-way. The property on the other side must be previously developed and have, for example, current or previous housing, parks, schools, or stores. Parks are considered previously developed; legally dedicated land in its natural state is considered undeveloped. When waterfront occurs on the other side of a street or right-of-way, the length of that waterfront may be excluded from the calculation.

Once a project boundary has been established, the project team should assemble information on the type and location of previous development within the boundary to determine whether the site qualifies as a previously developed site. Also investigate the type and location of previous development on parcels surrounding the project boundary to determine whether infill or adjacent status is possible (including the SLL Prerequisite 1, Smart Location, Option 2, which requires minimum surrounding intersection density in the case of adjacency).

Buildable Land

Buildable land is an important element of a project because it is the denominator in the calculation of land-use densities. The term is illustrated in Figure 5 and defined in the rating system as follows:

> **buildable land** the portion of the site where construction can occur, including land voluntarily set aside and not constructed upon. When used in density calculations, buildable land excludes public rights-of-way and land excluded from development by codified law or LEED for Neighborhood Development prerequisites. An applicant may exclude additional land not exceeding 15% of the buildable land base defined above, provided the following conditions are present:
>
> a. The land is protected from residential and nonresidential construction by easement, deed restriction, or other enforceable legal instrument.
>
> AND
>
> b. Either 25% or more of the boundary of each contiguous parcel proposed for exclusion borders a water body or areas outside the project boundary that are protected by codified law; or ownership of, or management authority over, the exclusion area is transferred to a public entity.

Figure 5. Project site with buildable and nonbuildable areas

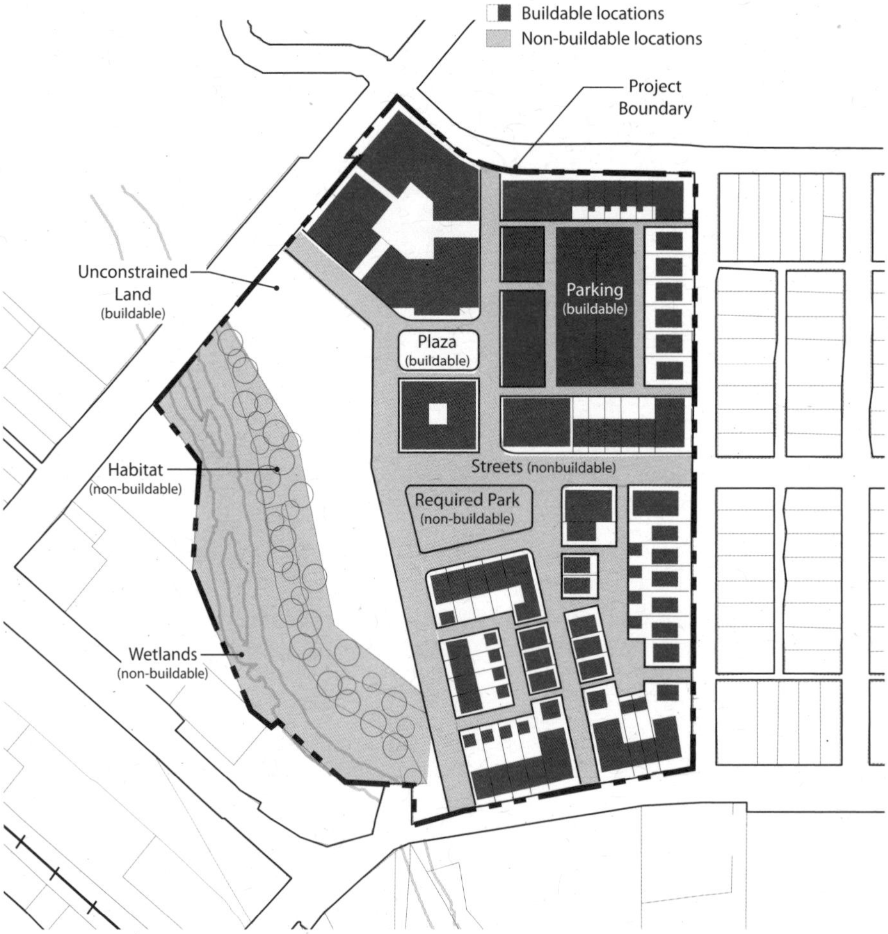

To delineate buildable land, first exclude nonbuildable areas. Allowable exclusions include public rights-of-way and land excluded from development by codified law or LEED-ND prerequisites.

In making nonbuildable exclusions, note that land voluntarily set aside for nonbuildable purposes, such as open space, must be considered buildable because it was available for construction but was set aside voluntarily. For example, 5 acres of park space required by local government code would be considered nonbuildable, but if a developer voluntarily sets aside an additional 3 acres for more park space, those 3 acres must be categorized as buildable land.

Once a base delineation of buildable and nonbuildable land has been made, a developer may additionally exclude up to 15% of the base buildable land area if the additional land is protected from construction and located next to water or other protected areas controlled by a public entity. Thus a project is not penalized in its density calculation for voluntarily increasing protected area amenities.

Development Footprint

The project's development footprint is essentially all of its impervious surfaces. The term is illustrated in Figure 6 and defined in the rating system as follows:

> **development footprint** the total land area of a project site covered by buildings, streets, parking areas, and other typically impermeable surfaces constructed as part of the project.

Footprint is used in multiple credit calculations, particularly where imperviousness is a factor, such as NPD Credit 5, Reduced Parking Footprint, and GIB Credit 8, Stormwater Management. Streets constructed with permeable pavement (at least 50% permeable) are not included in the development footprint.

Figure 6. Project site development footprint including all impervious surfaces

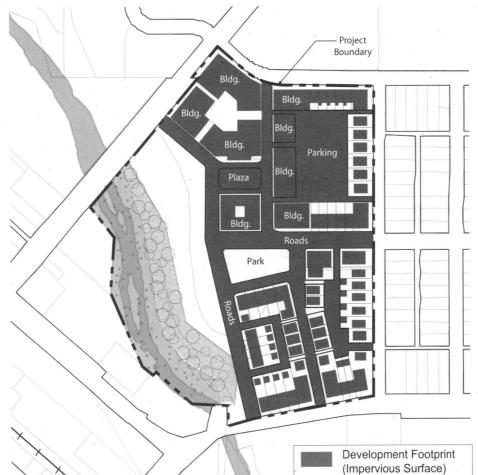

DEVELOPMENT PROGRAM

The development program is a tabular presentation of the use of land and the demolition, construction, renovation, and/or retention of buildings and infrastructure. The development program accounts for all land and water within the project boundary according to the buildable and nonbuildable considerations discussed above. Each land category is described according to the type and number of buildings and square footage within them, and then used consistently throughout the submission. In preparing the development program, consider the following:

- **New construction.** A majority of a project's square footage should be new construction, which is subject to all prerequisites and credits. New construction includes major renovations—that is, those affecting more than 50% of an existing building's square footage.

- **Existing buildings.** Projects may include existing buildings. These may or may not undergo changes as part of the project. If they are included in a project, the project team should carefully review each prerequisite and credit for applicability to existing buildings: Some credit calculations include existing buildings, and some do not. Table 4 summarizes treatment of existing and planned project features by credit.

- **Timeline.** Several provisions of the rating system are tied to milestone dates on the project's development timeline, beginning with property acquisition and extending through build-out and occupancy. The property acquisition date is the date that the project developer purchased or took equivalent control of a majority of the land area inside the project boundary. Some rating system provisions must be applied in perpetuity. Figure 7 shows major milestones and applicable credits on a timeline; it assumes concurrent build-out and occupancy.

Table 4. Applicability of LEED-ND credits to planned and existing features

	Option	Planned features	Existing features
Smart Location and Linkage			
Prerequisite 1, Smart Location	2. Adjacent Sites	—	Intersections, ROWs
	3. Projects in Transit Corridors	Buildings, transit	Buildings, transit
	4. Nearby Neighborhood Assets	Buildings	Buildings, diverse uses
Prerequisite 3, Wetland and Water Body Conservation	2. Sites with Wetlands, Water Bodies	Land-use densities	Land-use densities
Prerequisite 4, Agricultural Land Conservation	5. Sites with Impacted Soils	Land-use densities	Land-use densities
Credit 3, Locations With Reduced Automobile Dependence	1. Transit-Served Location	Buildings	Buildings, transit
Credit 4, Bicycle Network and Storage	a. Bicycle Network	Dwellings, uses	Dwellings, uses
	b. Bicycle Storage	Dwellings, uses	—
Credit 5, Housing and Jobs Proximity	1. Affordable Residential Component	Buildings	Buildings
	2. Residential Component	Buildings	Buildings
	3. Infill with Nonresidential Component	Buildings	Buildings
Neighborhood Pattern and Design			
Prerequisite 1, Walkable Streets	a. Principal Functional Entry	Buildings	—
	b. Building-Height-to-Street-Width Ratio	Buildings	Buildings
	c. Sidewalks	Sidewalks	—
	d. Garage Frontages	Streets	Streets
Prerequisite 2, Compact Development	1. Projects in Transit Corridors	Land uses, transit	Land uses, transit
	2. All Other Projects	Land uses, transit	Land uses, transit
Prerequisite 3, Connected and Open Community	1. Projects with Internal Streets	Streets, intersections	Streets, intersections
	2. Projects without Internal Streets	—	Streets, intersections
Credit 1, Walkable Streets	a. 25-Foot Setback	Buildings	Buildings
	b. 18-Foot Setback	Buildings	Buildings
	c. 1-Foot Setback	Buildings	Buildings
	d. Entries Every 75 Feet	Buildings	Buildings
	e. Entries Every 30 Feet	Buildings	Buildings
	f. Ground-Level Glass	Buildings	Buildings
	g. Minimal Blank Walls	Buildings	Buildings
	h. Unshuttered Retail Windows	Buildings	Buildings
	i. Onstreet Parking	Streets	Streets
	j. Continuous Sidewalks	Streets	Streets
	k. Ground-Floor Dwelling Units	Buildings	Buildings
	l. Ground-Floor Retail	Buildings	Buildings
	m. Building-Height-to-Street-Width Ratio	Buildings	Buildings
	n. 20-mph Streets	Streets	—
	o. 25-mph Streets	Streets	—
	p. Minimal Driveways	Streets	Streets
Credit 2, Compact Development	NA	Land-use densities	Land-use densities
Credit 3, Mixed-Use Neighborhood Centers	a. All Projects	Dwellings	Dwellings
	b. Projects with 150,000+ sf Retail	Buildings	Buildings

Table 4. Applicability of LEED-ND credits to planned and existing features (continued)

	Option	Planned features	Existing features
Neighborhood Pattern and Design (continued)			
Credit 4, Mixed-Income Diverse Communities	1. Diversity of Housing Types	Dwellings	Dwellings
	2. Affordable Housing	Dwellings	—
Credit 5, Reduced Parking Footprint	NA	Buildings	—
Credit 6, Street Network	NA	Cul-de-sacs	Abutting streets
Credit 7, Transit Facilities	NA	Buildings	Buildings
Credit 8, Transportation Demand Management	4. Vehicle Sharing	Buildings	Buildings
	5. Unbundling of Parking	Buildings	Buildings
Credit 9, Access to Civic and Public Space	NA	Buildings	Buildings
Credit 10, Access to Recreation Facilities	a. Proximity to Outdoor Facilities	Buildings	Buildings
Credit 11, Visitability and Universal Design	1. Projects with Dwelling Units	Dwellings	—
	2. Projects with Noncompliant ROWs	ROWs	ROWs
Credit 13, Local Food Production	1. Neighborhood Farms and Gardens	Dwellings	—
	2. Community-Supported Agriculture	Dwellings	—
	3. Proximity to Farmers' Market	Buildings	Buildings
Credit 14, Tree-Lined and Shaded Streets	NA	Buildings, streets	Buildings, streets
Credit 15, Neighborhood Schools	NA	Schools, buildings, streets	Buildings, streets
Green Infrastructure and Buildings			
Prerequisite 1, Certified Green Building	NA	Buildings	Renovations
Prerequisite 2, Minimum Building Energy Efficiency	NA	Buildings	Renovations
Prerequisite 3, Minimum Building Water Efficiency	NA	Buildings	Renovations
Credit 1, Certified Green Buildings	1. Projects with 10 or Fewer Buildings	Buildings	Buildings
	2. Projects of All Sizes	Buildings	Buildings
Credit 2, Building Energy Efficiency	a. Point Categories	Buildings	Renovations
Credit 3, Building Water Efficiency	NA	Buildings	Renovations
Credit 5, Existing Building Reuse	NA	—	Buildings
Credit 6, Historic Resource Preservation and Adaptive Use	NA	—	Buildings
Credit 7, Minimized Site Disturbance in Design and Construction	2. Undeveloped Area Is Undisturbed	Land uses	Land uses
Credit 9, Heat Island Reduction	1. Nonroof Measures	Nonroof hardscape	Nonroof hardscape
	2. High-Reflectance and Vegetated Roofs	Buildings	—
	3. Mixed Roof and Nonroof Measures	Mixed surfaces	Mixed surfaces
Credit 10, Solar Orientation	1. Block Orientation	Blocks	Blocks
	2. Building Orientation	Buildings	—
Credit 11, On-Site Renewable Energy Sources	NA	Buildings	—
Credit 12, District Heating and Cooling	NA	Buildings	—
Credit 13, Infrastructure Energy Efficiency	NA	Infrastructure	—
Credit 14, Wastewater Management	NA	Buildings	—
Credit 17, Light Pollution Reduction	NA	Land uses, buildings	Land uses, buildings

Figure 7. LEED-ND project timeline

Pre-project conditions – prior to property acquisition:
SLLp3 wetlands;
SLLc7 habitat/wetlands.

Property acquisition date

ND submission date – establishes existing conditions

Construction start

First building occupancy:
GIBc10 solar shading 25% max.

3 years after first bldg occupancy:
NPDc8 minimum length of subsidized transit passes.

20% occupancy:
NPDc8 start private transit at 20% of total sq.ft. occupancy;
NPDc8 start car sharing at 20% total DU and non-res sq.ft. occupancy.

5 years after first building occupancy:
NPDp2 and NPDc2 density achieved.

Construction completion/build-out

2 years after build-out:
NPDc7 add new transit stops/service.

20-50% occupancy:
NPDc3 diverse uses in place at 20-50% total sq.ft. occupancy.

3 years after build-out:
SLLc8 habitat maintenance commitment;
NPDc8 private transit service operation commitment.

50% occupancy:
SLLp1 start rail service at 50% total sq.ft. occupancy;
NPDc7 install transit shelters at 50% total sq.ft. occupancy;
NPDc13 start farmers market at 50% total sq.ft. occupancy;
NPDc15 open neighborhood school at 50% DU occupancy.

80% occupancy:
NPDc13 purchase CSA shares up to 80% of household occupancy.

10 years after build-out:
SLLc9 minimum duration of habitat conservation plan;
NPDc14 shading in place;
GIBc9 tree shading in place.

100% occupancy

Perpetuity:
SLLp3 protect habitat and mitigation area;
SLLp4 protect ag land and gardens;
SLLc6 protect steep slopes;
SLLc7 protect habitat;
SLLc8 protect habitat;
NPDc1 keep retail windows unshuttered;
NPDc13 unconstrained yards and dedicated growing space;
GIBc7 protect undisturbed areas; all projects protect trees;
GIBc17 adhere to light pollution requirements.

MAPPING

Because of the geographic and land-based calculations in the rating system, mapping is an important part of documenting a project's characteristics and verifying credit achievement. Project teams should use the following three types of maps (Figure 8).

- **Project site base.** A standardized project site base map should be used throughout the submission to illustrate relevant features inside the project boundary.

- **Vicinity base.** A standardized vicinity base map should be used throughout the submission to illustrate relevant features for up to 1 mile around the project boundary.

- **Special maps.** Certain credits require information that is more feasibly shown on special maps instead of the standard base maps. For example, maps of the high-priority redevelopment areas under Option 3 of SLL Credit 1, Preferred Locations, may cover entire communities.

Each map should have a title with the credit name and number, a compass rose or arrow indicating north, a scale, and the relevant features clearly labeled and dimensioned in sufficient detail to enable verification of credit compliance.

Visual verification of credit documentation is an important element of LEED-ND certification. Maps and other uploaded documents should be clear and of sufficiently high resolution to allow detailed review of project features. Overly large documents, however, are difficult to manage and may hinder the review process; create concise maps that document only the relevant credit requirements rather than provide broad documentation applicable to several credits.

Figure 8. Project site and vicinity base maps with standardized format, scale, applicable credit title, and full labeling and dimensioning of subject features

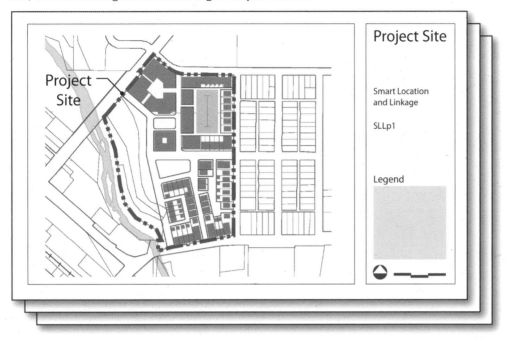

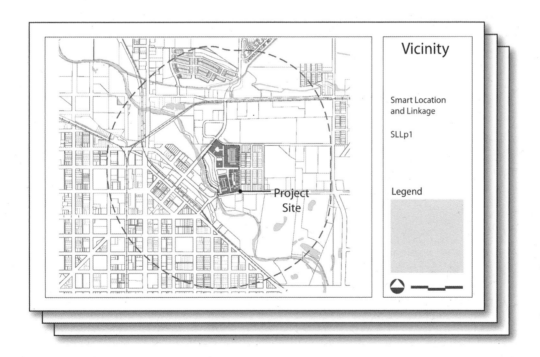

BASE CALCULATIONS

As shown in Table 5, several calculations are used across the rating system. Having performed these calculations at the outset, project teams can reuse the calculations and easily make credit-specific adjustments.

Table 5. Base calculations, by credit

Prerequisites and credits	Land-use densities	Intersection densities	Walking and bicycling distances	ROW-boundary intersects	Street and block frontage
Smart Location and Linkage					
Prerequisite 1, Smart Location		●	●	●	
Prerequisite 3, Wetland and Water Body Conservation	●				
Prerequisite 4, Agricultural Land Conservation	●				
Credit 1, Preferred Locations		●			
Credit 3, Locations with Reduced Automobile Dependence			●		
Credit 4, Bicycle Network and Storage			●		
Credit 5, Housing and Jobs Proximity			●		
Neighborhood Pattern and Design					
Prerequisite 1, Walkable Streets					●
Prerequisite 2, Compact Development	●		●		
Prerequisite 3, Connected and Open Community		●		●	●
Credit 1, Walkable Streets					●
Credit 2, Compact Development	●				
Credit 3, Mixed-Use Neighborhood Centers			●		
Credit 5, Reduced Parking Footprint					●
Credit 6, Street Network		●		●	
Credit 8, Transportation Demand Management			●		
Credit 9, Access to Civic and Public Space			●		
Credit 10, Access to Recreation Facilities			●		
Credit 13, Local Food Production	●		●		
Credit 15, Neighborhood Schools			●		
Green Infrastructure and Buildings					
Credit 7, Minimized Site Disturbance in Design and Construction	●				

Land-Use Densities

The rating system measures land-use density in two categories, residential and nonresidential. All project uses must be tabulated in one of these categories. Density is calculated according to the following definitions:

> **density** the amount of building structures constructed on the project site, measured for residential buildings as dwelling units per acre of buildable land available for residential uses, and for nonresidential buildings as the floor-area ratio of buildable land area available for nonresidential uses. In both cases, structured parking is excluded.

> **dwelling unit** living quarters intended for long-term occupancy that provide facilities for cooking, sleeping, and sanitation. This does not include hotel rooms.

> **floor-area ratio** (**FAR**) the density of nonresidential land use, exclusive of parking, measured as the total nonresidential building floor area divided by the total buildable land area available for nonresidential structures. For example, on a site with 10,000 square feet of buildable land area, an FAR of 1.0 would be 10,000 square feet of building floor area. On the same site, an FAR of 1.5 would be 15,000 square feet of built floor area; an FAR of 2.0 would be 20,000 built square feet and an FAR of 0.5 would be 5,000 built square feet.

These definitions are implemented as follows:

1. Sum the amounts of buildable land area by these categories: residential, nonresidential, mixed-use building area (land occupied by a building with a combination of residential and nonresidential uses), and other (e.g., voluntary set-asides of open space and recreation land). The total must equal 100% of the project's buildable land.

2. For mixed-use buildings, assign proportional shares of mixed-use building land area to the residential and nonresidential categories by following these steps: (1) determine the total floor area of the residential and nonresidential portions of mixed uses; (2) calculate the percentages of the total mixed-use floor area that the residential and nonresidential portions each represent; and (3) apply those percentages to the total mixed-use land area to determine the proportionate share of mixed-use building land area to be assigned to the residential and nonresidential buildable land categories.

3. Allocate shares of the "other" buildable land category to the residential and nonresidential land categories at the team's discretion. The allocated total must equal 100% of the "other" category.

4. Sum the residential and nonresidential land area amounts from above to obtain their respective total land areas.

5. Divide the project's total dwelling units and/or total nonresidential floor area by the total residential and/or nonresidential land areas, respectively. This gives residential density as dwelling units per acre of residential buildable land, and nonresidential density as a floor-area ratio for nonresidential buildable land.

The calculation of land-use densities for mixed-use projects varies in some credits, and project teams should review each instance to take into consideration any credit-specific allowances.

The project's base land-use densities may be adjusted in two instances: (1) the buildable land adjustment described above when extra protected areas are set aside; and (2) under SLL Prerequisite 4, Agricultural Land Conservation, where provision of a community garden enables a density increase (see SLL Prerequisite 4 for details). The latter adjustment applies only to SLL Prerequisite 4; the base or buildable land-adjusted densities must be used throughout the remainder of the project submission.

Intersection Densities

The density of street intersections in an area is used by transportation planners to measure connectivity for travel purposes. As intersection density increases, the number of travel routes increases, making trips shorter and more direct and more feasible for walking and bicycling. Intersection density is shown in Figure 9 and defined in the rating system as follows:

connectivity the number of publicly accessible street intersections per square mile, including intersections of streets with dedicated alleys and transit rights-of-way, and intersections of streets with nonmotorized rights-of-way (up to 20% of total intersections). If one must both enter and exit an area through the same intersection, such an intersection and any intersections beyond that point are not counted; intersections leading only to culs-de-sac are also not counted. The calculation of square mileage excludes water bodies, parks larger than 1/2-acre, public facility campuses, airports, rail yards, slopes over 15%, and areas nonbuildable under codified law or the rating system. Street rights-of-way may not be excluded.

Figure 9. Eligible and noneligible intersection determination for measuring connectivity with eligible intersections

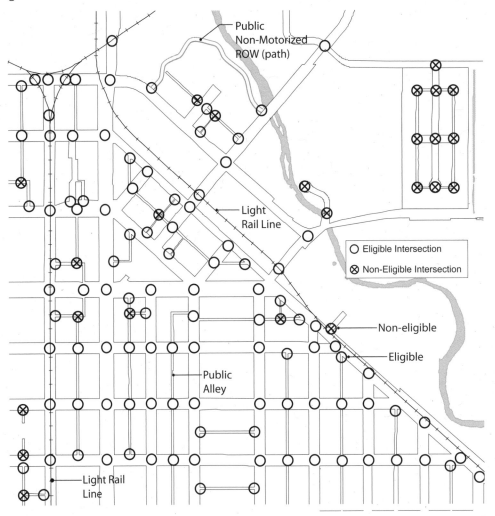

For the area in question, the project team should assemble maps of both internal streets (those inside the project boundary) and external streets in the surrounding area, exclude ineligible intersections, and count the remaining intersections. Digital GIS or CAD files of street and other right-of-way centerlines are normally available from the local government. With GIS or CAD files of surrounding centerlines, the team can add any proposed centerlines for streets or other rights-of-way inside the project, depending on the credit, and calculate intersection density by tabulating eligible intersections and the area in which they are situated. An intersection of an alley with an alley is not an eligible intersection. Intersections leading only to culs-de-sac cannot be counted; however, an intersection with a cul-de-sac can be counted if it also leads to an eligible intersection. The area containing the final intersection count must be prorated to the equivalent of a square mile. For example, 50 eligible intersections in a 0.75-square-mile project site equates to 67 intersections per square mile (50 / .75).

The definition allows several project features—parks, public facility campuses (such as universities, community colleges, or schools), rail yards, and airports—to be excluded from the land area for the purpose of calculating connectivity. The area of water bodies and steep slopes can also be excluded. As stated in the definition, the land area of streets or rights-of-way may not be excluded.

Walking and Bicycling Route Distances (Shortest Path Analysis)

Several prerequisites and credits require the measurement of walking and bicycling distances between origins and destinations along pedestrian and bicycle network routes. Review these two definitions:

> **bicycle network** a continuous network consisting of any combination of physically designated in-street bicycle lanes at least 5 feet wide, off-street bicycle paths or trails at least 8 feet wide for a two-way path and at least 5 feet wide for a one-way path, and/or streets designed for a target speed of 25 miles per hour or slower.

> **walk distance** the distance that a pedestrian must travel between origins and destinations without obstruction, in a safe and comfortable environment on a continuous network of sidewalks, all-weather-surface footpaths, crosswalks, woonerfs, or equivalent pedestrian facilities.

The walking or bicycling distance from the entrance of an origin building to destinations is specified in several credits; its calculation is illustrated in Figure 10. Sometimes known as shortest path analysis, the measurement is the distance a pedestrian or bicyclist would travel from an origin to the closest destination of a given type, such as the closest bus stop to a dwelling or office building. Origin building entrances serving multiple dwellings should be counted according to the number of dwellings accessed at those entrances. For example, 20 dwelling units accessed via one entrance to a multistory residential building would count as 20 units. A nonresidential building with one entrance leading to 15 office tenants and two retail tenants would count as 17 nonresidential uses.

Figure 10. Walking routes on pedestrian networks (and bicycle routes on bicycle networks) showing distances from building entrances to destinations

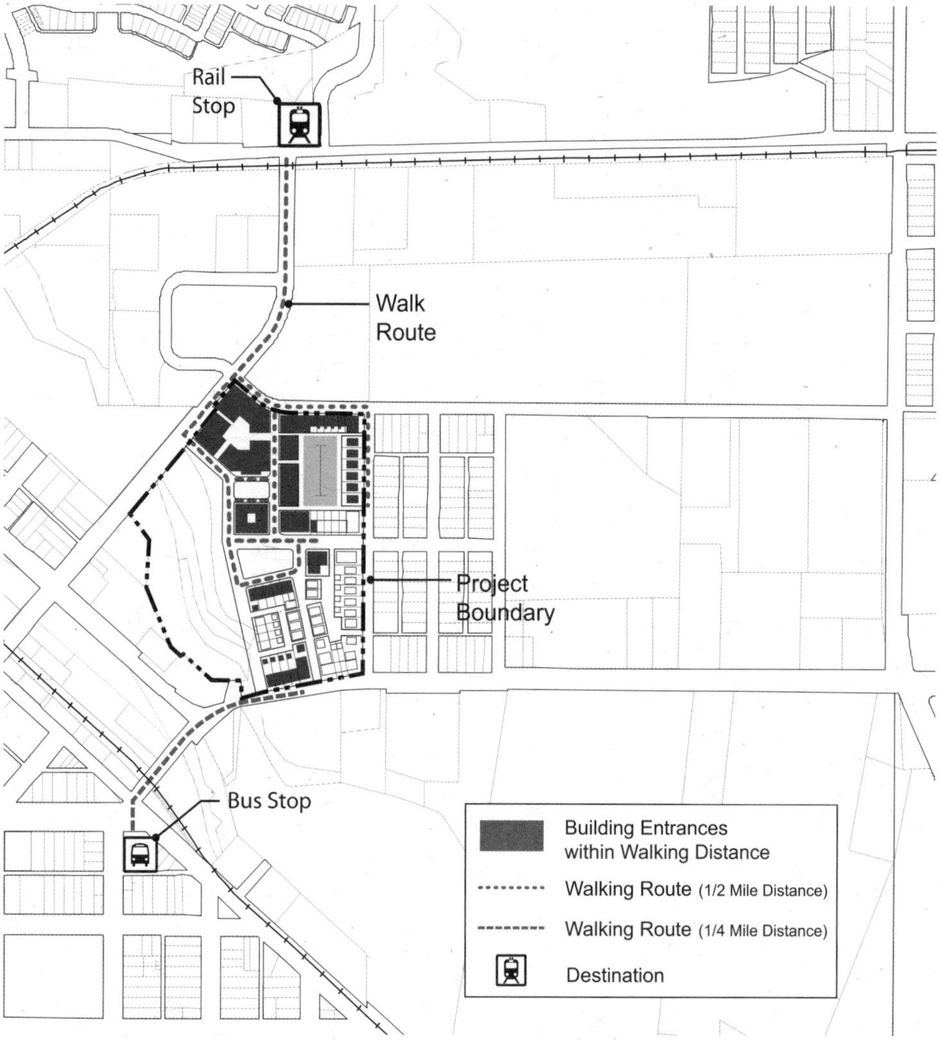

Rights-of-Way Intersecting Project Boundary

Three credits—SLL Prerequisite 1, Smart Location; NPD Prerequisite 3, Connected and Open Community; and NPD Credit 6, Street Network—require the measurement of distances between the points where internal rights-of-way pass through or terminate at the project boundary and connect with existing rights-of-way. Figure 11 shows how internal and external rights-of-way intersect the project boundary. For NPD Prerequisite 3 and NPD Credit 6, rights-of-way may terminate at the project boundary in addition to passing through the boundary. As shown in Figure 12, the intersect points of right-of-way centerlines on the project boundary are the points used to measure interval distances between intersects along the boundary. Maximum allowable distances between intersect points are stipulated in each credit.

Figure 11a. Internal right-of-way centerline intersect at project boundary with centerline continuation on existing external street

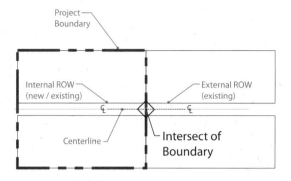

Figure 11b. Internal right-of-way centerline intersect at project boundary with centerline of existing street parallel to boundary

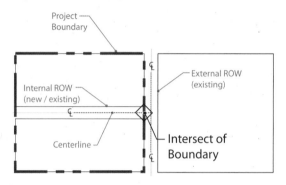

Figure 12a. Project boundary encompassing one block without internal rights-of-way and therefore no boundary intersects

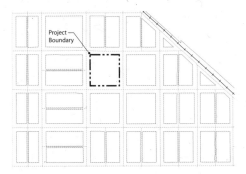

Figure 12b. Project boundary encompassing two blocks and intervening street creating two intersect interval distances

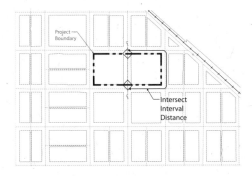

Figure 12c. Project boundary encompassing four blocks and intervening streets creating four intersect interval distances

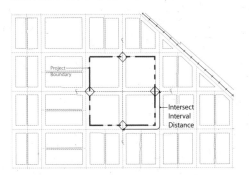

Figure 12d. Project boundary encompassing four blocks with intervening and surrounding streets creating 12 intersect interval distances

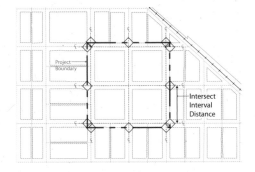

Street, Block, and Building Frontage

Three credits—NPD Prerequisite 1, Walkable Streets; NPD Credit 1, Walkable Streets; and NPD Credit 5, Reduced Parking Footprint—stipulate requirements for the frontages of streets, blocks, and buildings. The applicability of these terms to a typical streetscape is shown in Figure 13. Note that street frontage and block frontage are synonymous, and sidewalks are usually (but not always) located within street rights-of-way. Regardless of sidewalk location, the dividing point between streets and blocks is the right-of-way boundary or property line. When calculating street frontage, the team can exclude the width of any right-of-way that intersects the street.

Figure 13. Neighborhood pattern and design terminology applied to typical block

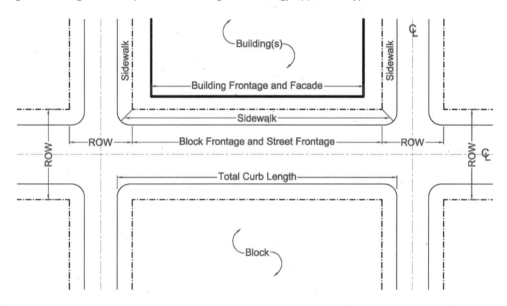

Project Geographic Center

Four credits—SLL Prerequisite 1, Smart Location; SLL Credit 5, Housing and Jobs Proximity; NPD Credit 4, Mixed-Income Diverse Communities; and NPD Credit 13, Local Food Production— require measuring the distance from a project's geographic center to certain features, such as farmers' markets. In CAD or GIS terms, the geographic center is the "centroid" of the polygon created by the project boundary. For projects using CAD or GIS, the centroid can be automatically identified.

DEFINITIONS

The rating system uses many terms whose definitions should be reviewed when a team selects credits to attempt. In the rating system, terms are italicized on their first appearance in a prerequisite or credit. Definitions appear in the Glossary at the end of this reference guide. Be aware of meanings specific to LEED-ND and how they may affect documentation requirements or a project's eligibility for points.

Smart Location and Linkage focuses on selection of sites that minimize the adverse environmental effects of new development and avoid contributing to sprawl and its consequences. Typical sprawl development—low-density, segregated housing and commercial uses located in automobile-dependent outlying areas—can harm the natural environment in a number of ways. Sprawl can consume forestland, destroy or fragment wildlife habitat, degrade water quality through destruction of wetlands and increased stormwater runoff, pollute the air and emit greenhouse gases through increased automobile travel, and often displace agriculture from prime farmland to locations where food production requires more energy and chemical inputs. In addition to these direct environmental effects, leapfrog development (a land-use pattern in which new development does not connect coherently to existing development, often leaving haphazard tracts of undeveloped land in between) can also harm the environment indirectly by promoting additional development in previously undeveloped areas.

Increased automobile travel is one of the most damaging consequences of sprawl. People living and working in outlying areas tend to drive greater distances, spend more time driving, own more cars, face a greater risk of traffic fatalities, and walk less. According to the Bureau of Transportation Statistics, vehicle use in the United States nearly tripled, from 1.1 trillion to 3 trillion miles per year, between 1970 and 2006.[1] Vehicles are responsible for more than 20% of U.S. greenhouse gas emissions.[2] Vehicle emissions contribute to climate change, smog, and particulate pollution, which all are harmful to human health and natural ecosystems. In addition, the parking and roadway surfaces required to support vehicular travel consume land and nonrenewable resources, disrupt natural stormwater flow, and enlarge urban heat islands.

Choosing a smart location can make a substantial difference: A recent study found that vehicle miles traveled could be reduced 10% to 30% through smart growth strategies.[3] Greenhouse gas emissions from traffic can be reduced as much as 24% with aggressive transportation reform.[4] Transportation surveys conducted by many metropolitan planning organizations across the country show that residents of close-in locations may drive only a third to half as much, on average, as do residents of the most far-flung locations in a metro region.

To reduce the effects of sprawl and create more livable communities, preference should be given to locations close to existing town and city centers, sites with good transit access, infill sites, previously developed sites, and sites adjacent to existing development. Selecting these sites can prevent development of outlying greenfield sites while reducing automobile travel and resulting emissions. In addition, these sites often have utilities, roads, and other infrastructure in place, reducing the need for construction of new infrastructure and minimizing the expansion of impervious surfaces that increase harmful stormwater runoff. In the locations that perform better environmentally, the benefits can often be multiple and reinforcing: convenient transportation choices such as buses, light rail, heavy trains, car pools, van pools, bicycle lanes, and sidewalks, for example, are generally more available near downtowns, neighborhood centers, and town centers, which are also the locations that produce shorter automobile trips. Research has shown that

1   National Transportation Statistics, Bureau of Transportation Statistics, U.S. Department of Transportation, 2008. Accessed at www.bts.gov/publications/national_transportation_statistics/.

2   Energy Information Administration, Emissions of Greenhouse Gases in the United States 2005. Report DOE/EIA-0573(2005). Released November 2006.

3   Amanda M. Eaken and David B. Goldstein, "Quantifying the Third Leg: The Potential for Smart Growth to Reduce Greenhouse Gas Emissions." Natural Resources Defense Council, 2008.

4   "Moving Cooler: An Analysis of Transportation Strategies for Reducing Greenhouse Gas Emissions.," Cambridge Systematics, Inc.. and the Urban Land Institute, 2009.

living in a mixed-use environment within walking distance of shops and services also encourages walking and bicycling, which improve cardiovascular and respiratory health and reduce the risk of hypertension and obesity.

An additional benefit of locations that require less driving is that households may be able to own fewer automobiles and cut transportation expenses. For commercial development, fewer automobiles may mean less investment in parking infrastructure, which can reduce the amount of land needed for a project, and lower construction costs. Abundant transportation choices can increase the value and marketability of a neighborhood development as well. More than 14.6 million households are expected to prefer housing within a half-mile of rail transit stops by 2025—more than double the number of households living in such locations today.[5]

Beyond the environmental damage caused by increased automobile dependence, fragmentation and loss of habitat due to sprawl are major threats to many imperiled species. Selection of sites that are within or adjacent to existing development can minimize habitat fragmentation and also help preserve areas for recreation. Wetlands provide very important wildlife habitat because they tend to be biologically rich. Development of wetlands or floodplains presents particularly serious environmental challenges because in addition to altering wildlife habitat, it can reduce water quality and increase the likelihood of flooding and associated consequences, such as erosion and loss of property. Left alone, these natural areas retain stormwater and floodwaters for slow release into river systems and aquifers, and they protect lakes and streams by trapping sediment.

Another important concern is development intrusion onto prime agricultural lands, which typically require less fertilization and irrigation and are therefore the most resource efficient and environmentally sound locations for farming. Leapfrog patterns of development not only take these lands out of agricultural production but can also fragment farming communities and consequently reduce the economic viability of the local agricultural economy. In the United States, 86% of fruits and vegetables and 63% of dairy products are produced very close to metropolitan areas, in the path of development.[6]

Many potential building sites in urban locations have been abandoned because of real or potential contamination from previous industrial or municipal activities. Remediation and reclamation of contaminated brownfield sites make them safer for the community and can also contribute to social and economic revitalization of depressed or disadvantaged neighborhoods. Development of these sites spares greenfields and utilizes existing infrastructure.

Finally, smart location choice also offers opportunities to repair the fabric of communities that are disjointed and sprawling. Suburban locations typically contain excellent redevelopment opportunities on grayfield sites, such as old airports, abandoned or underutilized shopping malls, and closed factories.

Resources for Learning More

Websites
American Farmland Trust
www.farmland.org/default.asp
This website offers education, fiscal analysis, support in developing agricultural land-use plans, and advice for preserving agricultural land.

---

5   Reconnecting America, Center for Transit-Oriented Development. *Hidden in Plain Sight: Capturing the Demand for Housing Near Transit.* 2004.
6   1997 U.S. Census of Agriculture, USDA Economic Research Service.

Natural Resources Defense Council, smart growth
www.nrdc.org
One of America's largest environmental organizations, NRDC provides reports and policy papers on diverse smart location topics, including "location efficiency," the Location Efficient Mortgage program, the measurable environmental benefits of smart growth neighborhoods, and strategies for solving sprawl.

Smart Growth America
www.smartgrowthamerica.org/
This coalition of organizations from around the United States posts the latest smart growth news and supports smart growth initiatives, particularly related to historic preservation, the environment, farmland and open space preservation, and neighborhood revitalization. It helps states, communities, and other interested stakeholders adopt policies and legislation that support compact development.

Smart Growth Network
www.smartgrowth.org
This network of nonprofit organizations and government agencies promotes smart growth practices. The website outlines smart growth principles, provides a guide to smart growth terms and technical concepts, and hosts a searchable catalogue of reports, websites, tools, and case studies dating from 1997.

U.S. Environmental Protection Agency, smart growth
www.epa.gov/dced/
The Development, Community and Environment Division of EPA has a smart growth program that provides research, tools, case studies, grants, and technical assistance.

Victoria Transportation Policy Institute
www.vtpi.org
This independent research organization provides consulting and publicly available research about solutions to emerging transportation issues, such as transportation demand management.

Print Media

Atlanta Region Daily per Capita Home-Based VMT (Criterion Planners, 2000).

Farming on the Edge Report (American Farmland Trust)
Available at www.farmland.org/resources/fote/default.asp.

Growing Cooler: The Evidence on Urban Development and Climate Change, by Reid Ewing, Keith Bartholomew, Steve Winkelman, Jerry Walters, and Don Chen (Urban Land Institute, 2007).

Holding Our Ground: Protecting America's Farms and Farmland, by Tom Daniels and Deborah Bowers (Island Press, 1997).

"The Influence of Land Use on Travel Behavior: Empirical Strategies," by Reid Ewing and Robert Cervero, *Transportation Research, Policy and Practice* 35 (2001): 823-845.

Measuring Sprawl and Its Impact, by Reid Ewing, Rolf Pendall, and Don Chen (Smart Growth America) Available at www.smartgrowthamerica.org/sprawlindex/MeasuringSprawl.PDF.

Our Built and Natural Environments: A Technical Review of the Interactions between Land Use, Transportation, and Environmental Quality (Development, Community, and Environment Division, U.S. Environmental Protection Agency, 2001).

Places to Grow: Growth Plan for the Greater Golden Horseshoe (Ministry of Public Infrastructure Renewal, Province of Ontario, 2006).

Retrofitting Suburbia: Urban Design Solutions for Redesigning Suburbs, by Ellen Dunham-Jones and June Williamson (John Wiley & Sons, 2008).

Saved by Development: Preserving Environmental Areas, Farmland, by Rick Pruetz (Arje Press, 1997).

Transportation Statistics Annual Report (Bureau of Transportation Statistics, U.S. Department of Transportation, 2005).

Understanding the Relationship between Public Health and the Built Environment, by LEED-ND Core Committee, Design, Community & Environment (2006)
Available at www.usgbc.org/ShowFile.aspx?DocumentID=1480.

"The Urban Form and Climate Change Gamble," by L.B. Frank, S. Kavage, and B. Appleyard, *Planning* 73(8) (2007): 18-23.

CREDIT	TITLE	POINTS
SLL Prerequisite 1	Smart Location	Required
SLL Prerequisite 2	Imperiled Species and Ecological Communities Conservation	Required
SLL Prerequisite 3	Wetland and Water Body Conservation	Required
SLL Prerequisite 4	Agricultural Land Conservation	Required
SLL Prerequisite 5	Floodplain Avoidance	Required
SLL Credit 1	Preferred Locations	10 points
SLL Credit 2	Brownfields Redevelopment	2 points
SLL Credit 3	Reduced Automobile Dependence	7 points
SLL Credit 4	Bicycle Network and Storage	1 point
SLL Credit 5	Housing and Jobs Proximity	3 points
SLL Credit 6	Steep Slope Protection	1 point
SLL Credit 7	Site Design for Habitat or Wetland and Water Body Conservation	1 point
SLL Credit 8	Restoration of Habitat or Wetlands and Water Bodies	1 point
SLL Credit 9	Long-Term Conservation Management of Habitat or Wetlands and Water Bodies	1 point

	ND
Prerequisite	SLL Prerequisite 1
Points	Required

Intent

To encourage development within and near *existing* communities and public transit infrastructure. To encourage improvement and redevelopment of existing cities, suburbs, and towns while limiting the expansion of the *development footprint* in the region to appropriate circumstances. To reduce vehicle trips and *vehicle miles traveled* (VMT). To reduce the incidence of obesity, heart disease, and hypertension by encouraging daily physical activity associated with walking and bicycling.

Requirements

FOR ALL PROJECTS

Either (a) locate the *project* on a site served by existing *water and wastewater infrastructure* or (b) locate the project within a legally adopted, publicly owned, planned water and wastewater service area, and provide new water and wastewater infrastructure for the project.

AND

OPTION 1. Infill Sites

Locate the project on an *infill site*.

OR

OPTION 2. Adjacent Sites with Connectivity

Locate the project on an *adjacent site* (i.e., a site that is adjacent to *previously developed* land; see Definitions) where the *connectivity* of the site and adjacent land is at least 90 intersections/square mile as measured within a 1/2-mile distance of a continuous segment of the *project boundary*, equal to or greater than 25% of the project boundary, that is adjacent to previous development. Existing external and internal intersections may be counted if they were not constructed or funded by the project *developer* within the past ten years. Locate and/or design the project such that a through-*street* and/or nonmotorized right-of-way intersects the project boundary at least every 600 feet on average, and at least every 800 feet, connecting it with an existing street and/or right of way outside the project; nonmotorized rights-of-way may count for no more than 20% of the total. The exemptions listed in NPD Prerequisite 3, Connected and Open Community, do not apply to this option.

Figure 1. Adjacent and connected project site based on minimum 25% of perimeter adjacent to previously developed parcels and at least 90 eligible intersections per square mile within 1/2 mile of boundary segment adjacent to previous development

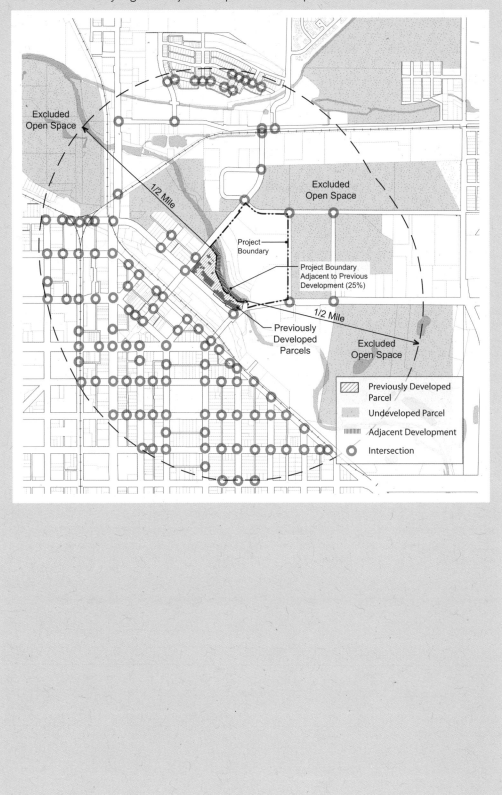

Figure 2. Project site with through-street right-of-way intersecting project boundary at least every 600 feet on average

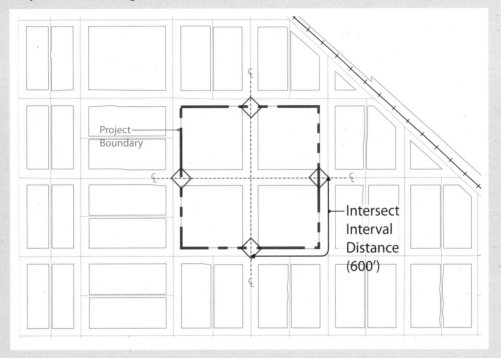

OR

OPTION 3. Transit Corridor or Route with Adequate Transit Service

Locate the project on a site with existing and/or planned transit service such that at least 50% of *dwelling units* and nonresidential building entrances (inclusive of existing buildings) are within a 1/4 mile *walk distance* of bus and/or streetcar stops, or within a 1/2 mile walk distance of *bus rapid transit* stops, light or heavy rail stations, and/or ferry terminals, and the transit service at those stops in aggregate meets the minimums listed in Table 1 (both weekday and weekend trip minimums must be met).

Weekend trips must include service on both Saturday and Sunday. Commuter rail must serve more than one *metropolitan statistical area* (MSA) and/or the area surrounding the core of an MSA.

Table 1. Minimum daily transit service

	Weekday trips	Weekend trips
Projects with multiple transit types (bus, streetcar, rail, or ferry)	60	40
Projects with commuter rail or ferry service only	24	6

SLL PREREQUISITE 1

If transit service is planned but not yet operational, the project must demonstrate one of the following:

a. The relevant transit agency has a signed full funding grant agreement with the Federal Transit Administration that includes a revenue operations date for the start of transit service. The revenue operations date must be no later than the occupancy date of 50% of the project's total building square footage.

b. For bus, streetcar, bus rapid transit, or ferry service, the transit agency must certify that it has an approved budget that includes specifically allocated funds sufficient to provide the planned service at the levels listed above and that service at these levels will commence no later than occupancy of 50% of the project's total building square footage.

c. For rail service other than streetcars, the transit agency must certify that preliminary engineering for a rail line has commenced. In addition, the service must meet either of these two requirements:

- A state legislature or local subdivision of the state has authorized the transit agency to expend funds to establish rail transit service that will commence no later than occupancy of 50% of the project's total building square footage.

OR

- A municipality has dedicated funding or reimbursement commitments from future tax revenue for the development of stations, platforms, or other rail transit infrastructure that will service the project no later than occupancy of 50% of the project's total building square footage.

Figure 3. Walking routes on pedestrian network showing distances from dwellings and nonresidential uses to transit stops.

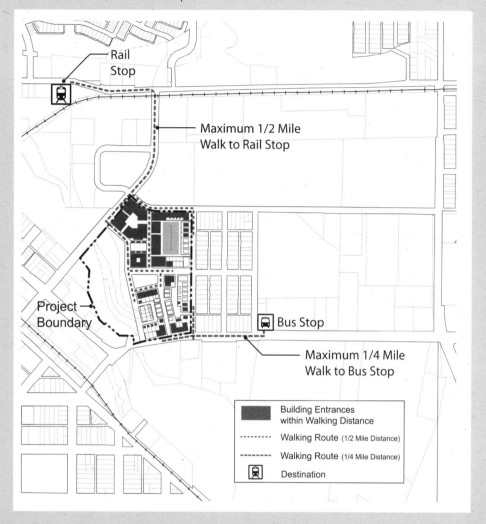

OR

OPTION 4. Sites with Nearby Neighborhood Assets

Include a residential component equaling at least 30% of the project's total building square footage (exclusive of portions of parking structures devoted exclusively to parking), and locate the project near existing neighborhood shops, services, and facilities ("diverse uses"; see Appendix) such that the project boundary is within 1/4-mile walk distance of at least five diverse uses, or such that the project's geographic center is within 1/2-mile walk distance of at least seven diverse uses. In either case the qualifying uses must include at least one food retail establishment and at least one service from each of two other categories, with the following limitations:

a. A single establishment may not be counted in two categories (e.g., a place of worship may be counted only once even if it also contains a daycare facility, and a retail store may be counted only once even if it sells products in several categories).

b. Establishments in a mixed-use building may each count if they are distinctly operated enterprises with separate exterior entrances, but no more than half of the minimum number of diverse uses can be situated in a single building or under a common roof.

c. Only two establishments in a single category may be counted (e.g., if five restaurants are within the required distance, only two may be counted).

Figure 4. Walking routes on pedestrian network showing distances from dwellings and nonresidential uses to diverse use destinations

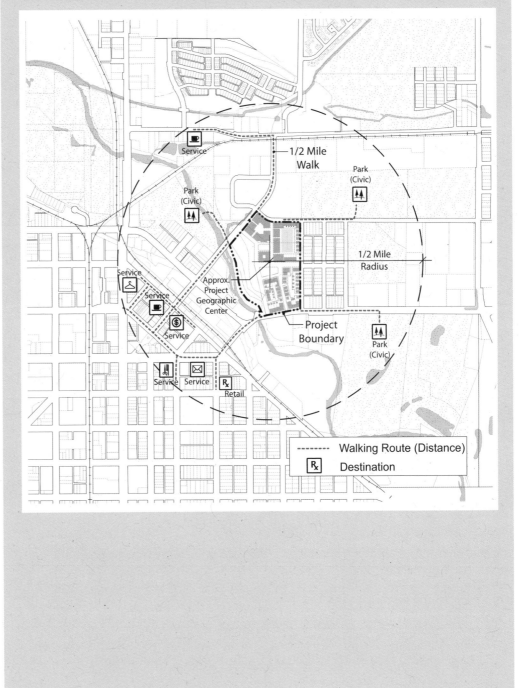

1. Benefits and Issues to Consider

Environmental Issues

For a summary of the numerous environmental benefits of choosing a project site near an existing community or infrastructure, please refer to the Introduction of the Smart Location and Linkage chapter.

Economic and Social Issues

Selecting a site near existing developed areas or targeted growth areas with planned public transit infrastructure may incur higher initial costs than acquiring comparable undeveloped land in outlying areas because of higher land values, remediation costs, and difficulties assembling parcels. It is sometimes possible to offset these costs by choosing less expensive sites that require more up-front effort or expertise to redevelop, such as brownfield or grayfield sites. Increased property values of redeveloped sites in existing areas often offset the higher initial investment required to purchase land in these areas.

The potential for higher property value stems from the numerous economic benefits often realized by residents and business owners in the project. A site with pedestrian access to public transportation, employment, and services that fulfill daily needs allows many households to save on transportation costs or eliminate a vehicle from the household entirely. Similarly, businesses that locate in developed areas may be able to tap into an existing base of customers and workers who live nearby.

2. Related Credits

Locating projects within or adjacent to areas that are already developed or selecting sites served by public transit or close to diverse uses may assist in earning the following related credits:

- SLL Credit 1, Preferred Locations
- SLL Credit 3, Locations with Reduced Automobile Dependence
- SLL Credit 5, Housing and Jobs Proximity
- NPD Credit 3, Mixed-Use Neighborhood Centers
- NPD Credit 6, Street Network

3. Summary of Referenced Standards

There are no referenced standards for this prerequisite.

4. Implementation

Regardless of prerequisite option, the project team should contact the local water and wastewater provider to obtain a map of the existing service area and any legally adopted planned service area. This information can be used to identify potential project sites or determine whether a particular site is in an existing or planned service area. Projects within a legally adopted, publicly owned planned water and wastewater service area must show the agency's commitment to extending service in a legally binding capital improvement program. Septic systems are not considered wastewater infrastructure; please note the definition of *water and wastewater infrastructure* in the Definitions section.

To identify locations that may qualify for Option 1, Infill Sites, or Option 2, Adjacent Sites with Connectivity, ask local government officials whether the municipality maintains any inventories of vacant or underutilized land.

To determine whether a particular site qualifies for Option 1, Infill Sites, gather information about adjacent parcels' previous development status and intersection density by contacting city or county officials. This information may be available in GIS format. Once the information has been obtained, see the Getting Started chapter for discussion about the maps and calculations necessary to document compliance with the infill site conditions.

To determine whether a location meets the requirements for Option 2, Adjacent Sites with Connectivity, contact city or county officials to obtain information on the street network in the area. This information may be available in GIS format. The methodology for calculating intersections per square mile is found in the Getting Started chapter.

To determine whether potential development sites meet the requirements for Option 3, Transit Corridor or Route with Adequate Transit Service, ask the local transit agency about any existing or planned transit routes and obtain the schedules of each route that meets the thresholds in the requirements.

To find project locations that meet the requirements for Option 4, Sites with Nearby Neighborhood Assets, determine whether any existing establishments that qualify as diverse uses (see Appendix) are near the project site. Obtain parcel- or point-level employment data from the local government's economic development department or from private market research data vendors (such as InfoUSA and Claritas). This information will help in mapping the clusters of diverse uses.

5. Timeline and Team

In the site selection phase, the project team should determine which options for the project site location will best meet the location requirements for this prerequisite. Beginning in the conceptual design phase for the project, the design team should ensure that the project is configured so that people can easily and safely reach transit stops, jobs, diverse uses, and residential areas outside the project boundary using multiple modes of travel.

6. Calculations

OPTION 1. Infill Sites

Condition A. Previous Development on Adjacent Parcels

Step 1. On a vicinity map, for the entire project perimeter, identify the parcels adjacent to the project perimeter. For each parcel, calculate the area that is previously developed. Determine the percentage of the parcel that is previously developed by dividing the previously developed area by the entire parcel area and multiplying by 100 (Equation 1). Each adjacent parcel that is at least 50% previously developed is then considered a "qualifying" parcel in these calculations.

Equation 1

$$\text{\% of adjacent parcel previously developed} = \frac{\text{Area of parcel that is previously developed}}{\text{Total area of parcel}} \times 100$$

Step 2. Sum the previously developed land area of each qualifying parcel identified in Step 1, divide by the total land area of all qualifying parcels (Equation 2), and multiply by 100. The result must be 75% or higher.

Equation 2

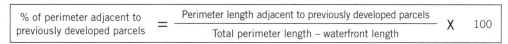

$$\text{\% previously developed area of combined qualifying parcels} = \frac{\text{Total previously developed area of qualifying parcels}}{\text{Total area of qualifying parcels}} \times 100$$

Step 3. Measure the entire project perimeter, and measure the length of the portions adjacent to any waterfront and the length of the portions adjacent to parcels that are at least 50% previously developed (qualifying parcels from Step 1). After subtracting waterfront length from the total perimeter length, divide the perimeter length adjacent to qualifying parcels by the total net perimeter length, and multiply by 100 to obtain the percentage of the perimeter bordering previously developed parcels (Equation 3). The result must be 75% or more.

Equation 3

$$\text{\% of perimeter adjacent to qualifying parcels} = \frac{\text{Perimeter length adjacent to qualifying parcels}}{\text{Total perimeter length} - \text{waterfront length}} \times 100$$

OPTION 2. Adjacent Sites with Connectivity

Step 1. Measure the entire project perimeter, and measure the length of the portions adjacent to any waterfront and the length of the portions adjacent to parcels that are at least 75% previously developed. After subtracting waterfront length from the total perimeter length, divide the perimeter length adjacent to parcels that are at least 75% previously developed by the total net perimeter length, and multiply by 100 to obtain the percentage of perimeter bordering previously developed parcels (Equation 4). The result must be a continuous segment of 25% or more.

Equation 4

$$\text{\% of perimeter adjacent to previously developed parcels} = \frac{\text{Perimeter length adjacent to previously developed parcels}}{\text{Total perimeter length} - \text{waterfront length}} \times 100$$

Step 2. Map the previously developed area near the project, taking care to include a surrounding area large enough to determine qualifying intersections. This will likely require a context map larger than 1/2-mile around the project. Next, map the lands within 1/2-mile from the qualifying continuous segment of project boundary established in Step 1. To do this, offset every point of the qualifying continuous segment by 1/2- mile to define a 1/2-mile adjacent calculation area. This area may include portions of land both inside and outside the project boundary. Identify existing qualifying intersections within the 1/2-mile adjacent calculation area. Do not count any planned intersections and any intersections that were funded or built within the past ten years by the project developer to determine the net number of intersections within the 1/2-mile adjacent calculation area. Determine the gross area in square miles of the 1/2-mile adjacent calculation area, and subtract eligible exclusions to determine the net area, including undeveloped land. Divide the number of qualifying intersections by the net area. The resulting number of intersections per square mile must be 90 or more (Equation 5).

Equation 5

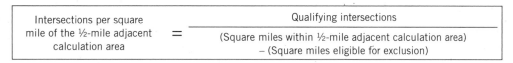

$$\text{Intersections per square mile of the } \tfrac{1}{2}\text{-mile adjacent calculation area} = \frac{\text{Qualifying intersections}}{(\text{Square miles within } \tfrac{1}{2}\text{-mile adjacent calculation area}) - (\text{Square miles eligible for exclusion})}$$

Step 3. Identify the through-streets and nonmotorized rights-of-way (ROWs) that intersect the project boundary for the continuous portion of the perimeter identified in Step 2; only 20% of the total can be nonmotorized. Measure the distance between the centerlines of each of these rights-of-way where they intersect with the project boundary. Confirm that none of the distances exceed 800 feet. Sum the distances between the intersecting through-streets or nonmotorized rights-of-way, and divide by the number of intersecting through-streets or nonmotorized rights-of-way, minus 1 (Equation 6). The result must 600 feet or less.

Equation 6

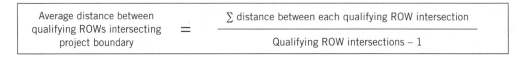

$$\text{Average distance between qualifying ROWs intersecting project boundary} = \frac{\sum \text{distance between each qualifying ROW intersection}}{\text{Qualifying ROW intersections} - 1}$$

OPTION 3. Transit Corridor or Route with Adequate Transit Service

Step 1. Use either of the following two methods to identify qualifying transit stops. See the Getting Started chapter for guidance on shortest path analysis.

Method A

- Use shortest path analysis to determine the walking distances from the project's dwelling units and nonresidential use building entrances to existing or planned transit stops within a 1/2-mile walk distance. For buildings with multiple units or nonresidential entrances, each unit or entrance must be counted separately (e.g., a multifamily residential building with 50 units counts as 50 entrances, and an office building with 10 suites counts as 10 entrances). Each point at which a vehicle stops to receive or discharge passengers is considered a separate stop; this includes stops facing each other on opposite sides of a street.

- Classify the identified transit stops by transit vehicle type (bus, streetcar, bus rapid transit, rail, commuter rail, or ferry).

- Using the shortest path results, count the dwelling units and nonresidential use entrances within a 1/4-mile walk of bus or streetcar stops, and within a 1/2-mile walk of bus rapid transit, rail, and/or ferry terminals.

Method B

- Use shortest path analysis to determine the walking distance from the farthest entrance to each nearby transit stop. If a vicinity map shows that other entrances are closer than the measured entrance to the farthest transit stop, the project may use that calculation to demonstrate that a transit stop and associated entrances qualify.

Step 2. For each transit stop qualifying in Step 1, count the number of transit trips each weekday (i.e., the number of transit vehicles stopping at each stop). Sum the number of trips provided each weekday at all transit stops qualifying in Step 1. The same vehicle may be counted more than once if it stops at multiple qualifying transit stops, but an individual transit stop cannot be counted more than once.

Step 3. For each transit stop qualifying in Step 1, identify transit service that is provided on Saturdays and Sundays. Using those routes, sum the number of trips on Saturdays, and then sum the number on Sundays. The same vehicle may be counted more than once if it stops at multiple qualifying transit stops, but an individual transit stop cannot be counted more than once.

OPTION 4. Sites with Nearby Neighborhood Assets

See the Getting Started chapter for guidance on shortest path analysis.

Step 1. This option is available only to projects with a residential component equaling at least 30% of the total building square footage. Calculate the percentage of the project that is residential by dividing the square feet of residential (exclusive of portions of parking structures devoted only to parking) by the total square feet of the project, and multiplying by 100 (Equation 7). The result must be 30% or higher.

Equation 7

$$\text{\% of project that is residential} = \frac{\text{Residential floor area (sf)}}{\text{Total project floor area (sf)}} \times 100$$

Step 2. On a vicinity map, identify diverse uses (see Appendix) within a 1/4-mile radius of the project's boundary or within a 1/2-mile radius of the project's geographic center.

Use shortest path analysis to create a table of walking distances from all street or nonmotorized right-of-way intersections on the project boundary to the diverse use locations. Using the shortest path results, sum the number of diverse uses within a 1/4-mile walk distance from the project boundary right-of-way intersect points. Subtract diverse uses that do not qualify, per the prerequisite requirements. The result must be 5 or more.

Alternatively, use shortest path analysis to create a table of walking distances from the project's geographic center to the diverse use locations. Using the shortest path results, sum the number of diverse uses within a 1/2-mile walk distance from the project's geographic center. Subtract diverse uses that do not qualify, per the prerequisite requirements. The result should be 7 or more.

7. Documentation Guidance

As a first step in preparing to complete the LEED-ND documentation requirements, work through the following measures. Refer to GBCI's website for the complete descriptions of all required documentation.

- Obtain information on adjacent parcels, including previously developed and undeveloped portions, diverse uses, and transit stop locations. Map the relevant features on a vicinity map.

- If the project is an adjacent site, retain a map of the street and nonmotorized right-of-way networks on adjacent portions.

- For sites with existing transit, obtain information on transit routes and schedules for any transit used for calculations.

- For sites with planned transit, obtain information on proposed transit routes.

- For sites with existing or planned transit, obtain information on the metropolitan service areas that have any commuter rail used for calculations.

- For planned transit service, contact relevant agencies and obtain information on funding and construction timeframes, per the prerequisite requirements.

8. Examples

Example 1. Infill Site

Table 2. Example determination for infill site

	Perimeter length (feet)	Perimeter length adjacent to parcels > 50% previously developed (feet)	Previously developed acres	Total acres	Intersections
Project site	5,000	4,300	N/A	26	N/A
Adjacent parcels	N/A	N/A	55	70	N/A
Aggregate parcel	16,000	13,500	N/A	N/A	
Parcels adjacent to aggregate parcel	N/A	N/A	105	125	N/A
Land within ½-mile of project perimeter	N/A	N/A	34*	45*	15

* Exclusive of rights-of-way.

In this example, the project meets Condition (a) (previous development on adjacent parcels that border perimeter) because the portion of the perimeter that borders parcels that are more than 50% previously developed is (4,300 / 5,000) x 100 = 86% (Equation 1). In addition, the adjacent parcels are in aggregate 78% previously developed: (55 / 70) x 100.

The project meets Condition (b) (previous development on parcels adjacent to aggregate parcel) because the aggregate parcel's portion of the perimeter that borders parcels that are more than 50% previously developed is (13,500 / 16,000) x 100 = 84% (Equation 1). In addition, the parcels adjacent to the aggregate parcel are in aggregate 84% previously developed: (105 / 125) x 100.

The project meets Condition (c) (previous development on surrounding land) because the land within 1/2-mile of the project perimeter is 76% previously developed: (34 / 45) x 100.

The project meets Condition (d) (connectivity of surrounding land) because the land within 1/2-mile of the project perimeter has more than 140 intersections per square mile (45 acres / 640 acres per square mile = .07 square miles; 15 intersections / .07 square mile = 214 intersections / square mile).

Please note the project needs to fulfill only one of the four conditions to qualify as an infill site.

Example 2. Adjacent Site with Connectivity

A project team wants to develop adjacent to land that is largely previously developed and seeks to qualify as an adjacent site with connectivity.

Table 3. Example determination for adjacent site with connectivity

	Perimeter length (feet)	Adjacent perimeter length (feet)	Intersections	Total acres
Project	7,600	2,750	17	76
Adjacent portion within ½ mile of project	N/A	N/A	13	110
Total	N/A	N/A	30	186

The percentage of the project's perimeter that is adjacent to previously developed land is
(2,750 / 7,600) x 100 = 36%.

The connectivity of the site and adjacent land is 30 intersections / (186 acres / 640 acres per square mile) = 103 intersections / square mile.

If the project meets the requirements related to the distances between through-streets and nonmotorized rights-of-way at the project perimeter, it meets the requirements for Option 2.

Example 3. Transit Corridor or Route with Adequate Transit Service

A 4-acre project featuring detached homes, a multiunit residential building with ground-floor retail, and two office buildings with ground-floor retail will have a bus rapid transit (BRT) line with one stop within the project and one outside the project boundary. The project team measures the distance from the entrances to determine whether at least 50% of the entrances are within 1/2-mile (2,640 feet) of at least one stop.

As Table 4 shows, 110 (83%) of the 132 entrances in the project fall within 1/2-mile of a BRT stop, satisfying the prerequisite requirements. Mixed-Use A and Detached Residential 3 and 4 do not have qualifying entrances because they are beyond a 1/2-mile walk distance.

Table 4. Example determination for distance to transit stops

Building	Entrances	Walk distance (feet)	Transit stop destination
Mixed-Use A (offices + retail)	21	2,750	BRT 2
Mixed-Use B (offices + retail)	31	1,234	BRT 1
Mixed-Use C (residential + retail)	76	900	BRT 1
Detached Residential 1	1	542	BRT 1
Detached Residential 2	1	278	BRT 2
Detached Residential 3	1	2,908	BRT 2
Detached Residential 4	1	3,760	BRT 1
Total qualifying entrances	110		

The transit service must be adequate as well as within the specified walking distance. The team researches the scheduled service and records the results (Table 5).

Table 5. Example determination for daily trips per transit stop

Transit stop	Service	Weekday trips	Saturday trips	Sunday trips
BRT 1	B33	42	27	21
BRT 2	B33	42	18	21
Total		84	45	42

This project meets the requirement for adequate transit service because it will be served by 84 (more than 60) weekday daily trips and 42 (more than 40) weekend daily trips within the required walking distances. Even though entrances in several buildings are close to the same transit stop, the trips at that stop are counted only once.

Example 4. Nearby Neighborhood Assets

A project has diverse uses near its perimeter, as shown in Table 6.

Table 6. Example list of nearby diverse uses

Category	Establishment	Diverse uses within ¼-mile walk of perimeter	Diverse uses within ½-mile walk of project center
Food retail	Supermarket	1	1
Community-serving retail	Hardware store	—	1
	Pharmacy	—	—
Services	Laundry	1	2
	Bank	—	3 (–1)
Civic and community facilities	Community center	—	—
	Post office	1	1
	Church	—	1
	School	—	1
Total diverse uses		3	10
Total qualifying diverse uses		3	9

Only three diverse uses, not the required five, are within a 1/4-mile walk of the project boundary. However, there are nine diverse uses, more than the required seven, within a 1/2-mile of the project's center. Because the team needs to meet only one of the two requirements, this project achieves the prerequisite. Note that one of the banks was excluded because only two establishments in any one category can be counted.

9. Exemplary Performance

This prerequisite is not eligible for exemplary performance under Innovation and Design Process.

10. Regional Variations

There are no regional variations associated with this prerequisite.

11. Resources

Websites
Metropolitan planning organizations
www.bts.gov/external_links/government/metropolitan_planning_organizations.html
This website lists metropolitan planning organizations around the United States.

Print Media
Environmental Characteristics of Smart-Growth Neighborhoods, Phase One (Natural Resources Defence Council and Criterion Planners, 2000), available at www.nrdc.org/cities/smartGrowth/char/charinx.asp.

Growing Cooler: The Evidence on Urban Development and Climate Change, by Reid Ewing, Keith Bartholomew, Steve Winkelman, Jerry Walters, and Don Chen (Urban Land Institute, 2007).

New Urbanism: Comprehensive Report and Best Practices Guide (New Urban Publications, 2003).

Our Built and Natural Environments: A Technical Review of the Interactions between Land Use,

Transportation, and Environmental Quality (Development, Community, and Environment Division, U.S. Environmental Protection Agency, 2001).

Planning and Urban Design Standards, by American Planning Association (John Wiley & Sons, 2006).

12. Definitions

adjacent site a site having at least 25% of its boundary bordering parcels that are each at least 75% previously developed. A street or other right-of-way does not constitute previously developed land; instead, it is the status of the property on the other side of the street or right-of-way that matters. Any fraction of the boundary that borders waterfront other than a stream is excluded from the calculation. A site is still considered adjacent if the 25% adjacent portion of its boundary is separated from previously developed parcels by undeveloped, permanently protected land averaging no more than 400 feet in width and no more than 500 feet in any one place. The undeveloped land must be permanently preserved as natural area, riparian corridor, park, greenway, agricultural land, or designated cultural landscape. Permanent pedestrian paths connecting the project through the protected parcels to the bordering site may be counted to meet the requirement of SLL Prerequisite 1, Option 2 (that the project be connected to the adjacent parcel by a through-street or nonmotorized right-of-way every 600 feet on average, provided the path or paths traverse the undeveloped land at no more than a 10% grade for walking by persons of all ages and physical abilities).

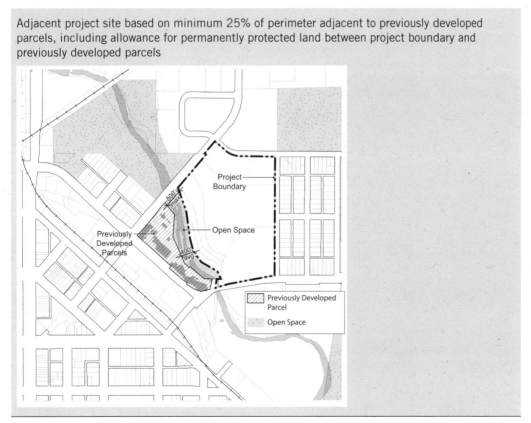

Adjacent project site based on minimum 25% of perimeter adjacent to previously developed parcels, including allowance for permanently protected land between project boundary and previously developed parcels

bus rapid transit an enhanced bus system that operates on exclusive bus lanes or other transit rights-of-way; it is designed to combine the flexibility of buses with the efficiency of rail.

connectivity the number of publicly accessible street intersections per square mile, including intersections of streets with dedicated alleys and transit rights-of-way, and intersections of streets with nonmotorized rights-of-way (up to 20% of total intersections). If one must both enter and exit an area through the same intersection, such an intersection and any intersections beyond that point are not counted; intersections leading only to culs-de-sac are also not counted. The calculation of square mileage excludes water bodies, parks larger than 1/2-acre, public facility campuses, airports, rail yards, slopes over 15%, and areas nonbuildable under codified law or the rating system. Street rights-of-way may not be excluded.

developer a public and/or private entity that controls a majority of the project's buildable land and is committed to making a majority of the investments required for the project implementation described in the LEED-ND submission.

development footprint the total land area of a project site covered by buildings, streets, parking areas, and other typically impermeable surfaces constructed as part of the project.

dwelling unit living quarters intended for long-term occupancy that provide facilities for cooking, sleeping, and sanitation. This does not include hotel rooms

existing present on the date of submission of LEED-ND certification documents; similarly, an element or condition that **exists** is present on the date that LEED-ND certification documents are submitted.

infill site a site that meets any of the following four conditions:

a. At least 75% of its boundary borders parcels that individually are at least 50% previously developed, and that in aggregate are at least 75% previously developed.

b. The site, in combination with bordering parcels, forms an aggregate parcel whose boundary is 75% bounded by parcels that individually are at least 50% previously developed, and that in aggregate are at least 75% previously developed.

c. At least 75% of the land area, exclusive of rights-of-way, within a 1/2-mile distance from the project boundary is previously developed.

d. The lands within a 1/2-mile distance from the project boundary have a preproject connectivity of at least 140 intersections per square mile.

A street or other right-of-way does not constitute previously developed land; it is the status of property on the other side of the street or right-of-way that matters. For conditions (a) and (b) above, any fraction of the perimeter that borders waterfront other than a stream is excluded from the calculation.

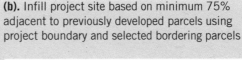

(b). Infill project site based on minimum 75% adjacent to previously developed parcels using project boundary and selected bordering parcels

(b). Infill project site based on minimum 75% adjacent to previously developed parcels using project boundary and selected bordering parcels

(c). Infill project site based on minimum 75% of land area within 1/2-mile of project boundary being previously developed

(d). Infill project site based on minimum 140 intersections/sq.mi. within 1/2-mile of project boundary

metropolitan (metro) and micropolitan (micro) statistical area a geographic entity defined by the U.S. Office of Management and Budget for use by federal statistical agencies in collecting, tabulating, and publishing federal statistics. A metro area contains a core urban area with a population of 50,000 or more, and a micro area contains an urban core with a population between 10,000 and 50,000. Each metro or micro area consists of one or more counties and includes the counties containing the core urban area, as well as any adjacent counties that have a high degree of social and economic integration (as measured by commuting to work) with the urban core. "Core-based statistical area" (CBSA) encompasses both metro and micro areas.

previously developed altered by paving, construction, and/or land use that would typically have required regulatory permitting to have been initiated (alterations may exist now or in the past). Previously developed land includes a platted lot on which a building was constructed if the lot is no more than 1 acre; previous development on lots larger than 1 acre is defined as the development footprint and land alterations associated with the footprint. Land that is not previously developed and altered landscapes resulting from current or historical clearing or filling, agricultural or forestry use, or preserved natural area use are considered undeveloped land. The date of previous development permit issuance constitutes the date of previous development, but permit issuance in itself does not constitute previous development.

project the land, water, and construction that constitutes the project application. A project applicant does not have to own or control all land or water within a project boundary, but all the area within the project boundary must comply with prerequisites and attempted credits.

project boundary the platted property line of the project defining land and water within it. Projects located on publicly owned campuses that do not have internal property lines must delineate a sphere-of-influence line to be used instead. *Project site* is equivalent to the land and water inside the project boundary. The project must not contain noncontiguous parcels, but parcels can be separated by public rights-of-way. Projects may also have enclaves of nonproject properties that are not subject to the rating system, but such enclaves cannot exceed 2% of the total project area and cannot be described as certified.

street a dedicated right-of-way that can accommodate one or more modes of travel, excluding alleys and paseos. A street is suitable for primary entrances and provides access to the front and/or sides of buildings and lots. A street may be privately owned as long as it is deeded in perpetuity for general public use. A street must be an addressable thoroughfare (for mail purposes) under the standards of the applicable regulating authority.

vehicle miles traveled (VMT) the number of miles driven by motorists in a specified time period, such as a day or a year, in absolute or per capita terms.

walk distance the distance that a pedestrian must travel between origins and destinations without obstruction, in a safe and comfortable environment on a continuous network of sidewalks, all-weather-surface footpaths, crosswalks, woonerfs, or equivalent pedestrian facilities.

water and wastewater infrastructure publicly owned water and wastewater infrastructure; this excludes septic and mound wastewater treatment systems.

IMPERILED SPECIES AND ECOLOGICAL COMMUNITIES CONSERVATION

	ND
Prerequisite	SLL Prerequisite 2
Points	Required

Intent

To conserve imperiled species and ecological communities.

Requirements

FOR ALL PROJECTS

Consult with the state Natural Heritage Program and state fish and wildlife agencies to determine whether species listed as threatened or endangered under the federal Endangered Species Act, the state's endangered species act, or species or ecological communities classified by NatureServe as GH (possibly extinct), G1 (critically imperiled), or G2 (imperiled) have been or are likely to be found on the *project* site because of the presence of suitable habitat and nearby occurrences. If the consultations are inconclusive and site conditions indicate that imperiled species or ecological communities could be present, using a qualified biologist, perform biological surveys using accepted methodologies during appropriate seasons to determine whether such species or communities occur or are likely to occur on the site.

OPTION 1. Sites without Affected Species or Ecological Community

The prerequisite is satisfied if the consultation and any necessary biological surveys determine that no such imperiled species or ecological communities have been found or have a high likelihood of occurring.

OR

OPTION 2. Sites with Affected Species or Ecological Community: Habitat Conservation Plan

Comply with an approved habitat conservation plan under the Endangered Species Act for each identified species or ecological community.

OR

OPTION 3. Sites with Affected Species or Ecological Community: Habitat Conservation Plan Equivalent

Work with a qualified biologist, a nongovernmental conservation organization, or the appropriate state, regional, or local agency to create and implement a conservation plan that includes the following actions:

a. Identify and map the extent of the habitat and the appropriate buffer, not less than 100 feet, according to best available scientific information.

b. To the maximum extent practicable, protect the identified habitat and buffer in perpetuity by donating or selling the land or a conservation easement on the land to an accredited land trust or relevant public agency.

c. If on-site protection can be accomplished, analyze threats from development and develop a monitoring and management plan that eliminates or significantly reduces the threats.

d. If any portion of the identified habitat and buffer cannot be protected in perpetuity, quantify the effects by acres or number of plants and/or animals affected, and protect from development in perpetuity habitat of similar or better quality, on-site or off-site, by donating or selling a conservation easement on it to an accredited land trust or relevant public agency. The donation or easement must cover an amount of land equal to or larger than the area that cannot be protected.

1. Benefits and Issues to Consider

Environmental Issues

Prevention of habitat encroachment is an essential element of sustainable site selection. Choosing a previously developed site offers the best chance to avoid sensitive species and ecological communities. It is also important, however, to recognize that even previously developed sites may contain such species. Proper treatment of previously developed sites with sensitive species or communities may help restore ecological balance to the area. On all sites, protecting sensitive species and communities will support biodiversity so that the natural areas of the site remain healthy.

Consider the local context when conducting an inventory of present or likely present species. Parcels bordering the project site may have protected habitat areas or corridors that the project can connect to, increasing the potential of any land set aside by the project to adequately protect species and decrease habitat fragmentation.

Areas set aside for the protection of species and ecological communities may also offer excellent educational opportunities, such as a visitors' station or nature walk. Portions of preserved areas can occasionally double as recreation amenities, depending on the sensitivity and needs of the particular species and ecological communities present.

Economic and Social Issues

A benefit of doing a comprehensive check for imperiled species prior to undertaking a project is the early discovery of any constraints on development. The presence of sensitive species and their habitat requirements may not be immediately apparent, and having this information in hand during initial site design can reduce the likelihood of costly redesign later.

Channeling development away from sensitive ecological areas may also encourage public support for a project and speed public review periods, thus minimizing or preventing obstacles traditionally encountered during project scoping.

2. Related Credits

Conserving environmentally sensitive land, whether by locating the project elsewhere or by designing the site to avoid, protect, or restore native natural communities, may assist in earning the following related credits:

- SLL Credit 6, Steep Slope Protection

- SLL Credit 7, Site Design for Habitat or Wetland and Water Body Conservation

- SLL Credit 8, Restoration of Habitat or Wetlands and Water Bodies

- SLL Credit 9, Long-Term Conservation Management of Habitat or Wetlands and Water Bodies

- GIB Credit 7, Minimized Site Disturbance in Design and Construction

3. Summary of Referenced Standards

Association of Fish and Wildlife Agencies, state endangered species acts
www.fishwildlife.org
Each state has a list of threatened and endangered species, maintained and administered by its fish and wildlife agency. In addition, many states have lists of candidate species and species of special concern. State endangered species acts vary in their criteria for listing and requirements for protection. The Association of Fish and Wildlife Agencies website has links to each state fish and wildlife agency.

National Marine Fisheries Service, endangered marine species
www.nmfs.noaa.gov/pr/species/esa_species.htm
The National Marine Fisheries Service is in charge of conservation guidelines and permitting for federally listed marine species.

NatureServe National Heritage Program, GH, G1, and G2 species and ecological communities
www.natureserve.org
NatureServe is a nonprofit conservation organization that represents an international network of biological inventories—known as natural heritage programs or conservation data centers—operating in all 50 U.S. states, Canada, Latin America, and the Caribbean. GH, G1, and G2 are part of a classification system maintained by this network of natural heritage programs in every state. Ecological communities are specific assemblages of species that are classified and defined by NatureServe using a standard classification system. NatureServe uses a number of criteria in assessing the status of species and ecological communities, including the number of populations, the size of populations, the viability of the species occurrences, the trends in population numbers, and the threats to species. GH species or ecological communities are possibly extinct and are known from only historical occurrences but still have some hope of rediscovery. G1 species or ecological communities are critically imperiled and are at very high risk of extinction globally because of extreme rarity (often five or fewer populations), very steep declines, or other factors. G2 are imperiled species or ecological communities at high risk of extinction globally because of very restricted range, very few populations (often 20 or fewer), steep declines, or other factors. If a species or ecological community has two ranks or a question mark beside the rank, the lowest rank number should be used in meeting this credit (e.g., a G2/G3 species and a G2 should both be considered G2s and included in this prerequisite).

U.S. Fish and Wildlife Service, threatened and endangered species
www.fws.gov/endangered/
This referenced standard addresses threatened and endangered wildlife and plants. The U.S. Fish and Wildlife Service also maintains a list of the country's native plants and animals that are candidates for addition to the federal list.

U.S. Fish and Wildlife Service, Endangered Species Act, habitat conservation plans
www.fws.gov/endangered/hcp/index.html
Entities conducting activities that might incidentally harm ("take") endangered or threatened wildlife on their land are required to obtain an incidental take permit from the U.S. Fish and Wildlife Service, under Section 10 of the Endangered Species Act; the permit provides legal protection from a violation. To obtain a permit, the applicant needs to develop a habitat conservation plan (HCP), designed to offset any harmful effects the proposed activity might have on the species. HCPs are approved by the USFWS if the applicant demonstrates that it has minimized and mitigated effects on endangered species to the maximum extent practicable, that the plan has adequate funding, and that the project will not jeopardize the survival or recovery of the species.

4. Implementation

As early as possible after site acquisition, consult with both the state fish and wildlife agency and the state natural heritage program about the potential for imperiled species or ecological communities to occur on the site. Project teams with sites that are previously developed or highly disturbed still need to perform this step, since imperiled species can occasionally occur in disturbed or built environments. Projects that have already conducted a biological survey of the site also need to consult with the state fish and wildlife agency and the state natural heritage program.

This prerequisite covers all species named in state, federal, and NatureServe lists. Not all GH, G1, and G2 species are listed under state or federal endangered species acts, and no ecological communities are listed under any endangered species acts. GH, G1, and G2 species and ecological communities are included in this prerequisite even if they are not listed under federal or state endangered species acts. Likewise, listed species that are not GH, G1, or G2 are also included in the prerequisite. Consult with the state fish and wildlife agency (for state and federally listed species) and the state's natural heritage program (for GH, G1, and G2 species and ecological communities) to ensure that the information is comprehensive.

If the result of the consultation with state agencies is inconclusive, decide whether site conditions indicate that species or ecological communities could be present. If site conditions clearly indicate that species are not present, the team need not conduct a biological survey. Examples of such site conditions include the following: the site is 100% previously developed; land on the site that is not previously developed is highly modified or consists entirely of invasive species; or the site is devoid of natural habitat and is surrounded by previously developed land.

If site conditions indicate that species or ecological communities could be present, a biological survey must be performed according to the prerequisite requirements by a qualified biologist. Qualified biologists should have knowledge of the local area, experience identifying species and habitats, and expertise in developing plans to conserve these habitats. Results from the biological survey, whether species presence is detected or absence is confirmed, should be provided to the state's natural heritage program.

If a federally listed species occurs on the property, the U.S. Fish and Wildlife Service should be notified immediately. If this agency determines that a habitat conservation plan (HCP) is required for the project to proceed, comply with Option 2, Habitat Conservation Plan. If an HCP is not required (i.e., if impacts are completely avoided, if the project receives a "take" permit through its wetland permitting, or if a federally listed plant is involved), comply with Option 3, Habitat Conservation Plan Equivalent.

If a state-listed species or a GH, G1, or G2 species or ecological community is found, the relevant state agency should be notified immediately, and the project will need to comply with state requirements as well as Option 3.

A project may be located within the coverage area of a regional HCP. Throughout most of California, as well as some counties in other states, regional HCPs have been developed to coordinate development permitting and conservation activities on a regional basis. Ask the state office of the U.S. Fish and Wildlife Service whether an approved HCP is in place for the project's region. If so, provide documentation that the site is covered by the regional HCP and that the project is complying with the plan.

For Option 3, in crafting a conservation strategy for on-site species or identifying off-site conservation sites, consider integrating conservation strategies with those of adjacent sites and conservation plans in the region. Consider mitigation not just for direct effects to habitat on the site but also for indirect effects on species from introduced exotic plants and animals (including domestic pets), mortality of animals from vehicles, water quality impacts, and other causes. For conserved areas, if possible, establish a funding source for ongoing management of habitat areas in perpetuity. Option 3 also requires donation or sale of land to accomplish habitat protection "to the maximum extent practicable." A land donation or sale must occur in all instances unless documented extenuating circumstances make such action clearly impractical. See the Land Trust Alliance contact information in the Resources section, below, for additional help with land donations and sales for protective purposes.

5. Timeline and Team

During the site selection process, the developer should contract with environmental professionals to conduct site assessments for imperiled species, wetlands and water bodies, floodplains, prime soils for agriculture, and other sensitive environmental features. Once a site has been selected, if sensitive environmental resources are found, the developer should contract with environmental professionals who can assess these features more thoroughly and develop a holistic plan to conserve the site's natural resources.

6. Calculations

There are no calculations for this prerequisite.

7. Documentation Guidance

As a first step in preparing to complete the LEED-ND documentation requirements, work through the following measures. Refer to GBCI's website for the complete descriptions of all required documentation.

- Retain written evidence that state agencies were consulted before the site was cleared.

- If an environmental impact report or statement is being prepared, retain information related to imperiled species. If GH, G1, and G2 species and ecological communities were not considered in the scope of the environmental impact report or statement, retain documentation that state agencies were consulted about these species and ecological communities.

- If the consultation was inconclusive and site conditions indicate that a biological survey is not necessary, document with photographs what the site looked like prior to clearing, if possible.

- If the project has an approved habitat conservation plan or is included in a regional HCP, create a vicinity map showing that the project falls within its scope.

- If preparing an HCP equivalent, acquire documentation from the U.S. Fish and Wildlife Service (for federally listed species) or the state fish and wildlife agency or natural heritage program (for state-listed species or GH, G1, and G2 species and ecological communities) that the project is complying with state or federal conservation requirements. Retain a site map indicating habitat areas and their buffers.

- For on-site habitat protection, prepare a summary of the development's threats to species on the site and summarize the expected monitoring and management activities.

- Obtain a letter from the relevant land trust or public agency that the transfer of land rights for habitat lands has taken place or will take place.

8. Examples

There are no examples for this prerequisite.

9. Exemplary Performance

This prerequisite is not eligible for exemplary performance under Innovation and Design Process.

10. Regional Variations

State endangered species acts vary in their requirements for species protection, so ask state fish and wildlife agencies for guidance. Species and ecological communities are classified as GH, G1, or G2 based on the same criteria throughout the United States, but the concentration of such species and ecological communities varies greatly by region. Most are found in the southern portions of the country and in Hawaii.

11. Resources

Websites

Land Trust Alliance

www.landtrustalliance.org

The Land Trust Alliance has an accreditation program for land trusts, and its website has links to land trusts across the United States.

NatureServe Explorer

www.natureserve.org/explorer/

This website lists the conservation status and other information for more than 65,000 species and ecological communities.

NatureServe, state natural heritage programs

www.natureserve.org/visitLocal/index.jsp

This website provides links to NatureServe's network of natural heritage programs operating in all 50 U.S. states, Canadian provinces and territories, and many countries and territories in Latin America and the Caribbean.

State fish and wildlife agencies

www.fishwildlife.org/where_us.html

The Association of Fish and Wildlife Agencies provides links to state fish and wildlife agencies in every state and in Canadian provinces.

Sustainable Sites Initiative

www.sustainablesites.org

The Sustainable Sites Initiative is an interdisciplinary effort by the American Society of Landscape Architects, the Lady Bird Johnson Wildflower Center, and the United States Botanic Garden to create voluntary national guidelines and performance benchmarks for sustainable land design, construction, and maintenance practices.

Print Media

Conservation Thresholds for Land Use Planners (Environmental Law Institute, 2003).

Design with Nature, by Ian L. McHarg (Doubleday & Company, 1969).

Habitat Protection Planning: Where the Wild Things Are, by Chris Duerksen et al. (American Planning Association, Planning Advisory Service Report Number 470/471, 1997).

Nature-Friendly Land Use Practices at Multiple Scales, by Rebecca Kihslinger and James McElfish (Environmental Law Institute, 2009).

12. Definitions

project the land, water, and construction that constitutes the project application. A project applicant does not have to own or control all land or water within a project boundary, but all the area within the project boundary must comply with prerequisites and attempted credits.

	ND
Prerequisite	SLL Prerequisite 3
Points	Required

Intent

To preserve water quality, natural hydrology, habitat, and biodiversity through conservation of *wetlands* and *water bodies*.

Requirements

Limit development effects on wetlands, water bodies, and surrounding buffer land according to the requirements below.

OPTION 1. Sites with No Wetlands, Water Bodies, Land within 50 Feet of Wetlands, or Land within 100 Feet of Water Bodies

Locate the *project* on a site that includes no wetlands, no water bodies, no land within 50 feet of wetlands, and no land within 100 feet of water bodies.

OR

OPTION 2. Sites with Wetlands, Water Bodies, Land within 50 Feet of Wetlands, or Land within 100 Feet of Water Bodies

a. Locate the project such that *preproject* wetlands, water bodies, land within 50 feet of wetlands, and land within 100 feet of water bodies is not affected by new development, unless the development is minor improvements or is on *previously developed* land.

OR

b. Earn at least 1 point under GIB Credit 8, Stormwater Management, and limit any impacts beyond minor improvements to less than the percentage of buffer land listed in Table 1.

Table 1. Maximum allowable area of impacts within buffer zone, by density

Residential density (DU/acre)*	Nonresidential density (FAR)*	Percentage of buffer land** where impacts beyond minor improvements are allowed
> 25	> 1.75	≤ 20%
> 18 and ≤ 25	> 1.25 to ≤ 1.75	≤ 15%
> 10 and ≤ 18	> .75 to ≤ 1.25	≤ 10%
≤ 10	≤ .75	≤ 5%

DU = dwelling unit; FAR = floor-area ratio.

* For this option, a mixed-use project may use either its residential or its nonresidential *density* to determine the percentage of allowable impacts, regardless of which is higher.

** For this option, buffer width may vary as long as the total buffer area is equal to the area within 50 feet of wetlands and/or within 100 feet of water bodies, minus excluded features (see below). The minimum buffer width, however, is 25 feet for wetlands and 50 feet for water bodies, measured from the edge. In the minimum buffer, only minor improvements and/or improvements that result in no ecological impairment of the wetland or water body, as determined by a qualified biologist, are allowed.

SLL PREREQUISITE 3

AND

FOR ALL PROJECTS

Comply with all local, state, and federal regulations pertaining to wetland and water body conservation.

The following features are not considered wetlands, water bodies, or buffer land that must be protected for the purposes of this prerequisite:

a. Previously developed land.

b. Man-made water bodies (such as industrial mining pits, concrete-lined canals, or stormwater retention ponds) that lack natural edges and floors or native ecological communities in the water and along the edge.

c. Man-made linear wetlands that result from the interruption of natural drainages by *existing* rights-of-way.

d. Wetlands that were man-made incidentally and have been rated "poor" for all measured wetland functions. Wetland quality assessment must be performed by a qualified biologist using a method that is accepted by state or regional permitting agencies.

Minor improvements within the buffer may be undertaken to enhance appreciation for the wetland or water body, provided such facilities are open to public access. Only the following improvements are permitted:

a. Bicycle and pedestrian pathways no more than 12 feet wide, of which no more than 8 feet may be impervious.

b. Activities to maintain or restore native natural communities and/or natural hydrology.

c. One single-story structure not exceeding 500 square feet per 300 linear feet of buffer, on average.

d. Grade changes necessary to ensure public access.

e. Clearings, limited to one per 300 linear feet of buffer on average, not exceeding 500 square feet each, for tables, benches, and access for nonmotorized recreational watercraft. Off-street parking is not considered a minor improvement.

f. Removal of hazardous trees; up to 75% of dead trees; trees less than 6 inches diameter at breast height; trees under 40% condition rating; and up to 20% of trees more than 6 inches diameter at breast height with a condition rating of 40% or higher. The condition rating must be based on an assessment by an arborist certified by the International Society of Arboriculture (ISA) using ISA standard measures.

g. *Brownfield* remediation activities.

Direct impacts to wetlands and water bodies are prohibited, except for minimal-impact structures, such as an elevated boardwalk, that allow access to the water for educational and recreational purposes. Structures that protrude into wetlands or water bodies may be replaced, provided the replacement structure has the same or smaller footprint and a similar height.

1. Benefits and Issues to Consider

Environmental Issues

Careful consideration of the location and condition of wetlands and water bodies is a crucial element in determining an appropriate project location. Water features serve numerous critical functions, providing habitat, maintaining microclimate, and recharging groundwater reserves. Dwindling water supplies in many areas of the country, particularly in the Southwest and Southeast, underscore the need for proper management of water resources. If maintained in a natural state, wetlands and water bodies can also play an important role in managing stormwater runoff from the site. If appropriate for the particular wetland or water body, providing public access is an effective way to instill a sense of stewardship in project residents and visitors.

Economic and Social Issues

Proximity to or views of a lake, river, or stream can be a significant selling point in a project, and it is important to carefully weigh the profit to be made from selling parcels near water bodies with the ecological health of the water features and the community benefits of public accessibility. Appropriate public accessibility to wetlands and water bodies can greatly increase the value of adjacent properties, offsetting the costs of hiring qualified professionals to assess the water features and design appropriate buffers and access points. Also, healthy wetlands and water bodies acting as natural stormwater management features may reduce the need to install costly cisterns or man-made stormwater treatment facilities.

Projects that avoid water features altogether may also realize cost savings by eliminating the need to hire specialized professionals to perform assessments, apply for additional permits with the local jurisdiction, or undertake restoration activities.

2. Related Credits

Conserving environmentally sensitive land, whether by locating the project elsewhere or by designing the site to avoid, protect, or restore natural hydrology and native habitat and biodiversity, may assist in earning the following related credits:

- SLL Credit 6, Steep Slope Protection

- SLL Credit 7, Site Design for Habitat or Wetland and Water Body Conservation

- SLL Credit 8, Restoration of Habitat or Wetlands and Water Bodies

- SLL Credit 9, Long-Term Conservation Management of Habitat or Wetlands and Water Bodies

- GIB Credit 7, Minimized Site Disturbance in Design and Construction

- GIB Credit 8, Stormwater Management

3. Referenced Standards

The International Society of Arboriculture sets standards for rating the condition of trees, and these ratings must be used to guide decisions about any tree removals in buffer zones.

4. Implementation

As part of an integrated design process to protect natural resources, conduct a thorough environmental survey identifying the site's sensitive environmental resources and their roles in its immediate vicinity and region. The site assessment should identify all water bodies and wetlands and take into account the hydrology, soils, and geomorphology of the site and its surrounding area. Wetlands should be delineated according to the Army Corps of Engineers' 1987 *Wetlands Delineation Manual*.

Delineated wetlands are included in the prerequisite regardless of whether they are considered jurisdictional wetlands under the Clean Water Act. For example, a small vernal pool that is not considered a jurisdictional wetland would still be protected under this prerequisite because it would be delineated according to the methodology in the Army Corps of Engineers' manual. In addition, adjacent land within 100 feet from the project's perimeter should be examined to determine whether the site contains buffer land for nearby wetlands or water bodies. Minimum and average widths for such buffers are shown in Figure 1. Intermittent wetlands within 100 feet of the project boundary or on the site should be assessed using the Army Corps method to see whether they qualify for delineation. Irrigation ditches are exempt from the prerequisite.

Figure 1. Wetland buffer widths showing minimum 25 feet and minimum average of 50 feet

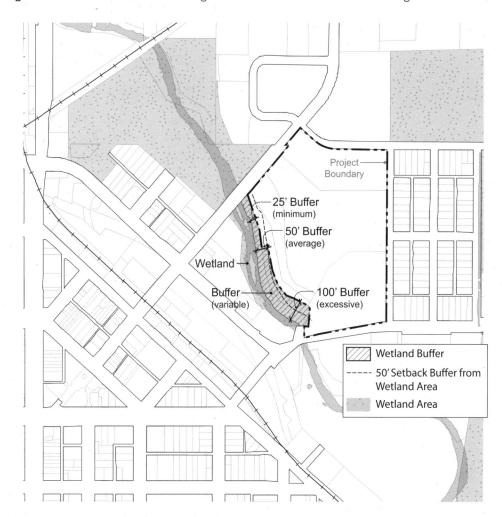

If wetlands, water bodies, or buffer land is located on the site, contact local, state, and federal authorities to determine what, if any, impacts to wetlands and water bodies or buffers are permitted. If compensatory mitigation is required by local or federal authorities, contact local or regional wetlands mitigation banks or state governmental agencies to determine how to compensate for impacts on on-site wetlands.

Once wetlands and water bodies are delineated, the site should be examined again to identify the four categories of features that are excluded from protection under this prerequisite: previously developed land, qualifying man-made water bodies, qualifying linear wetlands, and qualifying incidentally created poor-quality wetlands. For details, see the list under "For All Projects". Exclude these features from the list of wetlands and waterbodies to be protected.

For remaining wetlands, draw 50-foot buffers, along the horizontal plane, from the edge of the wetland delineation. For remaining water bodies, draw 100-foot buffers, measured along the horizontal plane, from the high tide (for coastal water bodies), the normal pool elevation (for inland water bodies), or the ordinary high-water mark (for both sides of streams and rivers), as appropriate. Make every effort to restrict development to areas outside the 50-foot and 100-foot buffers.

Minor improvements that may be made within the buffer land are described in the requirements. Maintenance or improvements to existing utilities located in easements within the buffer may be considered minor improvements, if the disturbance is temporary and native vegetation is restored as much as possible. For minor improvement (a), lighting that is included as part of pathways can be counted as part of the minor improvement. The pathways may be 8 to 12 feet wide, but width beyond 8 feet must be pervious. For (b), invasive species removal is included in restoration activities that are minor improvements. For (c), measure the closest distance between each small structure. Sum the distances between structures and divide by the number of structures, minus 1. The average distance should be less than 300 feet. For (d), ensure that grade changes are limited to those necessary for public access. For (e), do not exceed 500 square feet for each clearing, and limit clearings to one per 300 linear feet of buffer, on average. For (f), it is best to establish a canopy cover target if any trees will be removed. For all minor improvements, when working in areas of sensitive nature, reduce impacts from construction and public use as much as possible. For example, during construction of minor improvements within the buffer, reduce or eliminate the use of mechanical equipment.

For projects that pursue Option 2(b) and earn at least 1 point under GIB Credit 8, Stormwater Management, the size of pathways, buildings, or clearings may exceed the maximum size allowed for minor improvements. When this is the case, only the portion of the improvement that exceeds the maximum size of the minor improvement should be included in the calculation of the area of buffer land with impacts beyond minor improvements. For example, a project with an impervious pathway that is 14 feet wide should include only 6 feet of the pathway in the numerator for Equation 3 described below (the percentage of buffer land where impacts beyond minor improvements are allowed). Trail imperviousness is also adjustable using Option 2(b) allowances.

Brownfield sites are not treated in a separate category for this prerequisite. Brownfield remediation activities that take place within the buffer, however, are considered minor improvements. Previously developed land on brownfield sites is excluded from this prerequisite, just as previously developed land is excluded from the prerequisite for nonbrownfield sites. Brownfield remediation that involves direct disturbance of wetlands or water bodies may be allowable if the project can show that such remediation falls within minor improvement (b), activities to maintain or restore native natural communities and/or natural hydrology.

Similarly, reclaimed land is not treated in a separate category for this prerequisite. If the preproject condition of the land is a water body and the land is reclaimed as part of the project, the project would not meet the requirements of the prerequisite because it has direct impacts to water bodies. If the land was reclaimed before the property was acquired by the developer, the reclaimed land is not considered a water body. The property might be considered previously developed if development had occurred on the reclaimed land prior to acquisition. Alternatively, it would not be considered previously developed if the reclaimed land had never been developed prior to acquisition.

5. Timeline and Team

During the site selection process, the developer should contract with environmental professionals to conduct site assessments for imperiled species, wetlands and water bodies, floodplains, prime soils for agriculture, and other sensitive environmental features. Once a site has been selected, if sensitive environmental resources are found, the developer should contract with environmental professionals who can assess these features more thoroughly and develop a holistic plan to conserve the site's natural resources.

6. Calculations

OPTION 2. Sites with Wetlands, Water Bodies, Land within 50 Feet of Wetlands, or Land within 100 Feet of Water Bodies

There are no calculations for Option 2(a). For Option 2(b), follow these steps:

Step 1. Calculate the residential density of the site by dividing the total number of dwelling units (DU) by the acres of residential buildable land (see Glossary for the definition). This calculation follows the same methodology and should have the same result as the calculation for residential density for NPD Prerequisite 2, Compact Development.

Equation 1

$$\text{Residential density (DU/acre)} = \frac{\text{Total dwelling units}}{\text{Total buildable residential land (acres)}}$$

Step 2. Calculate the nonresidential density (FAR) of the site by dividing the square footage of nonresidential floor area by square footage of the nonresidential buildable land (see the definition of buildable land). This calculation follows the same methodology and should have the same result as the calculation for nonresidential density for NPD Prerequisite 2.

Equation 2

$$\text{Nonresidential density (FAR)} = \frac{\text{Total nonresidential floor area (sf)}}{\text{Total nonresidential buildable land (sf)}}$$

Step 3. Determine the area of the buffer for each wetland or water body whose buffer widths vary. The total area of the variable-width buffers must be the same as if the buffers had been measured consistently 50 feet from wetlands or 100 feet from waterbodies.

Step 4. Calculate the percentage of buffer land with impacts beyond minor improvements by dividing the area of affected buffer land by the total buffer land area. Do not include the wetland or water body itself in the buffer area calculation. Buffer land occupied by minor improvements should be included only in the denominator, not in the numerator.

Equation 3

$$\text{\% buffer land with impacts beyond minor improvements} = \frac{\text{Area of affected buffer land (acres)}}{\text{Total buffer area (acres)}} \times 100$$

7. Documentation Guidance

As a first step in preparing to complete the LEED-ND documentation requirements, work through the following measures. Refer to GBCI's website for the complete descriptions of all required documentation.

- Obtain or retain aerial photos of the site showing its appearance when it was acquired.

- If the site has a man-made water body that is being excluded because it lacks natural edges and floors or lacks native ecological communities in the water and along the edge, obtain aerial or ground photos of the water body, if possible.

- Retain environmental assessments for each wetland that is excluded because it was created incidentally by human activity and was determined to be performing poorly (i.e., given a "poor" rating) for all measured wetland functions. Retain the wetland quality assessment and evidence of the qualifications of the biologist conducting the assessment, and show that the assessment methodology is commonly used or required by state or local permitting agencies.

- If minor improvements are planned for the buffer area, ensure that improvements are mapped on the site plan, including dimensions of each minor improvement. If habitat restoration (b), tree removal (f), or brownfield remediation activities (g) will take place, retain a summary of the relevant activities and a report on tree condition rating, if applicable. Take photos of the activities and of the area after the activities are completed.

8. Example

A 30-acre site with no previously developed land has a stream along one border and a small wetland. The adjacent property has a concrete stormwater retention basin within 100 feet of the project site. The developer wishes to build out the entire property, except for protecting wetlands and buffers to meet the prerequisite. The developer can develop on buffer land adjacent to the nearby stormwater retention basin because it is excluded from the prerequisite.

Table 2. Example determination for area with permissible impacts beyond minor improvements

	Acres	Residential acres	Nonresidential acres	Dwelling units	Nonresidential square feet
Project site	30				
Nonbuildable land					
Stream (on-site portion)	0.5				
Stream buffer	2.5				
Wetland	3				
Wetland buffer	1				
Street rights-of-way	3.5				
Total nonbuildable land	10.5				
Buildable land	19.5	9.5	10	142	261,360

Residential density is calculated as follows:

Equation 4

$$\text{Residential density (DU/acre)} = \frac{142 \text{ dwelling units}}{9.5 \text{ acres}} = 14.9 \text{ DU/acre}$$

Nonresidential density, expressed as FAR, is calculated by converting acres to square feet (43,560 square feet per acre x 10 acres = 435,600 sf), then dividing the nonresidential floor area (sf) by the land area devoted to nonresidential development (sf) (Equation 5).

Equation 5

$$\text{Nonresidential density (FAR)} = \frac{261,360 \text{ sf}}{435,600 \text{ sf}} = 0.6 \text{ FAR}$$

For determining the proportion of buffer land that may have impacts beyond minor improvements, in this example the project team may choose either the residential density of 14.9 DU per acre or the nonresidential density of 0.6 FAR. The team will likely use the residential density because it allows 10% of buffer land to have impacts beyond minor improvements.

Calculate the total area of buffer land by summing each feature's buffer area: (2.5-acre stream buffer + 1-acre wetland buffer = 3.5-acre total buffer area).

To calculate the amount of buffer land that can be developed beyond minor improvements, use Equation 6.

Equation 6

$$\text{\% buffer land with impacts beyond minor improvements} = 10\% = \frac{\text{Area of impacted buffer land (acres)}}{\text{Total buffer area (acres)}} \times 100$$

Therefore, the maximum buffer area that may have impacts beyond minor improvements is 10% of 3.5 acres, or 0.35 acres. That 0.35 may be distributed anywhere on the buffer land except within 25 feet of the wetland or within 50 feet of the stream.

9. Exemplary Performance

This prerequisite is not eligible for exemplary performance under Innovation and Design Process.

10. Regional Variations

State and local regulations for wetland and riparian protection vary and may be more stringent than EPA and Army Corps of Engineers standards. Although wetlands throughout the United States are delineated using the same Army Corps of Engineers methodology, their prevalence varies by ecoregion.

11. Resources

Websites
Army Corps of Engineers, wetlands
www.wetlands.com/regs/tlpge02e.htm
The *Wetlands Delineation Manual* (1987) describes a methodology for determining wetlands that is commonly used throughout the United States.

Sustainable Sites Initiative
www.sustainablesites.org
The Sustainable Sites Initiative is an interdisciplinary effort by the American Society of Landscape Architects, the Lady Bird Johnson Wildflower Center, and the United States Botanic Garden to create voluntary national guidelines and performance benchmarks for sustainable land design, construction, and maintenance practices.

U.S. Environmental Protection Agency, Office of Wetlands, Oceans, and Watersheds
www.epa.gov/owow
This website offers watershed management tools, resource protection strategies, and regulatory information, plus publications on water conservation and landscaping practices.

Washington State Department of Ecology, wetlands
www.ecy.wa.gov/programs/sea/wetlands/index.html
This website contains information on wetland buffers, functions, and value.

Print Media

Conservation Thresholds for Land Use Planners (Environmental Law Institute, 2003).

Design with Nature, by Ian L. McHarg (Doubleday & Company, 1969).

Ecological Riverfront Design, by Betsy Otto, Kathleen McCormick, and Michael Leccese (American Planning Association, 2004).

"Guide to Judging the Condition of a Shade Tree," by Bruce L. Webster, *Journal of Arboriculture,* 4(11) (1978): 247-249.

Wetland Indicators: A Guide to Wetland Identification, Delineation, Classification, and Mapping, by Ralph W. Tiner (Lewis Publishers, 1999).

12. Definitions

brownfield real property, the expansion, redevelopment, or reuse of which may be complicated by the presence or possible presence of a hazardous substance, pollutant, or contaminate.

density the amount of building structures constructed on the project site, measured for residential buildings as dwelling units per acre of buildable land available for residential uses, and for nonresidential buildings as the floor-area ratio of buildable land area available for nonresidential uses. In both cases, structured parking is excluded.

existing present on the date of submission of LEED-ND certification documents; similarly, an element or condition that **exists** is present on the date that LEED-ND certification documents are submitted.

preproject before the LEED-ND project was initiated, but not necessarily before any development or disturbance took place. Preproject conditions describe the state of the project site on the date the developer acquired rights to a majority of its buildable land through purchase or option to purchase.

previously developed altered by paving, construction, and/or land use that would typically have required regulatory permitting to have been initiated (alterations may exist now or in the past). Previously developed land includes a platted lot on which a building was constructed if the lot is no more than 1 acre; previous development on lots larger than 1 acre is defined as the development footprint and land alterations associated with the footprint. Land that is not previously developed and altered landscapes resulting from current or historical clearing or filling, agricultural or forestry use, or preserved natural area use are considered undeveloped land. The date of previous development permit issuance constitutes the date of previous development, but permit issuance in itself does not constitute previous development.

project the land, water, and construction that constitutes the project application. A project applicant does not have to own or control all land or water within a project boundary, but all the area within the project boundary must comply with prerequisites and attempted credits.

water body the surface water of a stream (first-order and higher, including intermittent streams), arroyo, river, canal, lake, estuary, bay, or ocean, excluding irrigation ditches

wetland an area that is inundated or saturated by surface or ground water at a frequency and duration sufficient to support, and that under normal circumstances do support, a prevalence of vegetation typically adapted for life in saturated soil conditions. Wetlands generally include swamps, marshes, bogs, and similar areas, but exclude irrigation ditches unless delineated as part of an adjacent wetland.

AGRICULTURAL LAND CONSERVATION

	ND
Prerequisite	SLL Prerequisite 4
Points	Required

Intent

To preserve irreplaceable agricultural resources by protecting prime and unique soils on farmland and forestland from development.

Requirements

FOR ALL PROJECTS

Locate the *project* on a site that is not within a state or locally designated agricultural preservation district, unless any changes made to the site conform to the requirements for development within the district (as used in this requirement, district does not equate to land-use zoning).

AND

OPTION 1. Sites without Affected Soils

Locate the project *development footprint* such that it does not disturb *prime soils*, *unique soils*, or soils of state significance as identified in a state Natural Resources Conservation Service soil survey.

OR

OPTION 2. Infill Sites

Locate the project on an *infill site*.

OR

OPTION 3. Sites Served by Transit

Comply with SLL Prerequisite 1, Option 3, Transit Corridor or Route with Adequate Transit Service.

OR

OPTION 4. Development Rights Receiving Area

Locate the project within a designated receiving area for development rights under a publicly administered farmland protection program that provides for the transfer of development rights from lands designated for conservation to lands designated for development.

OR

OPTION 5. Sites with Impacted Soils

If development footprint affects land with prime soils, unique soils, or soils of state significance, as identified in a state Natural Resources Conservation Service soil survey, mitigate the loss through the purchase of easements providing permanent protection from development on land with comparable soils in accordance with the ratios based on densities per acre of *buildable land* as listed in Tables 1 and 2.

Table 1. Mitigation ratios for projects in metropolitan or micropolitan statistical areas, pop. 250,000 or more

Residential density (DU per acre of buildable land available for residential use)	Nonresidential density (FAR of buildable land available for nonresidential use)	Mitigation ratio (acres of easement : acres of project on prime, unique, or significant soil)
> 7 and ≤ 8.5	> 0.50 and ≤ 0.67	2 to 1
> 8.5 and ≤ 10	> 0.67 and ≤ 0.75	1.5 to 1
> 10 and ≤ 11.5	> 0.75 and ≤ 0.87	1 to 1
> 11.5 and ≤ 13	> 0.87 and ≤ 1.0	.5 to 1
> 13	> 1.0	No mitigation

Table 2. Mitigation ratios for projects in metropolitan or micropolitan statistical areas, pop. less than 250,000

Residential density (DU/acre of buildable land available for residential use)	Nonresidential density (FAR of buildable land available for nonresidential use)	Mitigation ratio (acres of easement : acres of project on prime, unique, or significant soil)
> 7 and ≤ 8	> 0.50 and ≤ 0.58	2 to 1
> 8 and ≤ 9	> 0.58 and ≤ 0.67	1 to 1
> 9 and ≤ 10	> 0.67 and ≤ 0.75	0.5 to 1
> 10	> 0.75	No mitigation
DU = dwelling unit; FAR = floor-area ratio.		

All off-site mitigation must be located within 100 miles of the project.

Up to 15% of the impacted soils area may be exempted from the *density* requirements if it is permanently dedicated for community gardens, and may also count toward the mitigation requirement for the remainder of the site. Portions of parking structures devoted exclusively to parking must be excluded from the numerator when calculating the *floor-area ratio* (FAR).

The mitigation ratio for a mixed-use project is calculated as follows:

1. Determine the total square footage of all residential and nonresidential uses.

2. Calculate the percentage residential and percentage nonresidential of the total square footage.

3. Determine the density of the residential and nonresidential components as measured in *dwelling units* per acre and FAR, respectively.

4. Referring to Tables 1 and 2, find the appropriate mitigation ratios for the residential and nonresidential components.

5. If the mitigation ratios are different, multiply the mitigation ratio of the residential component by its percentage of the total square footage, and multiply the mitigation ratio of the nonresidential component by its percentage.

6. Add the two numbers produced by Step 5. The result is the mitigation ratio.

1. Benefits and Issues to Consider

Environmental Issues

Prime and unique soils are particularly suited to the production of agricultural crops because they typically require fewer applications of fertilizers and pesticides to maintain a high yield. Farmland with these soils is in limited supply and disappearing at an alarming rate; therefore, care should be taken to avoid building on such land. The most reliable way to avoid prime farmland and the possible expense of mitigating its loss is to choose an infill or otherwise previously developed site.

The destruction of prime farmland is both a direct loss of a natural resource and a contributing factor in rising carbon emissions. As prime farmland is destroyed, food must be shipped increasing distances to reach major population centers, burning substantial amounts of fossil fuel. Prime farmland also plays an important role in recharging water tables and providing wildlife habitat.

Economic and Social Issues

Agriculture and associated industries are an important part of the national and local economy. Using prime farmland to produce food domestically keeps farmers employed and provides food security to the nation. Towns and cities near agricultural areas may also benefit from reduced food costs if residents are able to purchase food directly from farmers.

Some farmland provides exceptional views and aesthetic value. Agriculture is also a way of life in many communities, and its value as a defining characteristic and historic legacy should not be underestimated.

2. Related Credits

Calculations used to demonstrate compliance with this prerequisite may assist in achieving the following related credits:

- SLL Prerequisite 1, Smart Location
- SLL Credit 1, Preferred Locations
- SLL Credit 3, Locations with Reduced Automobile Dependence
- NPD Prerequisite 2, Compact Development
- NPD Credit 2, Compact Development
- NPD Credit 13, Local Food Production

3. Summary of Referenced Standards

U.S. Department of Agriculture, Natural Resources Conservation Service
www.nrcs.usda.gov (or www.mo15.nrcs.usda.gov/technical/soilsurveys.html)
The Natural Resources Conservation Service (NRCS) is responsible for identifying prime and unique soils. NRCS maintains detailed soil surveys and maps of every county in the United States and provides data for download to GIS mapping programs. "Prime" and "unique" soils are designated by NRCS, and "significant" soils are designated by states; all are included in NRCS soil surveys and maps.

4. Implementation

All Projects

When considering a potential project site, determine whether it is located in an agricultural preservation district and, if so, what the development restrictions are for that district. Note that this requirement does not mean a local government zoning district for agricultural land, but rather an independent special service district autonomous from local government zoning. Such preservation districts operate parallel to local zoning in some parts of the country, and this requirement ensures that projects are in full compliance in such instances. To determine whether preservation districts exist in the project area, contact the local agricultural department or land trust.

Soils

The prerequisite requires the project team to determine whether prime soils, unique soils, or soils of state significance occur on the site, and if so, whether any such valuable soils will be affected by the development footprint. To determine site soil types, visit the Natural Resources Conservation Service website and download GIS data for the appropriate state and county. NRCS keeps detailed surveys and maps for every county in the United States and provides most of this information on-line. Information is available for download to GIS mapping programs but can often be viewed without GIS directly through the NRCS website. If NRCS soil data for the project site are unavailable on-line, contact the state or regional NRCS office. Next, use the agency's state or local guidebooks, or contact its state or regional office, to determine whether the site's soil type is considered prime, unique, or "of state significance." It may be necessary to consult with an agricultural scientist if the soil type for the project site is unclear.

Response to Soil Findings

If the soil survey determines that valuable agricultural soils are not present on the site or not affected by the development footprint, use Option 1. If such soils are present and encroached upon by the development footprint, the project is exempt from this prerequisite under Option 2 if it is an infill site, or under Option 3 if it is a transit-served site (i.e., it complies with SLL Prerequisite 1, Option 3, Transit Corridor or Route with Adequate Transit Service).

If a project site has valuable agricultural soils that will be affected by the development footprint and it does not qualify for Options 2 or 3, it may attempt Option 4 if it is located in a designated receiving area for development rights under a public transfer of development rights (TDR) program. Such programs enable density entitlements from agricultural areas to be transferred to designated receiving areas. Contact the local government planning agency or land trust to find out about any TDR program operating in the area.

If a project with affected soils cannot qualify for Options 2, 3, or 4, the final compliance path, Option 5, requires on-site and/or off-site mitigation through purchase or donation of agricultural land protection easements. The mitigation must conserve soils of a comparable quality to those found in the project site, must be on site or within 100 miles of the project, and in a quantity tied to project density according to the project location in either a metropolitan or a micropolitan statistical area (populations more or fewer than 250,000 persons, respectively); see Table 1.

Community Garden Density Adjustment

Option 5 allows up to 15% of the affected agricultural soil area to be exempted from the density requirements if that land area is dedicated to community gardens. Projects attempting this alternative should recalculate their residential and/or nonresidential densities for this prerequisite using only the project's base densities. The garden adjustment affects project densities for purposes of this prerequisite only and is not used in any density calculations elsewhere in the rating system.

5. Timeline and Team

Early in the site planning process, the project team should consult with agricultural scientists, ecologists, or land-use planners who can provide site-specific expertise and interpret soil maps, land-use maps, and other data relevant to soils and agriculture on the site.

6. Calculations

Residential and nonresidential density calculations are described in the Getting Started chapter. Under Option 5, up to 15% of affected soils designated for community gardens can be exempted from the density requirements and count toward mitigation. To exercise this option, design a community garden and determine what percentage of affected soils it represents. The percentage must be 15 or less. Subtract this acreage from either the residential and/or non-residential buildable land denominator used to calculate density, and use that adjusted density in the prerequisite table to determine the required mitigation ratio. The community garden acreage can also be counted as mitigation acreage.

7. Documentation Guidance

As a first step in preparing to complete the LEED-ND documentation requirements, work through the following measures. Refer to GBCI's website for the complete descriptions of all required documentation.

- For a site with no affected soils, use the site base map showing the development footprint, and obtain NRCS soil maps if affected soils are on or near the project.

- For development rights receiving areas, obtain documentation of the project site location within a publicly administered farmland protection program that provides for the transfer of development rights from the project site to designated development lands.

- For a site with affected soils, obtain NRCS soil maps of both the project site and the off-site mitigation land. Also obtain a map that shows the distance from the project to the purchased easement.

8. Examples

Example 1. Residential Project with Community Garden Space

A project in a metropolitan statistical area with a population of 400,000 has 100 dwellings designed for 10 acres of buildable residential land, for a base residential density of 10 dwelling units per acre. This residential density requires a base mitigation ratio of 1.5 acres of easement to 1 acre of affected soil. The project design affects 2 acres of prime soil, so the required mitigation is 2 x 1.5 = 3 acres of easement.

The project adds a 0.26-acre community garden, which represents 13% of the affected soil area. This amount can be subtracted from the buildable land for purposes of calculating density and from the easement land area required for mitigation.

The adjusted buildable land is therefore 10 acres – 0.26 acre = 9.94 acres, which gives an adjusted residential density of 100 dwellings / 9.94 = 10.06 dwelling units per acre. The adjusted residential density of 10.06 dwelling units per acre has a mitigation ratio of 1:1, which equates to 2 acres of easement. The final adjustment is 2 acres of easement – 0.26 acre of garden = 1.74 acres of easement required.

Note that the density adjustment applies only to this prerequisite; it cannot be used for other credits in the rating system.

Example 2. Mixed-use Project

A project in a metropolitan statistical area of 100,000 has 30,000 sq. ft. of buildable residential land with a residential density of 8 dwelling units per acre. The project also contains 10,000 sq. ft. of non-residential buildable land with an FAR of .75. According to Table 2, the mitigation ratio required according to the residential density of 8 dwelling units per acre is 2 acres of easement to 1 acre of prime, unique, or significant soil (2:1). The mitigation ratio according to the non-residential FAR of .75 is .5:1.

Because the residential and non-residential components of the project fall into different mitigation categories, the final mitigation ratio is the result of a weighted average. The residential component is 75% of the total project square footage, therefore its adjusted mitigation requirement is .75 x 2 = 1.5. The non-residential component is 25% of the total project square footage, therefore its adjusted mitigation requirement is .125. Adding the two products together results in 1.625, which is the final acreage that must be compensated for every one acre impacted, i.e. the new mitigation ratio.

9. Exemplary Performance

This prerequisite is not eligible for exemplary performance under Innovation and Design Process.

10. Regional Variations

Several conditions and characteristics described in this credit—including the prevalence of agricultural land, the presence and level of protection for different kinds of soils, the existence of agricultural preservation districts or farmland protection programs, and the availability of transit—may differ significantly by region. Projects in rural areas are more likely to encroach on agricultural land than projects in urban and infill locations.

11. Resources

Websites

American Farmland Trust
www.farmland.org/default.asp
This website offers education, fiscal analysis, support in developing agricultural land-use plans, and advice for preserving agricultural land.

U.S. Census Bureau, metropolitan statistical areas
www.census.gov/population/www/metroareas/metroarea.html
This website provides lists of metropolitan and micropolitan statistical areas and definitions.

U.S. Department of Agriculture, Natural Resources Conservation Service
www.soils.usda.gov
NRCS, an agency of the U.S. Department of Agriculture, offers training, scientific support, soil conservation data, and surveys and maps for city and county planners.

U.S. Department of Agriculture, Natural Resources Conservation Service, state programs
www.nrcs.usda.gov/about/organization/regions.html
This link lists websites for all state-level NRCS programs.

Print Media

Biodiversity and the Ecosystem Approach in Agriculture and Forestry (UN Food and Agriculture Organization, 2003).

Clearing Land, by Jane Brox (American Farm, 2004).

Cost of Community Services Studies: Making the Case for Conservation (American Farmland Trust, 2002).

Holding Our Ground: Protecting America's Farms and Farmland, by Tom Daniels and Deborah Bowers (Island Press, 1997).

Land Conservation Financing, by Mike McQueen et al. (The Conservation Fund, 2003).

Land Preservation, by Christine Petersen (True Books, 2004).

Saved by Development: Preserving Environmental Areas, Farmland, by Rick Pruetz (Arje Press, 1997).

Saving American Farmland: What Works (American Farmland Trust, 1997).

12. Definitions

buildable land the portion of the site where construction can occur, including land voluntarily set aside and not constructed upon. When used in density calculations, buildable land excludes public rights-of-way and land excluded from development by codified law or LEED for Neighborhood Development prerequisites. An applicant may exclude additional land not exceeding 15% of the buildable land base defined above, provided the following conditions are present:

a. The land is protected from residential and nonresidential construction by easement, deed restriction, or other enforceable legal instrument.

AND

b. Either 25% or more of the boundary of each contiguous parcel proposed for exclusion borders a water body or areas outside the project boundary that are protected by codified law; or ownership of, or management authority over, the exclusion area is transferred to a public entity.

density the amount of building structures constructed on the project site, measured for residential buildings as dwelling units per acre of buildable land available for residential uses, and for nonresidential buildings as the floor-area ratio of buildable land area available for nonresidential uses. In both cases, structured parking is excluded.

development footprint the total land area of a project site covered by buildings, streets, parking areas, and other typically impermeable surfaces constructed as part of the project.

dwelling unit living quarters intended for long-term occupancy that provide facilities for cooking, sleeping, and sanitation. This does not include hotel rooms.

floor-area ratio (FAR) the density of nonresidential land use, exclusive of parking, measured as the total nonresidential building floor area divided by the total buildable land area available for nonresidential structures. For example, on a site with 10,000 square feet of buildable land area, an FAR of 1.0 would be 10,000 square feet of building floor area. On the same site, an FAR of 1.5 would be 15,000 square feet of built floor area; an FAR of 2.0 would be 20,000 built square feet and an FAR of 0.5 would be 5,000 built square feet.

infill site a site that meets any of the following four conditions:

a. At least 75% of its boundary borders parcels that individually are at least 50% previously developed, and that in aggregate are at least 75% previously developed.

b. The site, in combination with bordering parcels, forms an aggregate parcel whose boundary is 75% bounded by parcels that individually are at least 50% previously developed, and that in aggregate are at least 75% previously developed.

c. At least 75% of the land area, exclusive of rights-of-way, within a 1/2-mile distance from the project boundary is previously developed.

d. The lands within a 1/2-mile distance from the project boundary have a preproject connectivity of at least 140 intersections per square mile.

A street or other right-of-way does not constitute previously developed land; it is the status of property on the other side of the street or right-of-way that matters. For conditions (a) and (b) above, any fraction of the perimeter that borders waterfront other than a stream is excluded from the calculation.

(a). Infill project site based on minimum 75% of perimeter adjacent to previously developed parcels

(b). Infill project site based on minimum 75% adjacent to previously developed parcels using project boundary and selected bordering parcels

(c). Infill project site based on minimum 75% of land area within 1/2-mile of project boundary being previously developed

(d). Infill project site based on minimum 140 intersections/sq.mi. within 1/2-mile of project boundary

prime soil earth with chemical, hydrographic, and topological properties that make it especially suited to the production of crops, as defined by the U.S. Natural Resources Conservation Service.

project the land, water, and construction that constitutes the project application. A project applicant does not have to own or control all land or water within a project boundary, but all the area within the project boundary must comply with prerequisites and attempted credits.

unique soil earth with chemical, hydrographic, and topological properties that make it especially suited to specific crops, as defined by the U.S. Natural Resources Conservation Service.

FLOODPLAIN AVOIDANCE

	ND
Prerequisite	SLL Prerequisite 5
Points	Required

Intent

To protect life and property, promote open space and habitat conservation, and enhance water quality and natural hydrological systems.

Requirement

OPTION 1. Sites without Floodplains

Locate on a site that does not contain any land within a 100-year high- or moderate-risk floodplain as defined and mapped by the Federal Emergency Management Agency (FEMA) or a state or local floodplain management agency, whichever is more recent.

OR

OPTION 2. Infill or Previously Developed Sites with Floodplains

Locate the *project* on an *infill site* or a *previously developed site* or in a nonconveyance area of river or coastal floodplain without storm surge potential where compensatory storage is used in accordance with a FEMA-approved mitigation plan. Comply with the National Flood Insurance Program (NFIP) requirements for developing any portions of the site that lie within a 100-year high-or moderate-risk floodplain, as defined in Option 1. If the project includes construction of any critical facility, such as a hospital, water and sewage treatment facility, emergency center, or fire or police station, the critical facility must be designed and built so as to be protected and operable during a 500-year event, as defined by FEMA.

OR

OPTION 3. All Other Sites with Floodplains

If any part of the site is located within a 100-year high- or moderate-risk floodplain, as defined above, develop only on portions of the site that are not in the floodplain, or that have been previously developed, or that are in a nonconveyance area of river or coastal floodplain without storm surge potential where compensatory storage is used in accordance with a FEMA-approved mitigation plan. Previously developed portions in the floodplain must be developed according to NFIP requirements. If development includes construction of any critical facility, as described above, the critical facility must be designed and built so as to be protected and operable during a 500-year event, as defined by FEMA.

1. Benefits and Issues to Consider

Environmental Issues

Floodplains are typically ecologically rich and diverse, supporting habitat and producing excellent agricultural soil. Plant and animal species are often more varied and found at higher concentrations in floodplains than in the water bodies they border. Floodplains also play an important role in flood management, acting as natural overflow containment for water bodies. The gentle slope of a floodplain slows storms and wind as they move from water to land, protecting inland areas. Vegetation also anchors the soil, preventing erosion.

Economic and Social Issues

Floodplains change over time, and this natural variation is drastically affected by development on floodplains. If substantial development occurs in a floodplain, new maps must be produced to model the altered floodplain, resulting in costs and uncertainty for nearby residents. Additional expenses are incurred if engineers must be hired to model expected flooding and build infrastructure to protect populated areas from floods. In some coastal areas, the serious threat of floods and hurricanes also translates into expenses for emergency facilities, plans, and agencies. Accordingly, projects located in floodplains often need to pay higher insurance rates. Choosing a site away from floodplains reduces these initial costs as well as the risk of property damage.

2. Related Credits

Floodplains can often serve as stormwater retention areas, habitat areas, and recreational open space. Preserving and avoiding development in floodplains may assist in earning the following related credits:

- SLL Prerequisite 3, Wetland and Water Body Conservation
- SLL Credit 7, Site Design for Habitat or Wetland and Water Body Conservation
- GIB Credit 8, Stormwater Management

3. Summary of Referenced Standards

Federal Emergency Management Agency, definitions of *100-year floodplain and 500-year floodplain*
www.fema.gov
FEMA defines a 100-year floodplain, or "base flood," as the flood elevation that has a 1% chance of being reached or exceeded each year; it is not the most significant flood in a 100-year period. A 100-year flood could occur many times within a 100-year period. Similarly, a 500-year floodplain is the flood elevation that has a 0.2% chance of being reached or exceeded each year.

National Flood Insurance Program, development guidelines
www.fema.gov/business/nfip
The National Flood Insurance Program (NFIP), administered by FEMA, is sold through private insurance companies and agents but underwritten by the federal government. NFIP underwrites flood insurance coverage only in those communities that adopt and enforce floodplain regulations that meet or exceed minimum NFIP criteria. NFIP minimum requirements limit waterway obstructions, building or land alterations within floodplains, and some coastal development.

4. Implementation

Inventory 100-year high-risk or moderate-risk floodplains on and around the project site. If the project is attempting Option 2 or 3 and includes planned or existing critical facilities, such as hospitals, water and sewage treatment facilities, emergency centers, and fire or police stations, inventory 500-year floodplains as well.

Information about the location of floodplains is accessible directly from National Flood Insurance Program, administered by the Federal Emergency Management Administration (FEMA), usually in the form of flood insurance rate maps. However, many local governments can provide GIS map layers or other documentation of floodplain locations, and some local floodplain management agencies have more recent updates of maps than FEMA.

If no federal, state, or local flood mapping has been completed, a conditional letter of map revision or amendment (CLOMR or CLOMA) from FEMA can be used to identify floodplains. A development project that would alter a site's existing regulatory flood conditions generally requests a CLOMR (FEMA's comment on the project and its anticipated regulatory flood impacts) before requesting revisions to the flood insurance rate maps. (A CLOMA is issued by FEMA to correct errors in a flood insurance rate map.)

Previously Developed or Infill Sites

If the project is on an infill or previously developed site, 100-year high- or moderate-risk floodplain areas can be developed. These areas may be previously developed or previously undeveloped, but they must be in compliance with the National Flood Insurance Program's minimum floodplain development requirements. Alternatively, a project within a "nonconveyance area" of river or coastal floodplain can also develop a 100-year floodplain as long as this area has no storm surge potential and is in compliance with a FEMA-approved mitigation plan. Nonconveyance areas are low-lying ponds, backwater, or other areas adjacent to the floodplain that retain floodwater (instead of conveying it) at the flood elevation in the conveyance part of the floodplain.

Thus a project team has three ways to develop on a 100-year floodplain and still meet the requirements of the prerequisite: choose an infill site, choose a previously developed site, or locate the project in a qualifying nonconveyance area. The prerequisite makes no requirements on any portions of the project site outside the floodplain.

Since floodplain management and regulation of development are usually handled at the local or regional level by a floodplain management agency or local planning department, contact one of these agencies to learn about the floodplain development regulations applicable to the site. The agency should be able to confirm whether its regulations are in compliance with the minimum requirements of the National Flood Insurance Program. Many communities, especially in flood-prone areas, participate, and if the local floodplain ordinance complies with or exceeds NFIP requirements, this part of the prerequisite is met. Environmental scientists, hydrologists, planners, or other professionals with experience implementing local floodplain development requirements can also help navigate the regulations.

Standard NFIP minimum requirements include elevating development above the base flood elevation, "dry" flood-proofing nonresidential buildings, and obtaining permits for any type of development (including buildings, excavation, filling, mining, dredging, and land clearing) within the floodplain to ensure it does not alter or relocate a watercourse or cause flooding in adjacent communities. Under Options 2 and 3, strategies such as elevating buildings above flood levels or reworking the site to reduce flood hazards are allowed as long as they comply with NFIP requirements.

All Other Sites

If the project is not on a previously developed or infill site, previously undeveloped portions of the site within the 100-year high- or moderate-risk floodplain cannot be developed unless they lie in a qualifying nonconveyance area. This is a potentially far-reaching design constraint for any project and should be considered early in the conceptual design phase. Previously developed portions of the site within the 100-year high- or moderate-risk floodplain can be developed but only if they comply with NFIP minimum requirements (described above). If the project site includes a floodplain, the design team should look for opportunities to preserve the feature's ecological functions so that it provides benefits, such as stormwater retention, recreational open space, agricultural land, wildlife habitat, or wetland and riparian restoration.

Critical Facilities and 500-Year Flood Events (Options 2 and 3 only)

If any portion of a project site is covered by a 100-year high- or moderate-risk floodplain, the project can build or include existing "critical facilities" only if they will be protected and operable during a 500-year flood event. Critical facilities, as defined by FEMA, include important community-serving infrastructure like emergency services, hospitals, water treatment plants, and storage facilities for critical records. This requirement applies to all types of project sites, including infill, previously developed, adjacent, or previously undeveloped.

5. Timeline and Team

Early in the site design or entitlement process, the project team should consult with hydrologists, environmental engineers, or other qualified professionals who can provide site-specific expertise, interpret flood maps, and provide other data relevant to floodplain avoidance.

6. Calculations

There are no calculations for this credit.

7. Documentation Guidance

As a first step in preparing to complete the LEED-ND documentation requirements, work through the following measures. Refer to GBCI's website for the complete descriptions of all required documentation.

- Obtain maps of 100-year floodplains that affect the project site.

- If a critical facility, such as a hospital, water and sewage treatment facility, or emergency center, exists or will be built within the project and Option 2 or 3 is being used, obtain 500-year floodplain mapping.

- Obtain documentation that the local community participates in the National Flood Insurance Program, and develop a list of applicable NFIP requirements. Throughout the project, track how NFIP requirements are being met.

8. Examples

There are no examples for this prerequisite.

9. Exemplary Performance

This prerequisite is not eligible for exemplary performance under Innovation and Design Process.

10. Regional Variations

There are no regional variations associated with this credit.

11. Resources

Websites

Federal Emergency Management Agency, floodplains
www.fema.gov/plan/prevent/floodplain/fm_sg.shtm
Floodplain Management Requirements: A Study Guide and Desk Reference for Local Officials is designed to enhance the knowledge and skills of local floodplain management officials and be a desk

reference as specific issues arise in local communities. It includes an overview of floodplain management best practices, details on the National Flood Insurance Program, and an explanation of the roles of states and local communities in implementing its requirements.

Federal Emergency Management Agency, National Flood Insurance Program
www.fema.gov/business/nfip
This website provides the complete guide to federally backed flood insurance, with statistics, workshops and training, floodplain management recommendations, and ways to apply for assistance. Users can view or purchase historic floodplain maps for the entire United States or create flood insurance rate maps on-line.

Print Media

Floodplain Management: Ecologic and Economic Perspectives, by Nancy Philippi (Elsevier, 1996).

Floodplain Management: A New Approach for a New Era, by Bob Freitag et al. (Island Press, 2009).

Going with the Flow: Understanding the Effects of Land Management on Rivers and Floods, by Barbara Ellis-Sugai and Derek C. Godwin (Oregon State University, 2002).

12. Definitions

infill site a site that meets any of the following four conditions:

a. At least 75% of its boundary borders parcels that individually are at least 50% previously developed, and that in aggregate are at least 75% previously developed.

b. The site, in combination with bordering parcels, forms an aggregate parcel whose boundary is 75% bounded by parcels that individually are at least 50% previously developed, and that in aggregate are at least 75% previously developed.

c. At least 75% of the land area, exclusive of rights-of-way, within a 1/2-mile distance from the project boundary is previously developed.

d. The lands within a 1/2-mile distance from the project boundary have a preproject connectivity of at least 140 intersections per square mile.

A street or other right-of-way does not constitute previously developed land; it is the status of property on the other side of the street or right-of-way that matters. For conditions (a) and (b) above, any fraction of the perimeter that borders waterfront other than a stream is excluded from the calculation.

(a). Infill project site based on minimum 75% of perimeter adjacent to previously developed parcels

(b). Infill project site based on minimum 75% adjacent to previously developed parcels using project boundary and selected bordering parcels

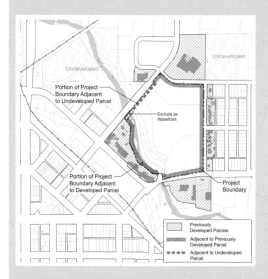

(c). Infill project site based on minimum 75% of land area within 1/2-mile of project boundary being previously developed

(d). Infill project site based on minimum 140 intersections/sq.mi. within 1/2-mile of project boundary

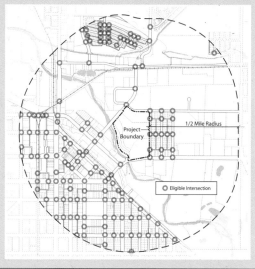

previously developed altered by paving, construction, and/or land use that would typically have required regulatory permitting to have been initiated (alterations may exist now or in the past). Previously developed land includes a platted lot on which a building was constructed if the lot is no more than 1 acre; previous development on lots larger than 1 acre is defined as the development footprint and land alterations associated with the footprint. Land that is not previously developed and altered landscapes resulting from current or historical clearing or filling, agricultural or forestry use, or preserved natural area use are considered undeveloped land. The date of previous development permit issuance constitutes the date of previous development, but permit issuance in itself does not constitute previous development.

project the land, water, and construction that constitutes the project application. A project applicant does not have to own or control all land or water within a project boundary, but all the area within the project boundary must comply with prerequisites and attempted credits.

PREFERRED LOCATIONS

	ND
Credit	SLL Credit 1
Points	1-10 points

Intent

To encourage development within *existing* cities, suburbs, and towns to reduce adverse environmental and public health effects associated with sprawl. To reduce development pressure beyond the limits of existing development. To conserve natural and financial resources required for construction and maintenance of infrastructure.

Requirements

Achieve any combination of requirements in the following three options:

OPTION 1. Location Type

Locate the *project* in one of the following locations:

    a. A *previously developed site* that is not an *adjacent site* or *infill site* (1 point).

    b. An adjacent site that is also a previously developed site (2 points).

    c. An infill site that is not a previously developed site (3 points).

    d. An infill site that is also a previously developed site (5 points).

AND/OR

OPTION 2. Connectivity

Locate the project in an area that has existing *connectivity* within 1/2 mile of the *project boundary*, as listed to Table 1.

Table 1. Points for connectivity within 1/2 mile of project

Intersections per square mile	Points
≥ 200 and < 250	1
≥ 250 and < 300	2
≥ 300 and < 350	3
≥ 350 and < 400	4
≥ 400	5

Intersections within the site may be counted if the intersections were not constructed or funded by the *developer* within the past ten years.

AND/OR

OPTION 3. Designated High-Priority Locations

Achieve the following (3 points):

- Earn at least 2 points under NPD Credit 4, Mixed-Income Diverse Communities, Option 2, Affordable Housing.

- In addition, locate the project in one of the following high-priority redevelopment areas: EPA National Priorities List, Federal Empowerment Zone, Federal Enterprise Community, Federal Renewal Community, Department of Justice Weed and Seed Strategy Community, Department of the Treasury Community Development Financial Institutions Fund Qualified Low-Income Community (a subset of the New Markets Tax Credit Program), or the U.S. Department of Housing and Urban Development's Qualified Census Tract (QCT) or Difficult Development Area (DDA).

1. Benefits and Issues to Consider

For a summary of the numerous environmental and economic benefits of choosing a project site in an existing community or near existing infrastructure, please refer to the Introduction to the Smart Location and Linkage chapter.

2. Related Credits

Projects that earn points in this credit are likely to be located in urban and suburban areas with proximity to diverse uses. Locating on previously developed sites allows projects to avoid many potential environmental effects from development. For these reasons, meeting requirements for this credit may assist in earning the following related credits:

- SLL Credit 3, Locations with Reduced Automobile Dependence
- SLL Credit 5, Housing and Jobs Proximity
- SLL Credit 7, Site Design for Habitat or Wetland and Water Body Conservation
- NPD Credit 3, Mixed-Use Neighborhood Centers
- NPD Credit 4, Mixed-Income Diverse Communities
- NPD Credit 6, Street Network
- GIB Credit 7, Minimized Site Disturbance in Design and Construction
- GIB Credit 8, Stormwater Management

3. Summary of Referenced Standards

U.S. Environmental Protection Agency, National Priority List

www.epa.gov/superfund/sites/npl

EPA maintains a list of sites around the United States that release or threaten to release hazardous substances, pollutants, or contaminants, as well as information about any clean-up in process. Projects on the National Priority List are targets for the federal Superfund program, which aims to clean up uncontrolled hazardous waste sites around the country.

U.S. Housing and Urban Development, Federal Empowerment Zone, Federal Enterprise Community, and Federal Renewal Community

www.hud.gov/offices/cpd/economicdevelopment/programs/rc/index.cfm

On its website, HUD provides an overview of these programs, as well as a locator tool to help developers determine whether a project lies within one of the designated zones or communities.

U.S. Department of Justice, Weed and Seed Strategy Community

www.ojp.usdoj.gov/ccdo/ws/welcome.html

This combination law enforcement and neighborhood restoration program in some instances receives assistance from the U.S. Attorney's Office to "seed" neighborhood restoration initiatives.

U.S. Department of Treasury, Community Development Financial Institutions Fund

www.cdfifund.gov

This federal grant program seeks to expand affordable credit, capital, and financial services for underserved populations through grants and tax credits. It is a subset of Treasury's New Markets Tax Credit Program (www.cdfifund.gov/what_we_do/programs_id.asp?programID=5), which provides a tax credit for investing in designated "community development entities."

U.S. Department of Housing and Urban Development, qualified census tracts and difficult development areas

www.huduser.org

A qualified census tract (QCT) is a census tract with a certain percentage of low-income households, as defined under Section 42 of the Internal Revenue Code. Difficult development areas (DDAs) are determined annually by HUD. Owners of rental properties in QCTs and DDAs qualify for the low-income housing tax credit, as defined under Section 42 of the Internal Revenue Code.

4. Implementation

Methods of identifying project locations that qualify as infill, previously developed, and adjacent under the rating system's definitions may be found in Getting Started and under SLL Prerequisite 1, Smart Location.

Contact the city or county in which the project is located to obtain information on the street network within a 1/2-mile radius of the project boundary. This information may be available in GIS format. The methodology for determining intersections per square mile is found in Getting Started and under Calculations, below.

To determine whether a project site qualifies for the Option 3 high-priority location categories, visit the websites listed under Summary of Referenced Standards, above. If website queries are inconclusive, contact the relevant federal agencies, using the contact information provided on the websites; the federal agencies may refer queries to the local government or local affordable housing or economic development organizations for more information. Also work with the local community to ensure that revitalization efforts and proposed uses enhance the culture, economy, and environment of the area.

5. Timeline and Team

In the site selection phase, the urban planner and developer should determine which options for the project site location will best meet the location requirements for this credit.

6. Calculations

OPTION 1. Location Type

To determine whether a project site is infill or adjacent, please see the calculations for SLL Prerequisite 1, Smart Location.

To determine whether the project is on a previously developed site and, if so, what areas are previously developed, use the definition of *previously developed* and guidance under Getting Started. Determine the percentage of the site that is previously developed by dividing the previously developed area by the entire site area and multiplying by 100 (Equation 1). The percentage must be 75% or higher.

Equation 1

$$\text{\% site area previously developed} = \frac{\text{Previously developed area (acres)}}{\text{Total area (acres)}} \times 100$$

OPTION 2. Connectivity

Step 1. Map the area that is 1/2-mile from the project perimeter. Count the qualifying intersections within the 1/2-mile area. Count the qualifying intersections existing on the site, if they were not constructed or funded within the past ten years by the developer. Calculate the percentage of intersections that involve nonmotorized rights-of-way by dividing the number of intersections with nonmotorized rights-of-way by the total number of intersections (Equation 2).

Equation 2

% qualifying intersections with nonmotorized rights-of-way	=	Qualifying intersections with nonmotorized rights-of-way / Total qualifying intersections	X 100

Intersections of streets with nonmotorized rights-of-way may count for up to 20% of total intersections.

Step 2. Determine the total area within 1/2-mile of the project perimeter. Add the area of any portion of the site that has qualifying intersections. Subtract eligible excluded area from the total area (see the definition of *connectivity*). Divide the number of intersections by the net area (Equation 3).

Equation 3

Intersections per square mile	=	Qualifying intersections / Area of surrounding land within ½-mile + area of site with intersections − eligible excluded areas (sq. mi.)

7. Documentation Guidance

As a first step in preparing to complete the LEED-ND documentation requirements, work through the following measures. Refer to GBCI's website for the complete descriptions of all required documentation.

- Obtain aerial photos of the site and the surrounding area in their preproject conditions.

- Retain information on which portions of the site were previously developed, the location of intersections, and if known, previous uses.

- To document an infill location, obtain land-use maps of surrounding property that delineate parcel boundaries.

- For intersections on the site that are counted under Option 2, determine whether any were funded or constructed by the developer within the past ten years; retain the correspondence.

- Retain correspondence with federal agencies and local authorities about whether the site is in a high-priority location.

8. Examples

Example 1. Previously Developed Site

The team for a 33-acre project wishes to determine whether the site qualifies as previously developed. The site has the following preproject conditions:

Table 2. Example determination for previously developed site

Use	Area (acres)
Inactive farm fields	16
Farm buildings and associated altered land	6
Area cleared and filled	8
Forested wetland	3
Total	33

The previously developed area is the farm buildings and associated altered land. Using Equation 1, the team calculates the percentage of the site that is previously developed: $(6/33) \times 100 = 18\%$. This land does not qualify as a previously developed site.

Example 2. Connectivity

A 5-acre site with previous development has a multiuse trail running through it. The team constructs a table describing the area and its intersections:

Table 3. Example determination for connectivity

	Area (sq. mi.)	Intersections with only motorized rights-of-way	Intersections with nonmotorized rights-of-way	Total intersections
Project site	.00781	2	1	3
Project site's excluded area	.00156	—	—	—
Surrounding ½-mile area	.932	210	11	221
Surrounding land's excluded area	.342	—	—	—

The percentage of total intersections that have nonmotorized rights-of-way is figured using Equation 2: $(12/224) \times 100 = 5.4\%$. All the nonmotorized intersections qualify. The intersections per square mile of the site and its surrounding area are calculated according to Equation 3: $224/.932 + (.00781-.00156) - .342 = 376$ intersections / square mile. This project qualifies for 4 points under Option 2.

9. Exemplary Performance

OPTION 1. Location Type

There is no exemplary performance point available for Option 1.

OPTION 2. Connectivity

Projects may earn an Innovation and Design Process credit for exemplary performance by demonstrating connectivity of 600 or more intersections per square mile.

OPTION 3. Designated High-Priority Location

There is no exemplary performance point available for Option 3.

10. Regional Variations

There are no regional variations associated with this credit.

11. Resources

Websites

Metropolitan planning organizations
www.bts.gov/external_links/government/metropolitan_planning_organizations.html
This website lists metropolitan planning organizations around the United States.

National Vacant Properties Campaign
www.vacantproperties.org
The campaign provides information, resources, tools, and assistance to support the revitalization of vacant properties.

Smart Growth America

www.smartgrowthamerica.org/

This coalition of organizations from around the United States posts the latest smart growth news and supports smart growth initiatives, particularly related to historic preservation, the environment, farmland and open space preservation, and neighborhood revitalization. It helps states, communities, and other interested stakeholders adopt policies and legislation that support compact development.

Smart Growth Network

www.smartgrowth.org

This network of nonprofit organizations and government agencies promotes smart growth practices. The website outlines smart growth principles, provides a guide to smart growth terms and technical concepts, and hosts a searchable catalogue of reports, websites, tools, and case studies dating from 1997.

Print Media

Designing Healthy Cities: Prescriptions, Principles, and Practice, by Joseph Aicher (Krieger Publishing, 1998).

Growing Cooler: The Evidence on Urban Development and Climate Change, by Reid Ewing, Keith Bartholomew, Steve Winkelman, Jerry Walters, and Don Chen (Urban Land Institute, 2007).

The Next American Metropolis, by Peter Calthorpe (Princeton Architectural Press, 1993).

Planning and Urban Design Standards, by American Planning Association (John Wiley & Sons, 2006).

Planning the Built Environment, by Larz Anderson (American Planning Association, 2000).

SmartCode Version 9 and Manual, by Duany Plater-Zyberk & Company (New Urban Publications, 2007), available at www.smartcodecentral.com.

Suburban Transformations, by Paul Lukez (Princeton Architectural Press, 2007).

Travel by Design: The Influence of Urban Form on Travel, by Marlon Boarnet (Oxford Press, 2001).

Urban Design Reclaimed: Tools, Techniques and Strategies for Planners, by Emily Talen (American Planning Association, 2009).

Urban Transformations: Understanding City Design and Form, by Peter Bosselmann (Island Press, 2008).

12. Definitions

adjacent site a site having at least 25% of its boundary bordering parcels that are each at least 75% previously developed. A street or other right-of-way does not constitute previously developed land; instead, it is the status of the property on the other side of the street or right-of-way that matters. Any fraction of the boundary that borders waterfront other than a stream is excluded from the calculation. A site is still considered adjacent if the 25% adjacent portion of its boundary is separated from previously developed parcels by undeveloped, permanently protected land averaging no more than 400 feet in width and no more than 500 feet in any one place. The undeveloped land must be permanently preserved as natural area, riparian corridor, park, greenway, agricultural land, or designated cultural landscape. Permanent pedestrian paths connecting the project through the protected parcels to the bordering site may be counted to meet the requirement of SLL Prerequisite 1, Option 2 (that the project be connected to the adjacent parcel by a through-street or nonmotorized right-of-way every 600 feet on average, provided the path or paths traverse the undeveloped land at no more than a 10% grade for walking by persons of all ages and physical abilities).

Adjacent project site based on minimum 25% of perimeter adjacent to previously developed parcels, including allowance for permanently protected land between project boundary and previously developed parcels

connectivity the number of publicly accessible street intersections per square mile, including intersections of streets with dedicated alleys and transit rights-of-way, and intersections of streets with nonmotorized rights-of-way (up to 20% of total intersections). If one must both enter and exit an area through the same intersection, such an intersection and any intersections beyond that point are not counted; intersections leading only to culs-de-sac are also not counted. The calculation of square mileage excludes water bodies, parks larger than 1/2-acre, public facility campuses, airports, rail yards, slopes over 15%, and areas nonbuildable under codified law or the rating system. Street rights-of-way may not be excluded.

developer a public and/or private entity that controls a majority of the project's buildable land and is committed to making a majority of the investments required for the project implementation described in the LEED-ND submission.

existing present on the date of submission of LEED-ND certification documents; similarly, an element or condition that **exists** is present on the date that LEED-ND certification documents are submitted.

infill site a site that meets any of the following four conditions:

    a. At least 75% of its boundary borders parcels that individually are at least 50% previously developed, and that in aggregate are at least 75% previously developed.

    b. The site, in combination with bordering parcels, forms an aggregate parcel whose boundary is 75% bounded by parcels that individually are at least 50% previously developed, and that in aggregate are at least 75% previously developed.

    c. At least 75% of the land area, exclusive of rights-of-way, within a 1/2-mile distance from the project boundary is previously developed.

d. The lands within a 1/2-mile distance from the project boundary have a preproject connectivity of at least 140 intersections per square mile.

A street or other right-of-way does not constitute previously developed land; it is the status of property on the other side of the street or right-of-way that matters. For conditions (a) and (b) above, any fraction of the perimeter that borders waterfront other than a stream is excluded from the calculation.

(b). Infill project site based on minimum 75% adjacent to previously developed parcels using project boundary and selected bordering parcels

(b). Infill project site based on minimum 75% adjacent to previously developed parcels using project boundary and selected bordering parcels

(c). Infill project site based on minimum 75% of land area within 1/2-mile of project boundary being previously developed

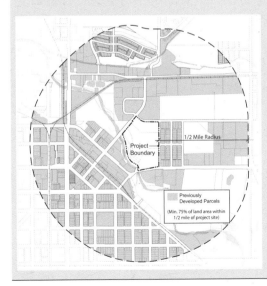

(d). Infill project site based on minimum 140 intersections/sq.mi. within 1/2-mile of project boundary

previously developed site a site that, preproject, consisted of at least 75% previously developed land.

project boundary the platted property line of the project defining land and water within it. Projects located on publicly owned campuses that do not have internal property lines must delineate a sphere-of-influence line to be used instead. Project site is equivalent to the land and water inside the project boundary. The project must not contain noncontiguous parcels, but parcels can be separated by public rights-of-way. Projects may also have enclaves of nonproject properties that are not subject to the rating system, but such enclaves cannot exceed 2% of the total project area and cannot be described as certified.

BROWNFIELDS REDEVELOPMENT

	ND
Credit	SLL Credit 2
Points	1-2 points

Intent

To encourage the reuse of land by developing sites that are complicated by environmental contamination, thereby reducing pressure on undeveloped land.

Requirements

OPTION 1. Brownfield Sites (1 point)

Locate the *project* on a site, part or all of which is documented as contaminated (by means of an ASTM E1903-97 Phase II Environmental Site Assessment or a local Voluntary Cleanup Program), or on a site defined as a *brownfield* by a local, state, or federal government agency; and remediate site contamination such that the controlling public authority approves the protective measures and/or cleanup as effective, safe, and appropriate for the future use of the site.

OR

OPTION 2. High-Priority Redevelopment Areas (2 points)

Achieve the requirements in Option 1;

AND

Locate the project in one of the following high-priority redevelopment areas: EPA National Priorities List, Federal Empowerment Zone, Federal Enterprise Community, Federal Renewal Community, Department of Justice Weed and Seed Strategy Community, Department of the Treasury Community Development Financial Institutions Fund Qualified Low-Income Community (a subset of the New Markets Tax Credit Program), or the U.S. Department of Housing and Urban Development's Qualified Census Tract (QCT) or Difficult Development Area (DDA).

1. Benefits and Issues to Consider

Environmental Issues

Many potential project sites in urban locations have been abandoned because of actual or possible contamination from previous industrial or municipal activities. The U.S. Environmental Protection Agency estimates that there are more than 450,000 brownfields in the United States.[7] Although brownfield sites might be costly or difficult to remediate, many are prime candidates for redevelopment. Remediation removes hazardous materials from a site's soil, groundwater, and any existing buildings, reducing the exposure of humans and wildlife to environmental pollution. In some instances, rather than remediate the contamination, it may be more sensible to leave contaminants in place and instead stabilize and isolate the contaminants to prevent human exposure.

Redevelopment of brownfield sites provides an alternative to developing on greenfield sites, preserving undeveloped areas for future generations and decreasing the overall environmental impact of development. Brownfields often have existing infrastructure improvements that make the construction of new utilities and roads unnecessary.

Economic and Social Issues

Remediation of brownfield sites can be costly and time consuming if extensive effort is required to characterize the contamination, evaluate cleanup options, and perform cleanup activities. However, substantially lower property costs can offset such costs and delays. The cost of remediation strategies varies by site and region.

Weigh the value of a remediated property against cleanup costs to determine whether the site is economically viable for redevelopment. In the past, developers have been reluctant to redevelop brownfield sites because of potential liability associated with previous owners' contamination. In recent years, EPA and many state and local government agencies have begun to provide incentives for brownfield redevelopment by revising regulations to reduce the liability of developers who choose to remediate contaminated sites.

Perceptions of a building site must also be considered. Owners may be wary of cleanup requirements and the potential for liability should contaminants migrate and affect neighbors. Potential building occupants may worry about health risks from breathing contaminated air or coming into contact with contaminated soil.

Many brownfields are in attractive locations and less expensive than similar uncontaminated properties. Additionally, remediation and reclamation of contaminated sites can increase local tax bases[8] and contribute to social and economic revitalization of depressed or disadvantaged neighborhoods. Some brownfields have a rich history and include historic buildings, locally significant architecture, or cultural landscapes.

2. Related Credits

Remediating and redeveloping a brownfield site may assist in earning the following related credits:

- GIB Credit 6, Historic Resource Preservation and Adaptive Use

- GIB Credit 8, Stormwater Management

---

7   U.S. Environmental Protection Agency, "Brownfields and Land Revitalization: About Brownfields." www.epa.gov/brownfields/about.htm (accessed November 2008).
8   Ibid.

3. Summary of Referenced Standards

U.S. Environmental Protection Agency

EPA Sustainable Redevelopment of Brownfields Program

www.epa.gov/brownfields

With certain legal exclusions and additions, a brownfield site is "real property, the expansion, redevelopment, or reuse of which may be complicated by the presence or potential presence of a hazardous substance, pollutant, or contaminant" (Public Law 107-118, H.R. 2869, Small Business Liability Relief and Brownfields Revitalization Act). See the website for additional information and resources.

ASTM International, Phase I environmental site assessment

www.astm.org

A Phase I assessment identifies potential or existing environmental contamination liabilities and typically addresses both the underlying land and any physical improvements to the property but does not include actual collection of physical samples or chemical analyses. It considers *potential* soil contamination, groundwater quality, and surface water quality and sometimes considers hazardous substance uptake by biota. The examination of a site may include the following specific actions: definition of any chemical residues within structures, identification of possible asbestos in building materials, inventory of hazardous substances stored or used on site, assessment of mold and mildew, and evaluation of other indoor air quality parameters. A Phase I environmental site assessment is not required to achieve SLL Credit 2, Brownfields Redevelopment, but is normally undertaken before a Phase II environmental site assessment. The current version of the standard is ASTM E1527-05.

ASTM International, Phase II environmental site assessment

www.astm.org

A Phase II environmental site assessment is an investigation that collects samples of soil, groundwater, or building materials and analyzes them for quantitative values of various contaminants. The most frequently tested substances are petroleum hydrocarbons, heavy metals, pesticides, solvents, asbestos, and mold. ASTM E1903-97 is the version of the standard that took effect in 2002.

State voluntary cleanup programs

Voluntary cleanup programs (VCPs) are administered by state governments according to a flexible framework provided by the U.S. Environmental Protection Agency. VCP programs differ from state to state, and project teams should contact the agency administering the state VCP for specific guidelines and requirements. Enrolling in a state VCP can mean that remediation plans will be approved at the state and federal levels through the same process. Some programs offer incentives and access to technical support or incentives.

U.S. Environmental Protection Agency, National Priority List

www.epa.gov/superfund/sites/npl

EPA maintains a list of sites around the United States that release or threaten to release hazardous substances, pollutants, or contaminants, as well as information about any clean-up in process. Projects on the National Priority List are targets for the federal Superfund program, which aims to clean up uncontrolled hazardous waste sites around the country.

U.S. Housing and Urban Development, Federal Empowerment Zone, Federal Enterprise Community, and Federal Renewal Community

www.hud.gov/offices/cpd/economicdevelopment/programs/rc/index.cfm

On its website, HUD provides an overview of these programs, as well as a locator tool to help developers determine whether a project lies within one of the designated zones or communities.

U.S. Department of Justice, Weed and Seed Strategy Community
www.ojp.usdoj.gov/ccdo/ws/welcome.html
This combination law enforcement and neighborhood restoration program in some instances receives assistance from the U.S. Attorney's Office to "seed" neighborhood restoration initiatives.

U.S. Department of Treasury, Community Development Financial Institutions Fund
www.cdfifund.gov
This federal grant program seeks to expand affordable credit, capital, and financial services for underserved populations through grants and tax credits. It is a subset of Treasury's New Markets Tax Credit Program (www.cdfifund.gov/what_we_do/programs_id.asp?programID=5), which provides a tax credit for investing in designated "community development entities."

U.S. Department of Housing and Urban Development, qualified census tracts and difficult development areas
www.huduser.org
A qualified census tract (QCT) is a census tract with a certain percentage of low-income households, as defined under Section 42 of the Internal Revenue Code. Difficult development areas (DDAs) are determined annually by HUD. Owners of rental properties in QCTs and DDAs qualify for the low-income housing tax credit, as defined under Section 42 of the Internal Revenue Code.

4. Implementation

Achieving this credit requires (1) documenting any part of a project site as contaminated or as a brownfield; and (2) remediating contamination. One extra point is available for redevelopment of brownfields in "high-priority" areas, as identified by federal agencies.

Documentation of Contaminated Site

Many sites have already been designated as brownfields by local, state, or federal agencies. If so, sufficient documentation for the purposes of LEED-ND already exists, and the project team can initiate remediation. There must be a brownfield or contaminated area within the project boundary for the project to achieve the credit. If contamination is found, project sponsors should contact state and local regulators to determine what rules govern the site and find financial assistance programs. It may also be helpful to contact the regional EPA Office of Solid Waste and Emergency Response, which may provide site characterization and remediation support.

If no area of the project site has been designated as a brownfield, but the project team suspects contamination because of a Phase I environmental site assessment or other evaluation, conduct a Phase II environmental site assessment to determine whether remediation is necessary. The Phase II assessment requires that an environmental professional test the soil, air, and water to identify what kinds of contaminants exist and at what levels. The tests vary but initially involve sending samples from the site to a laboratory for analysis. This sampling screens for broad categories of contaminants. If sufficient contamination is found or further investigation is needed, more sophisticated tests must be performed. The additional testing involves more time and expense but is needed to identify specific contaminants and determine effective remediation strategies, if required.

Remediation

Use remediation experts to develop a master plan for any site cleanup. Prioritize remediation activities according to available funds, site characteristics, and levels of cleanup required for future use. Establish a time frame for completing each activity.

The site should be cleaned using proven technologies that will not damage above-ground or underground natural features. The appropriate technology for a specific site depends on the contaminants present, hydrogeologic conditions, and other factors. Traditional remediation efforts for contaminated groundwater are termed pump-and-treat; they involve pumping contaminated groundwater to the surface and treating it with physical or chemical processes. Contaminated soils can be remediated in a variety of ways. Consider in situ remediation schemes that treat contaminants in place instead of off site. Advanced technologies such as bioreactors and in situ applications are sometimes more cost-effective than hauling large quantities of contaminated soil to an approved disposal facility. Innovative remediation efforts (such as solar detoxification technologies) are currently being developed and are expected to reduce remediation costs in the future. Evaluate the environmental implications of each strategy to make sure that it will not cause problems elsewhere. Once remediation is complete, continue to monitor the site for the identified contaminants.

High-Priority Designation

Determine whether the site is located in a "high-priority redevelopment area," as defined by the credit requirements. Generally, these are low-income or historically disadvantaged locations that face economic challenges to redevelopment and qualify for federal incentive programs. Contaminated areas on the EPA National Priorities List also qualify as high-priority redevelopment areas. Often, the easiest way to determine whether a project site is in such an area is to ask a local government's economic development, planning, community development, housing, or redevelopment agency or department. A local government agency that administers federal community development block grant funds is likely familiar with local recipients of federal programs, as are most local community development corporations that focus on affordable housing. Alternatively, the project team can search for information directly through individual federal agencies.

5. Timeline and Team

During the site planning process, the developer should contract with an environmental consultant to conduct site assessments, identify contaminants, determine a schedule for cleanup based on the remediation methods selected, and determine whether the project is located in a high-priority development area, as defined in the credit requirements. General contractors need to incorporate remediation activities into the construction schedule.

6. Calculations

There are no calculations for this credit.

7. Documentation Guidance

As a first step in preparing to complete the LEED-ND documentation requirements, work through the following measures. Refer to GBCI's website for the complete descriptions of all required documentation.

- Obtain a Phase II environmental site assessment or a state or local listing showing that the site contains contamination.

- Retain descriptions and maps of site contamination and remediation efforts undertaken by the project.

- Provide evidence that the site is in a high-priority development area, if applicable.

8. Examples

There are no examples for this prerequisite.

9. Exemplary Performance

This credit is not eligible for exemplary performance under Innovation and Design Process.

10. Regional Variations

There are no regional variations associated with this credit.

11. Resources

Websites

Brownfields Technology Support Center

www.brownfieldstsc.org

This public cooperative effort provides technical support to federal, state, and local officials on items related to site investigation and cleanup.

Environmental Law Institute, Brownfields Center

www.brownfieldscenter.org/big/about.shtml

The Environmental Law Institute's Brownfields Center provides information on brownfields cleanup and redevelopment, with a focus on the concerns and needs of community groups across the country.

U.S. Environmental Protection Agency, Brownfields Program

www.epa.gov/brownfields

This website contains information about EPA's Brownfields Program, including brownfields law, grants and tax incentives, technical tools and resources for remediation and development, and information on brownfields projects across the United States.

U.S. Department of Housing and Urban Development, Community Planning and Development

www.hud.gov/offices/cpd/index.cfm

HUD offers information about the Renewal Communities, Empowerment Zones, and Enterprise Communities programs and the Brownfields Economic Development Initiative grant program.

Print Media

Brownfields: A Comprehensive Guide to Redeveloping Contaminated Property, by Todd Davis (American Bar Association, 2002).

Brownfields: Redeveloping Environmentally Distressed Properties, by Harold Rafson et al. (McGraw-Hill, 1999).

Brownfield Redevelopment and the Quest for Sustainability, by Christopher De Sousa (Elsevier, 2008).

Redeveloping Brownfields for Landscape Architects, Site Planners, and Developers, by Thomas Russ (McGraw-Hill, 1999).

Sustainable Brownfield Regeneration: Livable Places from Problem Spaces, by Tim Dixon et al. (Blackwell, 2007).

12. Definitions

brownfield real property, the expansion, redevelopment, or reuse of which may be complicated by the presence or possible presence of a hazardous substance, pollutant, or contaminate.

REDUCED AUTOMOBILE DEPENDENCE

	ND
Credit	SLL Credit 3
Points	1-7 points

Intent

To encourage development in locations shown to have multimodal transportation choices or otherwise reduced motor vehicle use, thereby reducing greenhouse gas emissions, air pollution, and other adverse environmental and public health effects associated with motor vehicle use.

Requirements

OPTION 1. Transit-Served Location

Locate the *project* on a site with *existing* transit service such that at least 50% of *dwelling units* and nonresidential building entrances (inclusive of existing buildings) are within a 1/4-mile *walk distance* of bus or streetcar stops, or within a 1/2-mile walk distance of *bus rapid transit* stops, light or heavy rail stations, or ferry terminals, and the transit service at those stops in aggregate meets the minimums listed in Tables 1 and 2. Both weekday and weekend trip minimums must be met to earn points at a particular threshold.

Projects larger than 125 acres can meet the requirements by locating on a site with existing transit service such that at least 40% of dwelling units and nonresidential building entrances (inclusive of existing buildings) are within a 1/4-mile walk distance of bus or streetcar stops, or within a 1/2-mile walk distance of bus rapid transit stops, light or heavy rail stations, or ferry terminals, and the transit service at those stops in aggregate meets the minimums listed in Tables 1 and 2 (both weekday and weekend trip minimums must be met to earn points at a particular threshold), as long as the 40% complies with NPD Prerequisite 2 and any portion of the project beyond the 1/4-mile and/or 1/2-mile walk distances meets SLL Prerequisite 1, Option 3-compliant planned transit service.

Projects greater than 500 acres can meet the requirements by locating on a site with existing transit service such that at least 30% of dwelling units and nonresidential building entrances (inclusive of existing buildings) are within a 1/4-mile walk distance of bus or streetcar stops, or within a 1/2-mile walk distance of bus rapid transit stops, light or heavy rail stations, or ferry terminals, and the transit service at those stops in aggregate meets the minimums listed in Tables 1 and 2 (both weekday and weekend trip minimums must be met to earn points at a particular threshold), as long as the 30% complies with NPD Prerequisite 2 and any portion of the project beyond the 1/4-mile and/or 1/2-mile walk distances meets SLL Prerequisite 1, Option 3-compliant planned transit service.

For all projects, weekend daily trips must include service on both Saturday and Sunday. Commuter rail must serve more than one *metropolitan statistical area* (MSA) and/or the area surrounding the core of an MSA.

Table 1. Minimum daily transit service for projects with multiple transit types (bus, streetcar, rail, or ferry)

Weekday trips	Weekend trips	Points
60	40	1
76	50	2
100	65	3
132	85	4
180	130	5
246	150	6
320	200	7

Table 2. Minimum daily transit service for projects with commuter rail or ferry service only

Weekday trips	Weekend trips	Points
24	6	1
40	8	2
60	12	3

Projects served by two or more transit routes such that no one route provides more than 60% of the prescribed levels may earn 1 bonus point, up to the maximum 7 points.

Projects where existing transit service is temporarily rerouted outside the required distances for less than 2 years may meet the requirements if the local transit agency has committed to restoring the compliant routes with service at or above the prior level.

OR

OPTION 2. Metropolitan Planning Organization Location with Low VMT

Locate the project within a region served by a metropolitan planning organization (MPO) and within a transportation analysis zone where the current annual home-based *vehicle miles traveled* (VMT) per capita does not exceed 90% of the average of the metropolitan region. The research must be derived from household transportation surveys conducted by the MPO within ten years of the date of submission for LEED for Neighborhood Development certification. Additional credit may be awarded for increasing levels of performance, as indicated in Table 3.

Table 3. Points for low-VMT location

Percentage of average regional VMT per capita	Points
81–90%	1
71–80%	2
61–70%	3
51–60%	4
41–50%	5
31–40%	6
30 or less	7
VMT = vehicle miles traveled.	

Points earned under Options 1 and 2 may not be combined.

1. Benefits and Issues to Consider

Environmental Issues

The extensive use of single-occupancy vehicles and their reliance on petroleum contribute to environmental problems, such as global warming and resource depletion. Fortunately, alternatives to conventional transportation methods exist, and many people are willing to use other options if they are convenient. The use of mass transit helps reduce energy demand for transportation and associated greenhouse gas emissions, as well as the space needed for parking lots. Minimizing the amount of parking needed in a project, especially in surface parking lots, can make more land available for open space or other uses at greater development densities.

Reductions in single-occupancy vehicle use directly affect fuel consumption and air and water pollution from vehicle exhaust. On the basis of passenger miles traveled, public transportation is twice as fuel efficient as private vehicles and annually saves 45 million barrels of oil.[9] Another benefit of public transportation is the associated reduction in the need for infrastructure. Parking facilities and roadways for automobiles affect the environment because impervious surfaces, such as asphalt, increase stormwater runoff while contributing to urban heat island effects.

Choosing a location with access to robust public transportation and below-average automobile usage also indirectly reduces carbon emissions by making it feasible to design a compact, walkable project with minimal parking.

Economic and Social Issues

Many people, in their roles as residents, employees, students, and parents, view proximity to mass transit as a benefit, and this can increase the value and marketability of a project. The costs and time spent commuting can be significantly reduced by public transportation, allowing people more time with family and friends. Access to transit also helps business owners attract and retain employees. Reducing the size of parking areas based on anticipated use of public transportation may also free up land to provide amenities, such as parks or public plazas; if local utilities charge for stormwater based on impervious surface area, minimizing parking lots can lower stormwater fees. Alternatively, additional residential units or commercial space can be built on the land, increasing its earning power.

2. Related Credits

Site locations that are served by transit or have lower-than-average automobile use are likely to be served by multiple modes of travel, be near diverse uses, and have a compact, walkable street network. A location near existing transit allows for the opportunity to further reduce vehicle miles traveled if the project provides bus shelters and other transit facilities and institutes transportation demand management strategies. For these reasons, meeting SLL Credit 3 may assist in earning the following related credits:

- SLL Credit 1, Preferred Locations
- NPD Credit 2, Compact Development
- NPD Credit 3, Mixed-Use Neighborhood Centers
- NPD Credit 6, Street Network
- NPD Credit 7, Transit Facilities
- NPD Credit 8, Transportation Demand Management

9 American Public Transportation Association, "Use of Public Transportation by One in Ten Americans Would Lead to Cleaner Air and Reduce U.S. Oil Dependency by 40 Percent." APTA News Release, July 17, 2002. www.apta.com/media/releases/energystudy.cfm (accessed November 2008).

3. Summary of Referenced Standards

There are no referenced standards for this credit.

4. Implementation

For Option 1, contact the local transit service provider to obtain route information and a timetable of transit frequency for the area surrounding the project. Only existing transit service qualifies; planned transit may not be counted for this credit. For purposes of this option, a transit trip is defined as the stop of a transit vehicle at a transit stop, traveling in any direction. The termination of a route counts as two trips: The vehicle arrives at the end of its route and leaves at the beginning.

For Option 2, contact the metropolitan planning organization (MPO) for the project's region to determine whether the transportation analysis zone where the project is located has vehicle miles traveled (VMT) rates that are less than 90% of the average VMT rates in the region.

5. Timeline and Team

If the project is in the site selection phase, the design team should determine as soon as possible which alternative sites will best meet the public transportation access or reduced VMT requirements for this credit.

6. Calculations

OPTION 1. Transit-Served Location

Step 1. Determine the number of qualifying transit stops in either of two ways, as follows:

- Create a table of walking distances from the project's dwelling units and nonresidential use building entrances to existing transit stops within a 1/2-mile walk distance. For buildings with multiple units or nonresidential entrances, each unit or entrance must be counted separately (e.g., a multifamily residential building with 50 units counts as 50 entrances, and an office building with 10 separate suites counts as 10 entrances). Each point at which a vehicle stops to receive or discharge passengers is considered a separate stop; this includes stops facing each other on opposite sides of a street.

- Classify the identified transit stops by transit vehicle type (bus, streetcar, bus rapid transit, rail, or ferry).

- For each transit stop, calculate the percentage of dwelling unit entrances and nonresidential use building entrances within the specified walking distance (1/4-mile walk for bus and/or streetcar stops, 1/2-mile walk for bus rapid transit, rail, and/or ferry terminals).

Step 1 Alternative. Determine the walking distance from the farthest entrance to each nearby transit stop. This approach should be taken only for small projects with simple route geometries. If a vicinity map clearly shows that a sufficient number of other entrances are closer than the measured entrance to the farthest transit stop, then the project may use that calculation to demonstrate that a transit stop and associated dwelling units qualify.

Step 2. For each qualifying transit stop identified in Step 1, count the number of transit vehicles stopping each weekday; each is considered a transit trip. Sum the number of vehicles stopping per weekday at all transit stops qualifying in Step 1 to determine number of transit trips. The same vehicle may be counted more than once if it stops at multiple qualifying transit stops, but an individual transit stop cannot be counted more than once.

For each qualifying transit stop identified in Step 1, determine the transit service that is provided on Saturdays and Sundays. Count the number of transit vehicles stopping on Saturdays, and then count the number on Sundays. Sum the number of vehicles stopping on each weekend day at all transit stops qualifying in Step 1 (provide a total for Saturday and a total for Sunday). The same vehicle may be counted more than once if it stops at multiple qualifying transit stops, but an individual transit stop cannot be counted more than once.

Step 3. Use the appropriate table, based on the transit mode of qualifying stops, to determine the number of points earned. If the Saturday total is different from the Sunday total, use the smaller of the two totals.

Step 4. If the project has two or more transit routes serving transit stops qualifying under Step 1, determine whether any one route provides more than 60% of the total trips. If not, then the project qualifies for 1 bonus point, unless the project already qualifies for 7 points under Step 2.

OPTION 2. Metropolitan Planning Organization Location with Low VMT

Obtain from the regional MPO a travel survey–based calculation of the annual per capita VMT for the transportation analysis zone in which the project is located, along with a calculation of the average annual per capita VMT for the metropolitan region as a whole.

7. Documentation Guidance

As a first step in preparing to complete the LEED-ND documentation requirements, work through the following measures. Refer to GBCI's website for the complete descriptions of all required documentation.

- Obtain information on transit service routes and schedules.

- Obtain information on the metropolitan service areas that have any commuter rail used for calculations.

- For projects using VMT data from the metropolitan planning organization, retain information on the date of the household transportation survey on which VMT calculations are based.

8. Examples

Example 1. Transit-Served Location

A 5-acre project is located in a large city with multiple transit modes: rail, bus, bus rapid transit (BRT), and ferry. The project has two office buildings with retail, two multiunit residential buildings, and several detached residential buildings. The team identifies seven transit stops that might be within the qualifying walking distances to the building entrances.

Table 4. Example determination for distance to transit stops

Building	Entrances	Walk distance (feet)	Transit stop destination	Transit type
Mixed-Use A (offices + retail)	21	1,450	BRT 2	BRT
Mixed-Use B (offices + retail)	31	1,234	BRT 1	BRT
Multiunit Residential A	76	900	Rail 1	Rail
Multiunit Residential B	50	798	Bus 1	Bus
Detached Residential 1	1	542	Ferry 1	Ferry
Detached Residential 2	1	278	Bus 2	Bus
Detached Residential 3	1	2,508	BRT 2	BRT
Detached Residential 4	1	3,760	Rail 2	Rail
Total qualifying entrances	181			

As Table 4 shows, 181 entrances of 182 are within either a 1/4-mile walk of a bus stop or a 1/2-mile walk of bus rapid transit, rail, or ferry terminals. Detached Residential 4 does not qualify because the nearest transit stop is more than a 1/2-mile walk distance.

Table 5. Example determination for daily trips per transit stop

Transit stop	Location	Service	Weekday trips	Saturday trips	Sunday trips
Bus 1	Main St. and Wyoming Ave. (northbound)	P4	68	32	16
Bus 2	Arch St. and Ridge Rd. (westbound)	32, N22	76	48	32
BRT 1	Key Rd. and Handler St. (northbound)	80	76	36	0
BRT 2	Key Rd. and Handler St. (southbound)	80	76	36	0
Rail 1	Town Center Station	Eastern line	196	45	45
		Western line	196	45	45
Ferry 1	Town wharf	Mainland	10	5	2
		Total	698	247	140

The team then counts the number of trips per transit stop (Table 5). Even though entrances in several buildings are close to the same transit stop, the trips at that stop are counted only once. Rail 2 is not included because it is not within a 1/2-mile walk distance of any dwelling units. Although the weekday trips total exceeds the threshold for 7 points, the project earns only 5 points, corresponding to the threshold for weekend trips. The project receives 1 bonus point (bringing the total to 6 points) because no single route provides more than 60% of the total number of trips.

Example 2. Location with Low VMT

A project is located in a metropolitan region with an average 9,800 VMT per year per capita. Within the region, the project is in a transportation analysis zone with an average 6,650 VMT per year per capita. The zone's percentage of regional VMT is (6,650 / 9,800) x 100 = 68%. Under the Option 2, the project qualifies for 3 points.

9. Exemplary Performance

OPTION 1. Transit-Served Location

Projects may earn an Innovation and Design Process credit for exemplary performance by demonstrating increased transit frequency, as follows:

- Projects with a combination of transit service types (bus, rail, or ferry): 640 weekday trips, 400 weekend trips.

- Projects with commuter rail or ferry service only: 100 weekday trips, 18 weekend trips.

OPTION 2. Metropolitan Planning Organization Location with Low VMT

There is no exemplary performance point available for Option 2.

10. Regional Variations

There are no regional variations associated with this credit.

11. Resources

Websites

Location Efficient Mortgage

www.locationefficiency.com

This website includes an introductory brochure about the Location Efficient Mortgage, a program for homeowners.

Metropolitan planning organizations

www.bts.gov/external_links/government/metropolitan_planning_organizations.html

This website lists metropolitan planning organizations around the United States.

Reconnecting America

www.reconnectingamerica.org

Reconnecting America is a national nonprofit organization that is working to integrate transportation systems and the communities they serve. Its Center for Transit-Oriented Development focuses on coupling transit with development that improves housing affordability and choice, revitalizes downtowns and urban and suburban neighborhoods, and provides value for individuals, communities, and transportation agencies. The website contains a wealth of resources on best practices and news on transit-oriented development.

Print Media

Best Development Practices, by Reid Ewing (American Planning Association, 1996).

Designing Healthy Cities: Prescriptions, Principles, and Practice, by Joseph Aicher (Krieger Publishing, 1998).

"The Influence of Land Use on Travel Behavior: Empirical Strategies," by Reid Ewing and Robert Cervero, *Transportation Research, Policy and Practice* 35 (2001).

"Location Efficiency: Neighborhood and Socio-Economic Characteristics Determine Auto Ownership and Use: Studies in Chicago, Los Angeles, and San Francisco," by John Holtzclaw et al., *Transportation Planning and Technology* 25 (2002).

The New Transit Town: Best Practices in Transit-Oriented Development, by Hank Dittmar and Gloria Ohland (Island Press, 2003).

The Next American Metropolis, by Peter Calthorpe (Princeton Architectural Press, 1993).

Planning and Urban Design Standards, by American Planning Association (John Wiley & Sons, 2006).

Responsive Environments: A Manual for Designers, by Ian Bentley et al. (Architectural Press, 1985).

Transit Villages in the 21st Century, by M. Bernick and R. Cervero (McGraw-Hill, 1997).

12. Definitions

bus rapid transit (BRT) an enhanced bus system that operates on exclusive bus lanes or other transit rights-of-way; it is designed to combine the flexibility of buses with the efficiency of rail.

dwelling unit living quarters intended for long-term occupancy that provide facilities for cooking, sleeping, and sanitation. This does not include hotel rooms.

existing present on the date of submission of LEED-ND certification documents; similarly, an element or condition that **exists** is present on the date that LEED-ND certification documents are submitted.

metropolitan (metro) and micropolitan (micro) statistical area a geographic entity defined by the U.S. Office of Management and Budget for use by federal statistical agencies in collecting, tabulating, and publishing federal statistics. A metro area contains a core urban area with a population of 50,000 or more, and a micro area contains an urban core with a population between 10,000 and 50,000. Each metro or micro area consists of one or more counties and includes the counties containing the core urban area, as well as any adjacent counties that have a high degree of social and economic integration (as measured by commuting to work) with the urban core. "Core-based statistical area" (CBSA) encompasses both metro and micro areas.

vehicle miles traveled (VMT) the number of miles driven by motorists in a specified time period, such as a day or a year, in absolute or per capita terms.

walk distance the distance that a pedestrian must travel between origins and destinations without obstruction, in a safe and comfortable environment on a continuous network of sidewalks, all-weather-surface footpaths, crosswalks, woonerfs, or equivalent pedestrian facilities.

BICYCLE NETWORK AND STORAGE

	ND
Credit	SLL Credit 4
Points	1 point

Intent

To promote bicycling and transportation efficiency, including reduced *vehicle miles traveled* (VMT). To support public health by encouraging utilitarian and recreational physical activity.

Requirements

BICYCLE NETWORK

Design and/or locate the *project* to meet at least one of the three requirements below:

a. An *existing bicycle network* of at least 5 continuous miles in length is within 1/4-mile bicycling distance of the *project boundary*.

b. If the project is 100% residential, an existing bicycle network begins within 1/4-mile bicycling distance of the project boundary and connects to a *school* or *employment center* within 3 miles' bicycling distance.

c. An existing bicycle network within 1/4-mile bicycling distance of the project boundary connects to at least ten diverse uses (see Appendix) within 3 miles' bicycling distance from the project boundary.

AND

BICYCLE STORAGE

Provide bicycle parking and storage capacity to new buildings as follows:

a. **Multiunit residential.** Provide at least one secure, enclosed bicycle storage space per occupant for 30% of the *planned occupancy* but no fewer than one per unit. Provide secure visitor bicycle racks on-site, with at least one bicycle space per ten *dwelling units* but no fewer than four spaces per project site.

b. **Retail.** Provide at least one secure, enclosed bicycle storage space per new retail worker for 10% of retail worker planned occupancy. Provide visitor or customer bicycle racks on-site, with at least one bicycle space per 5,000 square feet of retail space, but no fewer than one bicycle space per business or four bicycle spaces per project site, whichever is greater. Provide at least one on-site shower with changing facility for any development with 100 or more new workers and at least one additional on-site shower with changing facility for every 150 new workers thereafter.

c. **Nonresidential other than retail.** Provide at least one secure, enclosed bicycle storage space per new occupant for 10% of planned occupancy. Provide visitor bicycle racks on-site with at least one bicycle space per 10,000 square feet of new commercial nonretail space but not fewer than four bicycle spaces per building. Provide at least one on-site shower with changing facility for any development with 100 or more new workers and at least one additional on-site shower with changing facility for every 150 new workers thereafter.

Secure, enclosed bicycle storage areas must be locked and easily accessible to residents and/ or workers. Provide informational signage on using the storage facilities.

Visitors' and customers' bicycle racks must be clearly visible from a main entry, located within 100 feet of the door, served with night lighting, and protected from damage from nearby vehicles. If the building has multiple main entries, bicycle racks must be proportionally dispersed within 100 feet of each.

Shower and changing facility requirements may be met by providing the equivalent of free access to on-site health club shower facilities, if the health club can be accessed without going outside. Provide informational signage on using the shower facilities.

1. Benefits and Issues to Consider

Environmental Issues

As an alternative to personal vehicle use, bicycling offers a number of environmental benefits. It produces no emissions, has zero demand for petroleum-based fuels, relieves traffic congestion, reduces noise pollution, and requires far less infrastructure for roadways and parking lots. Roadways and parking lots, in turn, produce stormwater runoff, contribute to the urban heat island effect, and encroach on green space. Bicycles are more likely to be used for relatively short commuting trips. Displacing automobile use with bicycling, even for short trips, carries a large environmental benefit because vehicle emissions are high in the first few minutes of driving, when cool operating temperatures make emissions control equipment less effective.

In projects that include or are near a school, providing the opportunity for students to bicycle along safe routes increases the likelihood that they will continue to use bicycles for transportation as adults, which is an important component of reducing cultural dependency on automobiles.

Combined, bicycle networks and storage facilities will encourage residents and workers in the project to ride bicycles for recreation, daily needs, and commuting. Supporting bicycling is one of the simplest, most cost-effective means of promoting public health in a community as well.

Economic and Social Issues

Choosing a project location where the infrastructure already supports safe and efficient bicycle use eliminates the cost associated with retrofitting existing streets, which can be difficult depending on the street grid. When buying a home, prospective residents may consider a bicycle network with off-road trails a valuable amenity.

The initial cost of building bicycle storage areas and changing facilities or showers is typically low relative to the overall project cost. When buildings accommodate bicycling infrastructure, occupants can realize health benefits by bicycling and walking to work and potentially save money on transportation costs. Bicycling and walking also expose people to the community, encourage interaction among neighbors, and allow for enjoyment of the area in ways unavailable to automobile passengers.

2. Related Credits

Providing bicycle parking and a bicycle network—including trails, on-street lanes, or low-speed streets—may assist in earning the following related credits:

- NPD Credit 5, Reduced Parking Footprint
- NPD Credit 7, Transit Facilities
- NPD Credit 8, Transportation Demand Management

3. Summary of Referenced Standards

There are no referenced standards for this credit.

4. Implementation

Achieving this credit usually involves three basic strategies: locating the project near an existing bike network, providing sufficient on-site bicycle storage, and providing shower facilities for employees. Note that 100% of all new multiunit residential buildings (four units or more) and all new nonresidential buildings must individually meet the storage and shower requirements. If only one building of several fails to meet the requirements, then the credit cannot be earned. Also note that unlike other LEED 2009 rating systems, which use occupancy metrics, LEED-ND bicycle parking and storage requirements are based on the number of dwellings and amount of square footage.

Bicycle Network

A "bicycle network," as defined in the rating system, can consist of on-street lanes, off-street trails, or low-speed streets. This provides an array of potential facilities appropriate to a variety of environments. Note that sidewalks are not part of the bicycle network definition. Obtain a map of the area's existing bicycle network and confirm which facilities meet the definition of a bicycle network. Bicycle network maps are often available from local municipalities or local advocacy groups. Determine which schools, employment centers, and diverse uses are located along the bicycle network within a 3-mile bicycle distance of the project boundary. For more than one building in a school campus or employment center, measure to the center. An infill or adjacent location will increase the likelihood of being within the required distance of these destinations. The distance that bicyclists may travel to reach the bicycle network (1/4-mile) is measured along any route that a bicyclist can physically travel, and bicycle amenities are not required for this distance. A bicycle network can pass either through the project boundary or within 1/4-mile of the project boundary and still qualify for the credit.

Bicycle Storage

To meet the credit requirements, each different building type requires some mix of bicycle storage for visitors and enclosed, secure bicycle storage for residents and workers. The only exception is for single-family and townhouse residential units, where no bike parking is required. Bicycle parking and storage systems vary in design and cost, and specific guidelines for installation and design are included in the Resources section, below. However, all bicycle parking must have night lighting and be protected from damage from motor vehicles. It must also be clearly visible, have appropriate signage, and be no more than 100 feet from the entrance of the building it serves. Other important considerations for all bike parking include security, stability, accessibility, durability, aesthetics, and a location that encourages "passive surveillance."

Enclosed storage for residents and employees must be lockable and accessible by key. Space must be designed specifically for secure bicycle storage to qualify for the credit; simply allowing bikes within dwelling units or unlocked office closets does not qualify for the credit.

Bicycle parking for visitors should be located such that it does not block the pedestrian path of travel or inhibit universal accessibility, and it should allow clearance for users to dismount, lock up, and circulate easily. Ideally, the racks should have two points of contact with the frame to prevent bicycles from falling.

Figure 1. Secure, enclosed bicycle storage areas, locked and easily accessible to residents and/or workers

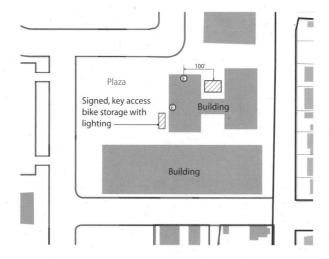

Showers and Changing Facilities

Shower and changing areas for cyclists should be easily accessible from enclosed bicycle storage areas; they can be unit showers or group showers. Free access to a health club's shower facilities also qualifies if cyclists do not have to travel outside from the job site to reach them.

Planned Occupancy

To determine the amount of enclosed, secure bicycle storage and the number of showers required for a project, determine the planned occupancy for both multiunit residential and nonresidential portions of the project. The project's multiunit residential planned occupancy will depend on the types of units included in the project; see the definition of planned occupancy.

Other Considerations

Several strategies that are not required by this credit will increase the overall quality of bicycle facilities. For instance, providing a bicycle repair shop, safety classes, or ridership information to project inhabitants encourages bicycle ridership and safety. Improving the project's internal bicycle network and locating near transit modes that cater to bikes also encourages ridership, as does providing clothing lockers in addition to showers for commuters. Bicycle parking or network requirements can also be written into CC&Rs or master plans to ensure their continuation.

Look for opportunities to cooperate with a municipality, nonprofit advocacy group, transit agency, or other third party to implement the credit. Examples include coordinated improvements to the bicycle network, joint bicycle parking installation, or shared material and planning resources.

5. Timeline and Team

On-site bicycle storage should be considered early in the project's design process. The developer should contract with design or transportation professionals who have experience designing bicycle storage, showers, and/or network facilities. Often, bicycle facilities are not considered until the very end of a design process, but planning for them early can improve their overall quality.

6. Calculations

Bicycle Storage, Multiunit Residential

Step 1. Identify the following for multiunit residential components of the project: (a) number of planned occupants; and (b) number of dwelling units.

Step 2. Determine the minimum number of secure, enclosed bicycle storage spaces for residents by taking the greater of the following: (a) 30% of planned multiunit occupants (Equation 1); or (b) number of multiunit residential dwelling units.

Equation 1

| Multiunit residential enclosed spaces | = | Planned multiunit residential occupants | X | 0.3 |

Step 3. Determine the minimum number of required multiunit residential visitor parking spaces by taking the greater of the following: 10% of multiunit residential dwelling units (Equation 2), or 4 spaces.

Equation 2

| Multiunit residential visitors' spaces | = | Multiunit residential dwelling units | X | 0.1 |

Bicycle Storage, Retail

Step 1. Identify the following for retail components of the project: number of planned workers, square footage of retail space, and number of retail businesses.

Step 2. Determine the minimum number of required secure, enclosed bicycle storage spaces for retail workers by calculating 10% of the number of planned retail worker occupants (Equation 3).

Equation 3

Retail workers' spaces	$=$	Planned retail workers	$\times$	0.1

Step 3. Determine the minimum number of required bicycle parking spaces for retail visitors by taking the greatest of the following: total retail square footage divided by 5,000 (Equation 4), number of retail businesses, or 4 spaces.

Equation 4

$$\text{Retail visitors' spaces} = \frac{\text{Total retail square footage}}{5{,}000}$$

Step 4. If the number of planned retail workers exceeds 100, determine the minimum number of required on-site showers with changing facilities according to Equation 5. The result of Equation 5 can be rounded up to the nearest whole number.

Equation 5

$$\text{Nonresidential workers' or occupants' showers} = \frac{\text{Planned workers or occupants} - 100}{150} + 1$$

Bicycle Storage, Nonresidential Other Than Retail

Step 1. Identify the following for nonresidential, nonretail components of the project: number of planned occupants, and square footage of nonresidential, nonretail space.

Step 2. Determine the minimum number of required secure, enclosed nonresidential, nonretail occupant spaces by calculating 10% of the number of planned occupants (Equation 6).

Equation 6

Nonresidential, nonretail occupants' spaces	$=$	Planned nonresidential, nonretail occupants	$\times$	0.1

Step 3. Determine the minimum number of required nonresidential, nonretail visitors' parking spaces by taking the greater of the following: total nonresidential nonretail square footage divided by 10,000 (Equation 7), or 4 spaces.

Equation 7

$$\text{Nonresidential, nonretail visitors' spaces} = \frac{\text{Nonresidential, nonretail square footage}}{10{,}000}$$

Step 4. If the number of planned nonresidential, nonretail workers exceeds, determine the minimum number of required on-site showers with changing facilities according to Equation 5. The result of Equation 5 can be rounded up to the nearest whole number.

7. Documentation Guidance

As a first step in preparing to complete the LEED-ND documentation requirements, work through the following measures. Refer to GBCI's website for the complete descriptions of all required documentation.

- Obtain or create a map of the bike bicycle network in the area of the project.

- Complete a survey of schools, employment centers, and other diverse uses within a 3-mile cycling distance of the project boundary, and map the results. The first 1/4-mile of cycling distance may be along streets without bicycle facilities if this is necessary to reach the bicycle network.

- Collect the following data: number of planned residential and nonresidential occupants, number of multiunit residential dwelling units, square footage of retail and other nonresidential spaces, and number of planned retail businesses.

8. Examples

There are no examples for this credit.

9. Exemplary Performance

This credit is not eligible for exemplary performance under Innovation and Design Process.

10. Regional Variations

There are no regional variations associated with this credit.

11. Resources

Websites

Association of Pedestrian and Bicycle Professionals
www.apbp.org/?page=Publications
The association's *Bicycle Parking Guidelines* provides an overview of best practices in bicycle parking.

Bicycle Solutions
www.bicyclesolutions.com/ps.html
Bicycle Solutions provides professional site analysis and product selection for bicycle parking in new and existing developments.

Victoria Transportation Policy Institute
www.vtpi.org
This independent research organization provides consulting and publicly available research about solutions to emerging transportation issues, such as transportation demand management.

Print Media

Bicycle Transportation: A Manual for Cycling Transportation Engineers, by John Forester (MIT Press, 1994).

Guidelines for the Development of Bicycle Facilities (American Association of State and Highway Transportation Officials, 1999).

Innovative Bicycle Treatments, by Jumana Nabti and Matthew Ridgway (Institute of Transportation Engineers, 2002).

Manual on Uniform Traffic Control Devices, U.S. Department of Transportation, Federal Highway Administration, revision 2, December 2007).

12. Definitions

bicycle network a continuous network consisting of any combination of physically designated in-street bicycle lanes at least 5 feet wide, off-street bicycle paths or trails at least 8 feet wide for a two-way path and at least 5 feet wide for a one-way path, and/or streets designed for a target speed of 25 miles per hour or slower.

dwelling unit living quarters intended for long-term occupancy that provide facilities for cooking, sleeping, and sanitation. This does not include hotel rooms.

employment center a nonresidential area of at least 5 acres with a job density of at least 50 employees per net acre.

existing present on the date of submission of LEED-ND certification documents; similarly, an element or condition that **exists** is present on the date that LEED-ND certification documents are submitted.

multiunit residential consisting of four or more residential units sharing a common entry.

planned occupancy the highest estimate of building occupants based on planned use(s) and industry standards for square foot requirements per employee. The minimum planned occupancy for multiunit residential buildings is 1 person for a studio unit, 1.5 persons for a one-bedroom unit, and 1.25 persons per bedroom for a two- bedroom or larger unit.

project the land, water, and construction that constitutes the project application. A project applicant does not have to own or control all land or water within a project boundary, but all the area within the project boundary must comply with prerequisites and attempted credits.

project boundary the platted property line of the project defining land and water within it. Projects located on publicly owned campuses that do not have internal property lines must delineate a sphere-of-influence line to be used instead. Project site is equivalent to the land and water inside the project boundary. The project must not contain noncontiguous parcels, but parcels can be separated by public rights-of-way. Projects may also have enclaves of nonproject properties that are not subject to the rating system, but such enclaves cannot exceed 2% of the total project area and cannot be described as certified.

school a kindergarten, elementary, or secondary institution for the academic instruction of children.

vehicle miles traveled (VMT) the number of miles driven by motorists in a specified time period, such as a day or a year, in absolute or per capita terms.

HOUSING AND JOBS PROXIMITY

	ND
Credit	SLL Credit 5
Points	1-3 points

Intent

To encourage balanced communities with a diversity of uses and employment opportunities.

Requirements

OPTION 1. Project with Affordable Residential Component (3 points)

Include a residential component equaling at least 30% of the *project*'s total building square footage (exclusive of parking structures), and locate and/or design the project such that the geographic center (or boundary if the project exceeds 500 acres) is within 1/2-mile *walk distance* of *existing* full-time-equivalent jobs whose number is equal to or greater than the number of *dwelling units* in the project; and satisfy the requirements necessary to earn at least one point under NPD Credit 4, Mixed-Income Diverse Communities, Option 2, Affordable Housing.

OR

OPTION 2. Project With Residential Component (2 points)

Include a residential component equaling at least 30% of the project's total building square footage (exclusive of parking structures), and locate and/or design the project such that the geographic center (or boundary if the project exceeds 500 acres) is within 1/2-mile walk distance of existing full-time-equivalent jobs whose number is equal to or greater than the number of dwelling units in the project.

OR

OPTION 3. Infill Project with Nonresidential Component (1 point)

Include a nonresidential component equaling at least 30% of the project's total building square footage (exclusive of parking structures), and locate on an *infill site* whose geographic center (or boundary if the project exceeds 500 acres) is within 1/2-mile walk distance of an existing rail transit, ferry, or tram stop and within 1/2-mile walk distance of existing dwelling units whose number is equal to or greater than 50% of the number of new full-time-equivalent jobs created as part of the project.

SLL	
ND	Credit 5

1. Benefits and Issues to Consider

Environmental Issues

Balancing housing and jobs in a region is an important strategy to combat sprawl and reduce carbon emissions. Strategically targeting areas with an existing stock of housing or jobs can slow the expansion of the regional footprint by eliminating the need for long commutes. Shorter commutes can reduce carbon emissions from vehicles and prevent unnecessary development of greenfields. Reduced commute times are also beneficial from a mental health perspective and free up time for family and recreation.

Economic and Social Issues

Clustering jobs and housing together supports the local economy by keeping tax dollars local. Residents are more likely to patronize local businesses if shops and services are conveniently located near the workplace. Shorter commute times may also result in increased worker productivity. Providing affordable housing in a job-rich area may be financially challenging, but local, state, and federal financial incentives may help. Low-income residents in particular can benefit from reduced transportation costs for traveling to work.

2. Related Credits

Locating jobs and affordable housing near each other may assist in earning the following related credits:

- SLL Prerequisite 1, Smart Location
- SLL Credit 1, Preferred Locations
- SLL Credit 3, Locations with Reduced Automobile Dependence
- NPD Credit 3, Mixed-Use Neighborhood Centers
- NPD Credit 4, Mixed-Income Diverse Communities

3. Summary of Referenced Standards

There are no referenced standards for this credit.

4. Implementation

There are two ways to earn points for housing and jobs proximity: by locating new housing near existing jobs, and by locating new jobs near existing housing and transit. Note that LEED-ND does not use the FTE definition of jobs found in other LEED 2009 rating systems. Instead, a job is simply a permanent, year-round, full-time position. Construction jobs related to the LEED-ND project or other developments in the vicinity do not count.

As with many other credits, proximity is measured by shortest path analysis along walking routes, not by a straight-line radius. See the Getting Started chapter for guidance on shortest path analysis. Walking routes can be measured only along paths of travel with pedestrian facilities, so when selecting a site, be aware of pedestrian barriers like freeways, railroads, water bodies, streets without crossings, or gaps in the pedestrian network. Unlike some other credits in the rating system, the SLL Credit 5 walk distance is measured from the project's geographic center, not from individual dwelling units and business entrances within the project.

Locating Housing Near Jobs

If a residential component is included in the project, the project site must be within walking distance of a large number of existing jobs. Downtown areas, main streets, regional employment districts, campuses, and other nonresidential nodes (centers of activity) can contain a high number of jobs in a compact area. Simply selecting an infill site with a diversity of uses nearby may enable a project to achieve this credit. One additional point may be earned by providing affordable rental or for-sale housing in the project, if such housing earns credit under NPD Credit 4, Mixed-Income Diverse Communities, Option 2, Affordable Housing.

Data for determining the location and number of existing full-time equivalent jobs within a 1/2-mile walk distance of the project are available from several sources. If the number of employers nearby is small, contacting each business and totaling their employment figures can be an efficient way to demonstrate compliance with the credit requirements. It is also possible to purchase point-source employment data from private vendors that conduct market research, such as InforUSA or Claritas. This enables the project team to map all jobs in the area and map walking distances to them. Other public sources of information about jobs include the local planning, finance, or economic development departments, fire department, a metropolitan planning organization, the tax assessor's office, and state economic development departments.

Locating Jobs Near Housing

Locate projects with a significant nonresidential component on infill sites that are near existing housing and rail or ferry transit. The number of nearby existing dwelling units can usually be obtained through the tax assessor's office or the local planning department. If these sources are not available, project sponsors may count housing units using a combination of aerial surveys and field surveys.

5. Timeline and Team

During the site selection and site planning phases, the project team should consider the availability of nearby jobs (for residential projects) or nearby housing (for jobs-creating projects). Local economics and market analysis professionals can help compile employment data.

6. Calculations

OPTION 2. Project with Residential Component

Step 1. Identify the percentage of the project's total building square footage that is residential.

Step 2. Count the existing jobs within a 1/2-mile walk distance of the project's geographic center. If the geographic center is a water body, use the closest reasonable land location instead. Divide the number of existing jobs by the number of residential dwelling units in the project (Equation 1). The resulting jobs-to-housing ratio must be at least 1:1.

Equation 1

$$\text{Jobs : housing ratio} = \frac{\text{Existing jobs}}{\text{New dwelling units}}$$

OPTION 3. Infill Project with Nonresidential Component

Step 1. Confirm that the project is located on an infill site. (See the infill site calculation in the Getting Started chapter.)

Step 2. Identify the percentage of the project's total building square footage that is nonresidential.

Step 3. Count the existing dwelling units within a 1/2-mile walk distance of the project's geographic center. Divide the number of existing dwelling units by the number of new full-time equivalent jobs provided by the project (Equation 2). The result must be at least 0.5.

Equation 2

$$\text{Housing : jobs ratio} = \frac{\text{Existing dwelling units}}{\text{New jobs}}$$

7. Documentation Guidance

As a first step in preparing to complete the LEED-ND documentation requirements, work through the following measures. Refer to GBCI's website for the complete descriptions of all required documentation.

- Identify a single location to be the project's geographic center.

- Collect data about the location and number of full-time equivalent jobs within 1/2-mile of the project's geographic center (if applicable).

- Collect data about existing dwelling units within 1/2-mile of the project's geographic center (if applicable).

8. Examples

There are no examples for this prerequisite.

9. Exemplary Performance

This credit is not eligible for exemplary performance under Innovation and Design Process.

10. Regional Variations

There are no regional variations associated with this credit.

11. Resources

Websites
Center for Neighborhood Technology
www.cnt.org
This website contains information about the benefits of jobs-housing balance and offers location-efficient research and tools.

Southern California Association of Governments, jobs-housing balance
www.scag.ca.gov/Housing/balance.html
This website defines *jobs-housing balance*, describes the benefits, and analyzes regional jobs-housing balance issues.

Print Media
The Transit Metropolis, by Robert Cervero (Island Press, 1998).

Jobs-Housing Balance Revisited: Trends and Impacts in the San Francisco Bay Area, by Robert Cervero, *Journal of the American Planning Association* (Autumn 1996).

Jobs-Housing Balance, by Jerry Weitz (American Planning Association, 2003).

Urban Design Reclaimed: Tools, Techniques and Strategies for Planners, by Emily Talen (American Planning Association, 2009).

12. Definitions

existing present on the date of submission of LEED-ND certification documents; similarly, an element or condition that **exists** is present on the date that LEED-ND certification documents are submitted.

dwelling unit living quarters intended for long-term occupancy that provide facilities for cooking, sleeping, and sanitation. This does not include hotel rooms.

infill site a site that meets any of the following four conditions:

a. At least 75% of its boundary borders parcels that individually are at least 50% previously developed, and that in aggregate are at least 75% previously developed.

b. The site, in combination with bordering parcels, forms an aggregate parcel whose boundary is 75% bounded by parcels that individually are at least 50% previously developed, and that in aggregate are at least 75% previously developed.

c. At least 75% of the land area, exclusive of rights-of-way, within a 1/2-mile distance from the project boundary is previously developed.

d. The lands within a 1/2-mile distance from the project boundary have a preproject connectivity of at least 140 intersections per square mile.

A street or other right-of-way does not constitute previously developed land; it is the status of property on the other side of the street or right-of-way that matters. For conditions (a) and (b) above, any fraction of the perimeter that borders waterfront other than a stream is excluded from the calculation.

(a). Infill project site based on minimum 75% of perimeter adjacent to previously developed parcels

(b). Infill project site based on minimum 75% adjacent to previously developed parcels using project boundary and selected bordering parcels

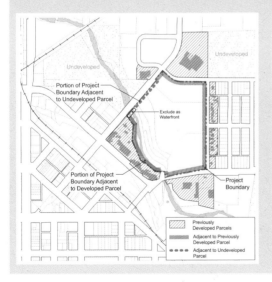

(c). Infill project site based on minimum 75% of land area within 1/2-mile of project boundary being previously developed

(d). Infill project site based on minimum 140 intersections/sq.mi. within 1/2-mile of project boundary

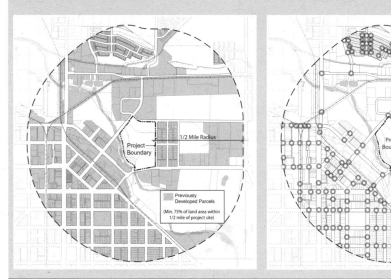

project the land, water, and construction that constitutes the project application. A project applicant does not have to own or control all land or water within a project boundary, but all the area within the project boundary must comply with prerequisites and attempted credits.

walk distance the distance that a pedestrian must travel between origins and destinations without obstruction, in a safe and comfortable environment on a continuous network of sidewalks, all-weather-surface footpaths, crosswalks, woonerfs, or equivalent pedestrian facilities.

STEEP SLOPE PROTECTION

	ND
Credit	SLL Credit 6
Points	1 point

Intent

To minimize erosion to protect habitat and reduce stress on natural water systems by preserving steep slopes in a natural, vegetated state.

Requirements

FOR ALL PROJECTS

All options apply to *existing* natural or constructed slopes. Portions of *project* sites with slopes up to 20 feet in elevation, measured from toe (a distinct break between a 40% slope and lesser slopes) to top, that are more than 30 feet in any direction from another slope greater than 15% are exempt from the requirements, although more restrictive local regulations may apply.

OPTION 1. No Disturbance of Slopes Over 15%

Locate on a site that has no existing slopes greater than 15%, or avoid disturbing portions of the site that have existing slopes greater than 15%.

OR

OPTION 2. Previously Developed Sites with Slopes Over 15%

On portions of *previously developed sites* with existing slopes greater than 15%, restore the slope area with *native plants* or noninvasive *adapted plants* according to Table 1.

Table 1. Required restoration area of slope

Slope	Restoration
> 40%	100%
26% to 40%	60%
15% to 25%	40%

In addition, develop *covenants, conditions, and restrictions* (CC&R); development agreements; or other binding documents that will protect the specified steep slope areas in perpetuity. Comply with the requirements of Option 3 on any slope over 15% that has not been previously developed.

OR

OPTION 3. Undeveloped Sites with Slopes Over 15%

On sites that are not previously developed, protect existing slopes over 15% as follows:

a. Do not disturb slopes greater than 40% and do not disturb portions of the project site within 50 feet horizontally of the top of the slope and 75 feet horizontally from the toe of the slope.

b. Limit development to no more than 40% of slopes between 25% and 40% and to no more than 60% of slopes between 15% and 25%.

c. Locate development such that the percentage of the *development footprint* that is on existing slopes less than 15% is greater than the percentage of *buildable land* that has existing slopes less than 15%.

d. Develop CC&R, development agreements, or other binding documents that will protect steep slopes in perpetuity.

1. Benefits and Issues to Consider

Environmental Issues

Steep slopes are an important and fragile part of the local ecosystem. Slopes play a vital role in preventing soil loss and erosion. They are also excellent candidates for planting native vegetation and creating wildlife habitat. Natural slopes may give clues as to the natural hydrology of the site, which is useful information when devising a stormwater management plan. All slopes, man-made or otherwise, should be considered integral to a stormwater management plan. Slopes may also act as a natural windbreak, sheltering the development, and provide visual interest.

Economic and Social Issues

Steep slopes are not an ideal land type for development because of the engineering challenge they pose. Redevelopment of previously developed steep slopes is usually less costly, though if the new development is substantially more intensive, reengineering may be necessary to accommodate the additional pressure on the land.

2. Related Credits

Conserving steep slopes, whether by locating the entire site away from such environmentally sensitive land or by designing the site to avoid, protect, or restore sensitive natural resources, may assist in earning the following related credits:

- SLL Credit 7, Site Design for Habitat or Wetland and Water Body Conservation
- SLL Credit 8, Restoration of Habitat or Wetlands and Water Bodies
- SLL Credit 9, Long-Term Conservation Management of Habitat or Wetlands and Water Bodies
- GIB Credit 7, Minimized Site Disturbance in Design and Construction
- GIB Credit 8, Stormwater Management

3. Summary of Referenced Standards

There are no referenced standards for this credit.

4. Implementation

As part of an integrated design process to protect natural resources, conduct a thorough survey identifying the site's sensitive environmental resources and their roles in its immediate vicinity and region. Take into account the site's and surrounding area's geomorphology, soils, including erodibility, and hydrology. Note that the credit covers both naturally occurring slopes and man-made slopes, such as those resulting from grading cuts and fills.

The goal of limiting disturbance to the stated parameters in the credit requirements is to consolidate all areas of disturbance on the areas of least slope and to minimize changes in grade, cleared area, and volume of cut or fill on the site. The figures below provide guidance on how the credit is applied on a typical slope.

Contact a soil engineering consultant with experience in preserving steep slopes. Terrain computer models can also assist with site design on areas with steep slopes. In general, seek to connect protected steep slopes with areas of natural habitat or wetlands and water bodies on the site and adjacent sites. Also try to ensure the connectivity of the built environment to ensure walkability and compact development. Because steep slopes create opportunities to provide either aesthetically pleasing views or eyesores, care should be taken to design the site with vistas of natural areas or appropriate architecture in mind.

For restoration of native or adapted vegetation to previously developed slopes, please see the Implementation section of SLL Credit 8, Restoration of Habitat or Wetlands and Waterbodies. Vegetation restoration on steep slopes should take into account northern versus southern exposure, ease of establishment on steep slopes, and likelihood of maintaining soil stability through the establishment period. Selection of vegetation and restoration techniques should also take into account the hydrology and soils of the slopes and the nature of development or conserved natural resources upslope and downslope of the newly vegetated areas. The conservation and restoration strategy for steep slopes should also include plans and funding for managing the restored vegetation so that it continues to provide ecological and aesthetic benefits into the future.

For all options, portions of project sites with slopes up to 20 feet in elevation (toe to top) that are more than 30 feet in any direction from another slope greater than 15% are exempt from the requirements, although more restrictive local regulations may apply. Note that Option 1 applies to permanent disturbance only, not construction-related activities (which are addressed in GIB Prerequisite 4, Construction Activity Pollution Prevention, and GIB Credit 7, Minimized Site Disturbance in Design and Construction).

5. Timeline and Team

During the site selection process, the developer should contract with environmental professionals to conduct site assessments for steep slopes, imperiled species, wetlands and water bodies, floodplains, prime soils for agriculture, and other sensitive environmental features. Once a site has been selected, if sensitive environmental resources are found, the developer should contract with environmental professionals who can assess these features more thoroughly and develop a holistic plan to conserve the site's natural resources. Once steep slopes are identified for preservation or restoration, the project team, including environmental professionals, can plan for preservation and restoration activities that will commence once entitlement is complete. Restoration activities can begin at any time—before, during, or after construction—but special care should be taken to avoid erosion and sedimentation from steep slopes during construction.

6. Calculations

There are no calculations for this credit.

7. Documentation Guidance

As a first step in preparing to complete the LEED-ND documentation requirements, work through the following measures. Refer to GBCI's website for the complete descriptions of all required documentation.

- Retain any topographic maps of the property in preproject conditions, with slopes relevant to this credit delineated.

- Retain copies of CC&Rs, deed restrictions, conservation easements, or other tools to protect land in perpetuity.

- Retain lists of the native and adapted plants to be used in restoration.

- For previously undeveloped sites with slopes greater than 15%, create a table itemizing the size of the preservation and restoration areas for each slope increment, and the percentage of each slope increment area being restored.

8. Examples

OPTION 3(c)

A 100-acre site that is not previously developed has 35 acres with steep slopes and 60 acres of nonbuildable land. The developer wishes to avoid disturbing steep slopes and comply with the requirements for Option 3 of this credit.

Table 2. Example determination for steep slope protection

	Project (acres)	Slopes ≤ 15% (acres)	Slopes > 15% (acres)	Development footprint (acres)	Development footprint on slopes > 15% (acres)
Project site	100	65	35	32	< 8
Nonbuildable land	60	35	25	2 (street right-of-ways)	
Buildable land	40	30	10	30	

The development footprint covers 32 acres, which includes some slopes greater than 15% and some less than 15%. Because 30 of the 40 acres (75%) of buildable land has slopes less than 15%, at least 75% of the development footprint must be on slopes less than 15%. Therefore, no more than 8 acres (25%) of the development footprint can be on slopes greater than 15%.

Figure 1. OPTION 1, No Disturbance of Slopes over 15%

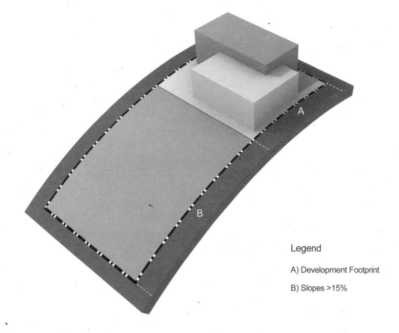

Legend

A) Development Footprint

B) Slopes >15%

Figure 2. OPTION 2, Previously Developed Sites with Slopes over 15%

This figure indicates the amount of restored native vegetation that would be necessary to achieve Option 2. The project in the figure could also use Option 1, since no part of the site with a slope greater than 15% is being built upon.

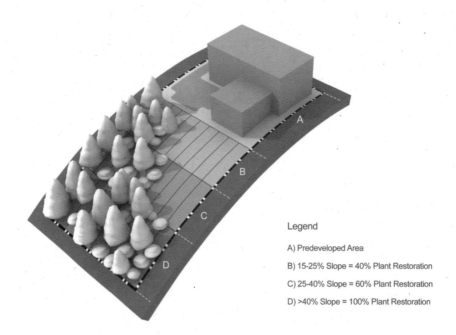

Legend

A) Predeveloped Area

B) 15-25% Slope = 40% Plant Restoration

C) 25-40% Slope = 60% Plant Restoration

D) >40% Slope = 100% Plant Restoration

Figure 3. OPTION 3, Undeveloped Sites with Slopes over 15%

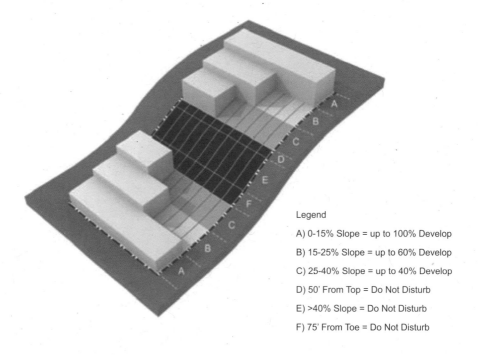

Legend

A) 0-15% Slope = up to 100% Develop

B) 15-25% Slope = up to 60% Develop

C) 25-40% Slope = up to 40% Develop

D) 50' From Top = Do Not Disturb

E) >40% Slope = Do Not Disturb

F) 75' From Toe = Do Not Disturb

Figure 4. Exemption for steep slope requirement

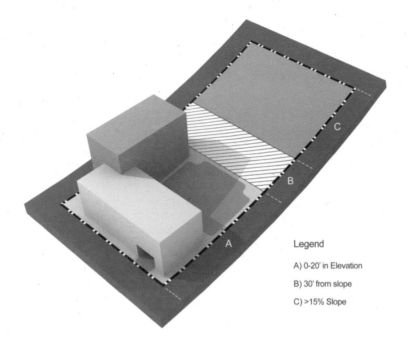

Legend

A) 0-20' in Elevation

B) 30' from slope

C) >15% Slope

9. Exemplary Performance

This credit is not eligible for exemplary performance under Innovation and Design Process.

10. Regional Variations

State and local government regulations to protect steep slopes vary and may be more stringent than the credit requirements.

11. Resources

Websites

American Society of Landscape Architects, digital terrain modeling

www.asla.org/nonmembers/DgtlTMod.htm

This website provides an index of digital terrain modeling programs, practitioners, and data sources.

Land Trust Alliance

www.landtrustalliance.org

The Land Trust Alliance has an accreditation program for land trusts, and its website has links to land trusts across the United States.

Native Plant Information Network

www.wildflower.org

This resource includes a native plants database and national suppliers directory.

Plant Native

www.plantnative.org

This organization is dedicated to moving native plants and "naturescaping" into mainstream landscaping practices. Its website offers native plant landscaping suggestions for each state.

Sustainable Sites Initiative

www.sustainablesites.org

The Sustainable Sites Initiative is an interdisciplinary effort by the American Society of Landscape Architects, the Lady Bird Johnson Wildflower Center, and the United States Botanic Garden to create voluntary national guidelines and performance benchmarks for sustainable land design, construction, and maintenance practices.

U.S. Department of Agriculture, plants database

www.plants.usda.gov

This website contains a database of plants with information on whether they are native or introduced to certain states. It also lists state and federal noxious weeds.

Print Media

Design with Nature, by Ian L. McHarg (Doubleday & Company, 1969).

12. Definitions

adapted (or introduced) plant a species that reliably grows well in a given habitat with minimal attention from humans in the form of winter protection, pest protection, water irrigation, or fertilization once its root systems are established in the soil. Adapted plants are low maintenance but not invasive.

buildable land the portion of the site where construction can occur, including land voluntarily set aside and not constructed upon. When used in density calculations, buildable land excludes public rights-of-way and land excluded from development by codified law or LEED for Neighborhood Development prerequisites. An applicant may exclude additional land not exceeding 15% of the buildable land base defined above, provided the following conditions are present:

    a. The land is protected from residential and nonresidential construction by easement, deed restriction, or other enforceable legal instrument.

AND

    b. Either 25% or more of the boundary of each contiguous parcel proposed for exclusion borders a water body or areas outside the project boundary that are protected by codified law; or ownership of, or management authority over, the exclusion area is transferred to a public entity.

covenants, conditions, and restrictions (CC&Rs) limitations that may be placed on a property and its use and are made a condition of holding title or lease.

development footprint the total land area of a project site covered by buildings, streets, parking areas, and other typically impermeable surfaces constructed as part of the project.

existing present on the date of submission of LEED-ND certification documents; similarly, an element or condition that **exists** is present on the date that LEED-ND certification documents are submitted.

native (or indigenous) plant a plant species that did or would have occurred on the site or within the subject county prior to the widespread land alterations that accompanied European settlement. Cultivars of native plants may be considered native plants.

previously developed site a site that, preproject, consisted of at least 75% previously developed land.

project the land, water, and construction that constitutes the project application. A project applicant does not have to own or control all land or water within a project boundary, but all the area within the project boundary must comply with prerequisites and attempted credits.

SITE DESIGN FOR HABITAT OR WETLAND AND WATER BODY CONSERVATION

	ND
Credit	SLL Credit 7
Points	1 point

Intent

To conserve *native plants*, wildlife habitat, *wetlands*, and *water bodies*.

Requirements

OPTION 1. Sites without Significant Habitat or Wetlands and Water Bodies

Locate the *project* on a site that does not have significant habitat, as defined in Option 2 of this credit, or land within 100 feet of such habitat, and fulfill the requirements of Options 1 or 2(a) under SLL Prerequisite 3, Wetland and Water Body Conservation.

OR

OPTION 2. Sites with Significant Habitat

Work with both the state's Natural Heritage Program and the state fish and wildlife agency to delineate identified significant habitat on the site. Do not disturb significant habitat or portions of the site within an appropriate buffer around the habitat. The geographic extent of the habitat and buffer must be identified by a qualified biologist, a nongovernmental conservation organization, or the appropriate state or regional agency. Protect significant habitat and its identified buffers from development in perpetuity by donating or selling the land, or a conservation easement on the land, to an accredited land trust or relevant public agency (a deed covenant is not sufficient to meet this requirement). Identify and commit to ongoing management activities, along with parties responsible for management and funding available, so that habitat is maintained in *preproject* condition or better for a minimum of three years after the project is built out. The requirement for identifying ongoing management activities may also be met by earning SLL Credit 9, Long-Term Conservation Management of Wetlands and Water Bodies.

Significant habitat for this credit includes the following:

a. Habitat for species that are listed or are candidates for listing under state or federal endangered species acts, habitat for species of special concern in the state, and/or habitat for those species and/or ecological communities classified as G1, G2, G3, and/or S1 and S2 species by NatureServe.

b. Locally or regionally significant habitat of any size, or patches of predominantly native vegetation at least 150 acres (even if some of the 150 acres lies outside the *project boundary*).

c. Habitat flagged for conservation under a regional or state conservation or green infrastructure plan.

OR

OPTION 3. Sites with Wetlands and Water Bodies

Design the project to conserve 100% of all water bodies, wetlands, land within 100 feet of water bodies, and land within 50 feet of wetlands on the site. Using a qualified biologist, conduct an assessment, or compile *existing* assessments, showing the extent to which those water bodies and/or wetlands perform the following functions: (1) water quality maintenance, (2) wildlife habitat protection, and (3) hydrologic function maintenance, including flood protection. Assign appropriate buffers (not less than 100 feet for water bodies and 50 feet for wetlands) based on the functions provided, contiguous soils and slopes, and contiguous land uses. Do not disturb wetlands, water bodies, and their buffers, and protect them from development in perpetuity by donating or selling the land, or a conservation easement on the land, to an accredited land trust or relevant public agency (a deed covenant is not sufficient to meet this requirement). Identify and commit to ongoing management activities, along with parties responsible for management and funding available, so that habitat is maintained in preproject condition or better for a minimum of three years after the project is built out. The requirement for identifying ongoing management activities may also be met by earning SLL Credit 9, Long-Term Conservation Management of Wetlands and Water Bodies. The project does not meet the requirements if it has negative effects on habitat for species identified in Option 2(a).

FOR ALL PROJECTS

The following features are not considered wetlands, water bodies, or buffer land that must be protected:

a. *Previously developed* land.

b. Man-made water bodies (such as industrial mining pits, concrete-lined canals, or stormwater retention ponds) that lack natural edges and floors or native ecological communities in the water and along the edge

c. Man-made linear wetlands that result from the interruption of natural drainages by existing rights-of-way.

d. Wetlands that were created incidentally by human activity and have been rated "poor" for all measured wetland functions. Wetland quality assessment must be performed by a qualified biologist using a method that is accepted by state or regional permitting agencies.

1. Benefits and Issues to Consider

For an explanation of the numerous benefits of avoiding sensitive habitat, wetlands, and water bodies, please refer to the Benefits and Issues sections under SLL Prerequisite 2, Imperiled Species and Ecological Communities Conservation, and SLL Prerequisite 3, Wetland and Water Body Conservation.

2. Related Credits

Conserving environmentally sensitive land, whether by locating the project elsewhere or by designing the site to avoid, protect, or restore natural hydrology and native communities, may assist in earning the following related credits:

- SLL Credit 6, Steep Slope Protection

- SLL Credit 8, Restoration of Habitat or Wetlands and Water Bodies

- SLL Credit 9, Long-Term Conservation Management of Habitat or Wetlands and Water Bodies

- GIB Credit 7, Minimized Site Disturbance in Design and Construction

- GIB Credit 8, Stormwater Management

3. Summary of Referenced Standards

U.S. Fish and Wildlife Service, threatened and endangered species
www.fws.gov/endangered/
This referenced standard addresses threatened and endangered wildlife and plants. The U.S. Fish and Wildlife Service also maintains a list of the country's native plants and animals that are candidates for addition to the federal list.

National Marine Fisheries Service, endangered marine species
www.nmfs.noaa.gov/pr/species/esa_species.htm
The National Marine Fisheries Service is in charge of conservation guidelines and permitting for federally listed marine species.

Association of Fish and Wildlife Agencies, state endangered species acts
www.fishwildlife.org
Each state has a list of threatened and endangered species, maintained and administered by its fish and wildlife agency. In addition, many states have lists of candidate species and species of special concern. State endangered species acts vary in their criteria for listing and requirements for protection. The Association of Fish and Wildlife Agencies website has links to each state fish and wildlife agency.

NatureServe Natural Heritage Program, G1, G2, G3, S1, and S2 species and ecological communities
www.natureserve.org
NatureServe is a nonprofit conservation organization that represents an international network of biological inventories—known as natural heritage programs or conservation data centers—operating in all 50 U.S. states, Canada, Latin America and the Caribbean. G1 and G2 are part of a classification system maintained by this network of natural heritage programs in every state. Ecological communities are specific assemblages of species that are classified and defined by NatureServe using a standard classification system. NatureServe uses a number of criteria in assessing the status of species and ecological communities, including the number of populations, the size of populations, the viability of the species occurrences, the trends in population numbers, and the threats to species.

G1 species or ecological communities are critically imperiled and at very high risk of extinction globally because of extreme rarity (often five or fewer populations), very steep declines, or other factors. G2 species or ecological communities are imperiled and at high risk of extinction globally because of very restricted range, very few populations (often 20 or fewer), steep declines, or other factors. G3 species or ecological communities are vulnerable and at moderate risk of extinction because of a restricted range, relatively few populations (often 80 or fewer), recent and widespread declines, or other factors.

S1 species or ecological communities are critically imperiled and especially vulnerable to extirpation in the state because of extreme rarity (often five or fewer occurrences), very steep declines, or other factors. S2 species or ecological communities are imperiled and very vulnerable to extirpation in the state because of rarity, very restricted range, very few populations (often 20 or fewer), steep declines, or other factors.

If a species or ecological community has two ranks or a question mark beside the rank, the lower rank number should be used in meeting this credit (e.g., a G2/G3 species and a G2? should both be considered G2s and included in this credit).

4. Implementation

ALL OPTIONS

As part of an integrated design process to protect natural resources, conduct a thorough environmental survey identifying the site's sensitive environmental resources and their roles in its immediate vicinity and region. Take into account the site's and surrounding area's hydrology, soils, and geomorphology.

As in SLL Prerequisite 2, Imperiled Species and Ecological Communities Conservation, consult with both the state fish and wildlife agency and the state natural heritage program to determine whether any of the imperiled species or ecological communities listed in Option 2(a) could occur on the site. If the result of the consultation is inconclusive and site conditions indicate that imperiled species could be present, conduct a biological survey during appropriate seasons, using accepted methods. If imperiled species, wetlands, or water bodies are found, contact the appropriate state and federal agencies and comply with all relevant local, state, and federal regulations.

OPTION 2. Sites with Significant Habitat

If site conditions and/or the consultation with state agencies indicate that significant habitat (as defined in the credit requirements) could be found, ensure that the environmental site assessment surveys for the project identifies, delineates, and assesses all types of significant habitat described in the credit requirements. In addition, contact local, state, and federal fish and wildlife agencies, as well as local land trusts and naturalist societies, and find out whether they have identified the site or its species and ecological communities as significant habitat.

If significant habitat is found, work with one of the agencies or groups described above or a qualified biologist to delineate and assess the habitat and appropriate buffers. It is best to work with the agency or organization that flagged the site to ensure that appropriate measures are taken to conserve the significant habitat. Ensure that buffer delineation and management activities take into account the full array of factors that will affect the habitat, including human intrusion, disturbance or predation by pets, potential invasive species introduction, hydrological modification, noise, and light pollution. If possible, consider establishing a source for funding management of habitat areas in perpetuity.

OPTION 3. Sites with Wetlands and Water Bodies

Ensure that the environmental site assessment includes a detailed assessment of the wetlands and/or water bodies. Such an assessment should be performed by a qualified biologist and follow a methodology that is required, commonly used, or recommended by local, state, or regional wetland permitting agencies. Results from the assessment should detail the functions provided by the wetland or water body, and buffer delineation and ongoing management should ensure that those functions will not be impaired. Take any necessary steps to avoid impacts by establishing large buffers, protecting steep slopes, managing stormwater, and providing linkages to adjacent protected areas. If possible, establish a funding source for ongoing management of habitat areas in perpetuity. Although the credit requires that wetlands, water bodies, and their buffers not be disturbed, habitat or hydrological restoration activities that involve temporary disturbance may be acceptable.

5. Timeline and Team

During the site selection process, the developer should contract with environmental professionals to conduct site assessments for imperiled species, wetlands and water bodies, floodplains, prime soils for agriculture, and other sensitive environmental features. Once a site has been selected, if sensitive environmental resources are found, the developers should contract with environmental professionals who can assess these features more thoroughly and develop a holistic plan to conserve the site's natural resources.

6. Calculations

There are no calculations for this credit.

7. Documentation Guidance

As a first step in preparing to complete the LEED-ND documentation requirements, work through the following measures. Refer to GBCI's website for the complete descriptions of all required documentation.

- Retain written evidence of consultation with state agencies and correspondence with local and regional fish and wildlife agencies and conservation organizations, indicating whether the site or its resources are flagged in state wildlife conservation plans or green infrastructure plans.

- Retain aerial photos or vicinity maps of the site.

- If habitat is found for species identified in Option 2(a), acquire documentation from the U.S. Fish and Wildlife Service (for federally listed species) or the state fish and wildlife agency (for state-listed species or G1-3 or S1-2 species or ecological communities) that the project is complying with state or federal conservation requirements.

- Prepare a summary of the environmental site assessment, as well as the assessment of wetland or water body functions. Acquire documentation that the functional assessment methodology is commonly used or required by state or regional permitting agencies.

- Prepare a summary of the conservation strategy for wetlands and water bodies, including buffer delineation, stormwater management, and ongoing management activities, per the credit requirements.

- Retain environmental assessments for each wetland being excluded, the wetland quality assessment, and the qualifications of the biologist conducting the assessment.

8. Examples

There are no examples for this credit.

9. Exemplary Performance

This credit is not eligible for exemplary performance under Innovation and Design Process.

10. Regional Variations

State endangered species acts vary in their requirements for species protection, so ask state fish and wildlife agencies for guidance. State and local regulations for wetland and riparian protection vary and may be more stringent than EPA and Army Corps of Engineers standards.

11. Resources

Websites

Army Corps of Engineers, wetlands

www.wetlands.com/regs/tlpge02e.htm

The *Wetlands Delineation Manual* (1987) describes a methodology for determining wetlands that is commonly used throughout the United States.

Center for Natural Lands Management

www.cnlm.org

This website contains a property analysis record, a tool commonly used to calculate the cost over time of managing natural areas.

Land Trust Alliance

www.landtrustalliance.org

The Land Trust Alliance has an accreditation program for land trusts, and its website has links to land trusts across the United States.

NatureServe, state natural heritage programs

www.natureserve.org/visitLocal/index.jsp

This website provides links to NatureServe's network of natural heritage programs operating in all 50 U.S. states, Canadian provinces and territories, and many countries and territories in Latin America and the Caribbean.

State fish and wildlife agencies

www.fishwildlife.org/where_us.html

The Association of Fish and Wildlife Agencies provides links to state fish and wildlife agencies in every state and in Canadian provinces.

Sustainable Sites Initiative

www.sustainablesites.org

The Sustainable Sites Initiative is an interdisciplinary effort by the American Society of Landscape Architects, the Lady Bird Johnson Wildflower Center, and the United States Botanic Garden to create voluntary national guidelines and performance benchmarks for sustainable land design, construction, and maintenance practices.

The Nature Conservancy

www.nature.org

www.conserveonline.org/workspaces/cbdgateway/

The Nature Conservancy has chapters in all 50 states, owns and manages nature preserves, holds conservation easements, and has developed ecoregion plans that identify important conservation areas and significant habitat. Its Conservation by Design Gateway website provides guidance, tools, resources, and case studies for conservation projects at all scales. The Conservation Action Planning section is particularly relevant for this credit.

U.S. Environmental Protection Agency, Office of Wetlands, Oceans, and Watersheds
www.epa.gov/owow
This website offers watershed management tools, resource protection strategies, and regulatory information, plus publications on water conservation and landscaping practices.

Washington State Department of Ecology, wetlands
www.ecy.wa.gov/programs/sea/wetlands/index.html
This website contains information on wetland buffers, functions, and value.

Print Media

Conservation Thresholds for Land Use Planners (Environmental Law Institute, 2003).

Design with Nature, by Ian L. McHarg (Doubleday & Company, 1969).

Ecological Riverfront Design, by Betsy Otto, Kathleen McCormick, and Michael Leccese (American Planning Associaiton, 2004).

Green Infrastructure, by Mark A. Benedict and Edward T. McMahon (Island Press, 2006).

Handbook of Water Sensitive Planning and Design, edited by Robert L. France (Lewis Publishers, 2002).

Nature-Friendly Land Use Practices at Multiple Scales, by Rebecca Kihslinger and James McElfish (Environmental Law Institute, 2009).

Practical Ecology for Planners, Developers and Citizens, by Dan L. Perlman and Jeffrey C. Milder (Island Press, 2005).

Wetland Indicators: A Guide to Wetland Identification, Delineation, Classification, and Mapping, by Ralph W. Tiner (Lewis Publishers, 1999).

Wetlands, Streams and Other Waters, by Kenneth Bogdan et al. (Solano Press, 2004).

12. Definitions

existing present on the date of submission of LEED-ND certification documents; similarly, an element or condition that **exists** is present on the date that LEED-ND certification documents are submitted.

native (or indigenous) plant a plant species that did or would have occurred on the site or within the subject county prior to the widespread land alterations that accompanied European settlement. Cultivars of native plants may be considered native plants.

preproject before the LEED-ND project was initiated, but not necessarily before any development or disturbance took place. Preproject conditions describe the state of the project site on the date the developer acquired rights to a majority of its buildable land through purchase or option to purchase.

previously developed altered by paving, construction, and/or land use that would typically have required regulatory permitting to have been initiated (alterations may exist now or in the past). Previously developed land includes a platted lot on which a building was constructed if the lot is no more than 1 acre; previous development on lots larger than 1 acre is defined as the development footprint and land alterations associated with the footprint. Land that is not previously developed and altered landscapes resulting from current or historical clearing or filling, agricultural or forestry use, or preserved natural area use are considered undeveloped land. The date of previous development permit issuance constitutes the date of previous development, but permit issuance in itself does not constitute previous development.

project the land, water, and construction that constitutes the project application. A project applicant does not have to own or control all land or water within a project boundary, but all the area within the project boundary must comply with prerequisites and attempted credits.

project boundary the platted property line of the project defining land and water within it. Projects located on publicly owned campuses that do not have internal property lines must delineate a sphere-of-influence line to be used instead. Project site is equivalent to the land and water inside the project boundary. The project must not contain noncontiguous parcels, but parcels can be separated by public rights-of-way. Projects may also have enclaves of nonproject properties that are not subject to the rating system, but such enclaves cannot exceed 2% of the total project area and cannot be described as certified.

water body the surface water of a stream (first-order and higher, including intermittent streams), arroyo, river, canal, lake, estuary, bay, or ocean, excluding irrigation ditches.

wetland an area that is inundated or saturated by surface or ground water at a frequency and duration sufficient to support, and that under normal circumstances do support, a prevalence of vegetation typically adapted for life in saturated soil conditions. Wetlands generally include swamps, marshes, bogs, and similar areas, but exclude irrigation ditches unless delineated as part of an adjacent wetland.

RESTORATION OF HABITAT OR WETLANDS AND WATER BODIES

	ND
Credit	SLL Credit 8
Points	1 point

Intent

To restore *native plants*, wildlife habitat, *wetlands*, and *water bodies* that have been harmed by previous human activities.

Requirements

Using only native plants, restore *predevelopment* native ecological communities, water bodies, or wetlands on the *project* site in an area equal to or greater than 10% of the *development footprint*. Work with a qualified biologist to ensure that restored areas will have the native species assemblages, hydrology, and other habitat characteristics that likely occurred in predevelopment conditions. Protect such areas from development in perpetuity by donating or selling the land, or a conservation easement on the land, to an accredited land trust or relevant public agency (a deed covenant is not sufficient to meet this requirement). Identify and commit to ongoing management activities, along with parties responsible for management and funding available, so that restored areas are maintained for a minimum of three years after the project is built out or the restoration is completed, whichever is later. The requirement for identifying ongoing management activities may also be met by earning SLL Credit 9, Long-Term Conservation Management of Wetlands and Water Bodies. The project does not meet the requirements if it has negative effects on habitat for species identified in Option 2(a) of SLL Credit 7, Site Design for Habitat or Wetland and Water Body Conservation.

1. Benefits and Issues

Environmental Issues

Restoration of sensitive lands offers opportunity to enhance the natural state of the site and even promote the survival of any threatened habitat or species. Using native plantings can help restore the local ecosystem and help control stormwater runoff. Native plantings attract native animals and insect life, which may be beneficial for agricultural production or pest control. Restored wetlands and water bodies often help recharge underground water reserves and can also act as natural stormwater management features.

As the restoration proceeds over time, residents and visitors to the project should be given the opportunity to learn what is taking place. Adequate public education will help ensure that the sensitive land is respected in the future.

Economic and Social Issues

Native plants often require less maintenance than conventional plants and have a greater chance of surviving in the long term. Restoration activities may be costly, depending on the quantity and quality of the restoration. However, cost justification may be easier if restored areas can double as open space, provide views, or assist with stormwater management. Local conservation groups or the municipality may have an interest in seeing sensitive lands restored, and partnerships should be explored.

2. Related Credits

Conserving environmentally sensitive land, whether by locating the project elsewhere or by designing the site to avoid, protect, or restore natural hydrology and native natural communities, may assist in earning the following related credits:

- SLL Credit 6, Steep Slope Protection
- SLL Credit 7, Site Design for Habitat or Wetland and Water Body Conservation
- SLL Credit 9, Long-Term Conservation Management of Habitat or Wetlands and Water Bodies
- GIB Credit 7, Minimized Site Disturbance in Design and Construction
- GIB Credit 8, Stormwater Management

3. Summary of Referenced Standards

There are no referenced standards for this credit.

4. Implementation

As in SLL Prerequisite 2, Imperiled Species and Ecological Communities Conservation, consult with both the state fish and wildlife agency and the state natural heritage program to determine whether any of the imperiled species or ecological communities listed in Option 2(a) of SLL Credit 7, Site Design for Habitat or Wetland and Water Body Conservation, could occur on the site. If the result of the consultation is inconclusive and site conditions indicate that imperiled species could be present, conduct a biological survey during appropriate seasons, using accepted methods. If imperiled species, wetlands, or water bodies are found on the site, contact the appropriate state and federal agencies and comply with all relevant local, state, and federal regulations.

As part of an integrated design process to protect natural resources, conduct a thorough environmental survey identifying the site's sensitive environmental resources and their roles in its immediate vicinity and region. Take into account the site and surrounding area's hydrology, soils, and geomorphology. Select restoration areas that will provide multiple ecological benefits, such as connectivity to nearby natural areas, water quality improvements, flood control, and educational opportunities. In addition, enhance the urbanism of the site by designing a compact development, maintaining walkability within the project and to adjacent areas, and providing pleasant views and opportunities to connect with and experience the natural world.

A qualified biologist can help assess the predevelopment conditions on the site, including conditions prior to any previous agricultural use. The assessment may involve locating historical aerial photos and records associated with the site or immediate area. Restoration that involves creating wetlands or streams where they did not previously exist does not meet this credit's requirements. In addition, restoration of areas that are disturbed during construction does not qualify for the credit unless it improves the ecological conditions compared with their preconstruction state.

The restoration process should include removal of invasive exotic species and ongoing management to prevent recolonization by invasive species. A qualified biologist can help develop a planting plan that uses native plants. Landscape architects, local or regional governmental agencies, educational facilities, native plant societies, and plant nurseries that specialize in native species may also be able to assist in identifying native species and plant sources. Native plant selection should strive to complement and enhance the genetic diversity of the site, and projects should confirm that the plants and animals that will be restored to the site are native to the area. Planting nonnative adapted species in restoration areas does not meet the credit requirements because such vegetation is inherently not native habitat.

For hydrological restoration, consider "daylighting" streams that were channeled underground, removing agricultural tiles that drained wetlands, and using other techniques to mimic natural hydrology. Habitat restoration, and particularly hydrological restoration, will be most effective if it is integrated with other measures, both on the site and on adjacent sites, that influence water quality and quantity, including stormwater management, steep slope protection, site design for conservation, and construction activity pollution prevention.

A management plan for the restored area should take into account the full array of factors that will affect its ongoing health, including human intrusion, disturbance or predation by pets, the potential for invasive species to recolonize, and hydrological modification. If possible, establish a funding source for ongoing management of restored areas in perpetuity.

5. Timeline and Team

The developer should contract with environmental professionals and, if possible, collaborate with natural resource agencies, conservation organizations, native plant societies, and academic institutions whose specialists can assess the site thoroughly and develop a holistic plan to conserve the site's natural resources. Such professionals have the expertise to identify restoration areas and develop a successful restoration and management strategy. Typically, a restoration area is delineated during master planning, and restoration activities can begin at any time—before, during, or after construction. Intensive restoration effort may take from a few weeks to a season to multiple seasons. Once intensive restoration is well underway or completed, the project begins actively managing the restored area, per the credit requirements.

6. Calculations

Calculate the amount of land area where native habitat and/or predevelopment water bodies or wetlands will be restored. Calculate the development footprint (see the Definitions section for additional guidance). Divide the amount of the restored area by the development footprint to obtain the restored area's percentage of development footprint (Equation 1). The result must be 10% or greater.

Equation 1

$$\% \text{ development footprint restored} = \frac{\text{Total restored area (acres)}}{\text{Total development footprint (acres)}} \times 100$$

7. Documentation Guidance

As a first step in preparing to complete the LEED-ND documentation requirements, work through the following measures. Refer to GBCI's website for the complete descriptions of all required documentation.

- Retain written evidence of consultation with state agencies with regard to all types of species listed in Option 2(a) of SLL Credit 7, Site Design for Habitat or Wetland and Water Body Conservation, prior to clearing the site.

- Obtain or retain historic aerial photos or historical records that demonstrate the habitat or wetlands/water bodies that were on the site prior to any agricultural, industrial, or commercial development.

- Prepare a description and a map of the restoration strategy. Retain information on the qualifications of the biologist who developed the restoration strategy, and retain descriptions of any collaborating institutions and correspondence with them.

8. Examples

There are no examples for this credit.

9. Exemplary Performance

Projects may earn an Innovation and Design Process credit for exemplary performance by restoring an area equal to 20% or more of the development footprint.

10. Regional Variations

There are no regional variations associated with this credit.

11. Resources

Websites
Global Restoration Network
www.globalrestorationnetwork.org
This resource offers a database and web-based portal for hard-to-find information on ecological restoration techniques, with case studies.

National Academy of Sciences, wetlands restoration
www.mitigationactionplan.gov/nas404program.pdf
The National Academy of Sciences has developed operational guidelines for creating or restoring wetlands that are ecologically self-sustaining; these recommendations have been adopted by the Army Corps of Engineers.

Native Plant Information Network
www.wildflower.org
This resource includes a native plants database and national suppliers directory.

Plant Native
www.plantnative.org
This organization is dedicated to moving native plants and "naturescaping" into mainstream landscaping practices. Its website offers native plant landscaping suggestions for each state.

Sustainable Sites Initiative

www.sustainablesites.org

The Sustainable Sites Initiative is an interdisciplinary effort by the American Society of Landscape Architects, the Lady Bird Johnson Wildflower Center, and the United States Botanic Garden to create voluntary national guidelines and performance benchmarks for sustainable land design, construction, and maintenance practices.

The Nature Conservancy

www.nature.org

www.conserveonline.org/workspaces/cbdgateway/

The Nature Conservancy has chapters in all 50 states, owns and manages nature preserves, holds conservation easements, and has developed ecoregion plans that identify important conservation areas and significant habitat. Its Conservation by Design Gateway website provides guidance, tools, resources, and case studies for conservation projects at all scales. The Conservation Action Planning section is particularly relevant for this credit.

U.S. Department of Agriculture, plants database

www.plants.usda.gov

This website contains a database of plants with information on whether they are native or introduced to certain states. It also lists state and federal noxious weeds.

Print Media

Stream Corridor Restoration: Principles, Processes and Practice, by Federal Interagency Stream Corridor Working Group (2001), available at www.nrcs.usda.gov/technical/stream_restoration.

Daylighting: New Life for Buried Streams, by Richard Pinkham (Rocky Mountain Institute, 2000), available at www.rmi.org/images/other/Water/W00-32_Daylighting.pdf.

12. Definitions

development footprint the total land area of a project site covered by buildings, streets, parking areas, and other typically impermeable surfaces constructed as part of the project.

native (or indigenous) plant a plant species that did or would have occurred on the site or within the subject county prior to the widespread land alterations that accompanied European settlement. Cultivars of native plants may be considered native plants.

predevelopment before any development occurred on the site. Predevelopment conditions describe the natural conditions of the site prior to any human alteration, such as development of roads or buildings.

project the land, water, and construction that constitutes the project application. A project applicant does not have to own or control all land or water within a project boundary, but all the area within the project boundary must comply with prerequisites and attempted credits.

water body the surface water of a stream (first-order and higher, including intermittent streams), arroyo, river, canal, lake, estuary, bay, or ocean, excluding irrigation ditches.

wetland an area that is inundated or saturated by surface or ground water at a frequency and duration sufficient to support, and that under normal circumstances do support, a prevalence of vegetation typically adapted for life in saturated soil conditions. Wetlands generally include swamps, marshes, bogs, and similar areas, but exclude irrigation ditches unless delineated as part of an adjacent wetland.

LONG-TERM CONSERVATION MANAGEMENT OF HABITAT OR WETLANDS AND WATER BODIES

	ND
Credit	SLL Credit 9
Points	1 point

Intent

To conserve *native plants*, wildlife habitat, *wetlands*, and *water bodies*.

Requirements

Create and commit to implementing a long-term (at least ten-year) management plan for new or *existing* on-site native habitats, water bodies, and/or wetlands and their buffers, and create a guaranteed funding source for management. Involve a qualified biologist or a professional from a natural resources agency or natural resources consulting firm in writing the management plan and conducting or evaluating the ongoing management. The plan must include biological objectives consistent with habitat and/or water resource conservation, and it must identify (1) procedures, including personnel to carry them out, for maintaining the conservation areas; (2) estimated implementation costs and funding sources; and (3) threats that the *project* poses for habitat and/or water resources within conservation areas (e.g., introduction of exotic species, intrusion of residents in habitat areas) and measures to substantially reduce those threats. The project does not meet the requirements if it has negative effects on habitat for species identified in Option 2(a) of SLL Credit 7, Site Design for Habitat or Wetland and Water Body Conservation.

1. Benefits and Issues

Environmental Issues

An effective long-term management plan helps ensure that any conservation or restoration activities undertaken by the project will have a lasting effect on the local ecosystem. If restoration has been undertaken, it may take a long time for the area to stabilize and begin producing noticeable benefits. Well-managed sensitive lands and water bodies can serve as educational facilities for the public, as well as provide excellent sites for conservation research.

Economic Issues

Finding funding for long-term management of conserved areas can prove as challenging as underwriting restoration activities. The best strategy is to explore partnerships with the many entities that may be interested in seeing the land preserved, such as the municipality, conservation groups, or academic institutions.

2. Related Credits

Conserving environmentally sensitive land, whether by locating the project elsewhere or by designing the site to avoid, protect, or restore natural hydrology and native natural communities, may assist in earning the following related credits:

- SLL Credit 6, Steep Slope Protection

- SLL Credit 7, Site Design for Habitat or Wetland and Water Body Conservation

- SLL Credit 8, Restoration of Habitat or Wetlands and Water Bodies

- GIB Credit 7, Minimized Site Disturbance in Design and Construction

- GIB Credit 8, Stormwater Management

3. Summary of Referenced Standards

There are no referenced standards for this credit.

4. Implementation

As for SLL Prerequisite 2, Imperiled Species and Ecological Communities Conservation, consult with both the state fish and wildlife agency and the state natural heritage program to determine whether any of the imperiled species or ecological communities listed in Option 2(a) of SLL Credit 7, Site Design for Habitat or Wetland and Water Body Conservation, could occur on the site. If the result of the consultation is inconclusive and site conditions indicate that imperiled species could be present, conduct a biological survey during appropriate seasons, using accepted methods. If imperiled species, wetlands, or water bodies are found on the site, contact the appropriate state and federal agencies and comply with all relevant local, state, and federal regulations.

Work with a qualified biologist and other collaborators in delineating areas to be managed and crafting a management plan. The management plan must meet all credit requirements. In addition, develop a plan to conduct biological monitoring over time and use the information to adjust management activities.

If possible, establish a funding source for ongoing management of natural areas in perpetuity. For management in perpetuity, typically the developer will establish an endowment that generates adequate income each year.

5. Timeline and Team

As early as possible after site acquisition and managed lands are identified, the developer should contract with arborists, wetland ecologists, or other environmental professionals with the expertise to assess the site thoroughly, develop a holistic plan to conserve its natural resources, and craft a monitoring and management plan that meets the credit requirements and maintains ecological integrity over time. If possible, collaborate with natural resource agencies, conservation organizations, native plant societies, or academic institutions. A management plan can be written at any time after a conservation area has been identified, and implementation typically begins once the area has been conserved or restored. Management plans can be written and implemented before, during, or after construction, but plan implementation should start no later than one year following full build-out.

6. Calculations

There are no calculations for this credit.

7. Documentation Guidance

As a first step in preparing to complete the LEED-ND documentation requirements, work through the following measures. Refer to GBCI's website for the complete descriptions of all required documentation.

- Retain written evidence that state agencies were consulted about all the species listed in Option 2(a) of SLL Credit 7, Site Design for Habitat or Wetland and Water Body Conservation, before the site was cleared.

- Retain information on the qualifications of the biologist developing the management plan, and retain names and qualifications of any experts or institutions contributing to the management plan.

8. Examples

There are no examples for this credit.

9. Exemplary Performance

This credit is not eligible for exemplary performance under Innovation and Design Process.

10. Regional Variations

There are no regional variations associated with this credit.

11. Resources

Websites

Center for Natural Lands Management

www.cnlm.org

This website contains a property analysis record, a tool commonly used to calculate the cost over time of managing natural areas.

Sustainable Sites Initiative

www.sustainablesites.org

The Sustainable Sites Initiative is an interdisciplinary effort by the American Society of Landscape Architects, the Lady Bird Johnson Wildflower Center, and the United States Botanic Garden to create voluntary national guidelines and performance benchmarks for sustainable land design, construction, and maintenance practices.

The Nature Conservancy

www.nature.org

www.conserveonline.org/workspaces/cbdgateway/

The Nature Conservancy has chapters in all 50 states, owns and manages nature preserves, holds conservation easements, and has developed ecoregion plans that identify important conservation areas and significant habitat. Its Conservation by Design Gateway website provides guidance, tools, resources, and case studies for conservation projects at all scales. The Conservation Action Planning section is particularly relevant for this credit.

12. Definitions

existing present on the date of submission of LEED-ND certification documents; similarly, an element or condition that **exists** is present on the date that LEED-ND certification documents are submitted.

native (or indigenous) plant a plant species that did or would have occurred on the site or within the subject county prior to the widespread land alterations that accompanied European settlement. Cultivars of native plants may be considered native plants.

project the land, water, and construction that constitutes the project application. A project applicant does not have to own or control all land or water within a project boundary, but all the area within the project boundary must comply with prerequisites and attempted credits.

water body the surface water of a stream (first-order and higher, including intermittent streams), arroyo, river, canal, lake, estuary, bay, or ocean, excluding irrigation ditches.

wetland an area that is inundated or saturated by surface or ground water at a frequency and duration sufficient to support, and that under normal circumstances do support, a prevalence of vegetation typically adapted for life in saturated soil conditions. Wetlands generally include swamps, marshes, bogs, and similar areas, but exclude irrigation ditches unless delineated as part of an adjacent wetland.

Neighborhood Pattern and Design emphasizes the creation of compact, walkable, vibrant, mixed-use neighborhoods with good connections to nearby communities. These neighborhoods provide many important benefits to residents, employees, and visitors and to the environment.

In particular, because compact neighborhoods use land and infrastructure efficiently, they reduce fragmentation of wildlife habitat and farmland loss resulting from development, provide opportunities to reduce driving and resultant emissions, conserve economic resources, and help reduce the spread of low-density development across a region's landscape. Residents enjoy convenient access to shops, basic services, and public spaces within walking and bicycling distance, and when people choose to drive, they take shorter automobile trips, saving time and avoiding emissions. Compact development also facilitates access to public transportation because transit becomes more economically viable when supported by higher concentrations of population. All told, doubling density in a metropolitan region is associated with a 20% to 50% reduction in vehicle miles traveled.[1]

In addition, the small block sizes associated with compact neighborhoods encourage walking and bicycling because of the increased connectivity, shorter travel distances, slower automobile traffic, and more inviting pedestrian environment. The slower traffic speeds typically found in dense developments also can reduce injury rates. (The environmental and public health benefits that accompany increased transportation choices and reduced rates of driving are further discussed in the introduction to Smart Location and Linkage.)

Along with higher densities and a diversity of land uses, features such as sidewalks and trails, street trees, pedestrian-friendly building façades, small setbacks, minimal parking lot area, and measures to slow automobiles also increase pedestrian activity. Public spaces, such as parks and plazas, can encourage social interaction and active recreation while helping control stormwater runoff and reducing urban heat island effects. Community gardens also promote social interaction and physical activity while increasing access to fresh, locally grown produce.

Communities with diverse housing types that accommodate a range of incomes, ages, and physical abilities permit residents to live closer to their workplaces, help the community retain residents, and allow families to remain in the neighborhood as their circumstances change over time. Community involvement in project design and planning can help the project complement adjacent neighborhoods, meet the needs of residents and workers, and nurture a cooperative relationship with the project's neighbors.

Resources for Learning More

Websites

American Planning Association

www.planning.org

The major professional planning association in the United States, APA organizes conferences and workshops and communicates planning news, legislation and policy, and research.

---

1   Holtzclaw, John, et al., "Location Efficiency: Neighborhood and Socio-Economic Characteristics Determine Auto Ownership and Use: Studies in Chicago, Los Angeles, and San Francisco." Transportation Planning and Technology 25 (2002).

Center for Neighborhood Technology

www.cnt.org

This website contains a searchable database of research about sustainable neighborhood design, lists of events, and a listserv documenting developments in the field.

The Congress for the New Urbanism

www.cnu.org

The major group promoting New Urbanism in the United States hosts an annual conference, has information about design and development tools (including LEED-ND), grants awards for exemplary projects, indexes New Urbanist projects, and hosts networking events for New Urbanist practitioners through its chapters.

Form Based Codes Institute

www.formbasedcodes.org/index.html

FBCI promotes the use of form-based codes, which are a method of regulating development to achieve a specific urban form. Form-based codes are intended to create a predictable public realm primarily by controlling physical form, with a lesser focus on land use, through city or county regulations.

Reconnecting America

www.reconnectingamerica.org

Reconnecting America is a nonprofit organization seeking to integrate transportation systems and the communities they serve. It promotes awareness, conducts research, and supports legislation for transit-oriented compact development. The organization's publications include a transit technologies worksheet.

Smart Growth Network

www.smartgrowth.org

This network of nonprofit organizations and government agencies promotes smart growth practices. The website outlines smart growth principles, provides a guide to smart growth terms and technical concepts, and hosts a searchable catalogue of reports, websites, tools, and case studies dating from 1997.

SmartCode, Duany Plater-Zyberk & Co.

www.smartcodecentral.org/

SmartCode is a transect-based design and development code available for all scales of planning, from region to community and from block to building. It is intended to help keep towns compact and rural lands open while reforming the destructive sprawl-producing patterns of single-use zoning.

Trust for Public Land

www.tpl.org/tier2_pa.cfm?folder_id=705

TPL's Parks for People initiative uses geographical information systems (GIS) mapping technology to show which neighborhoods most need parks and playgrounds. TPL works with community leaders to identify opportunities for park creation, secure park funding, and acquire parklands. The initiative's website contains a range of resources about neighborhood and community parks.

Urban Land Institute

www.uli.org

This nonprofit organization promotes the responsible use of land to enhance the total environment, provides customized research and advisory services, and sponsors meetings.

Print Media

Charter of the New Urbanism, by The Congress for the New Urbanism (McGraw-Hill, 1999).

"The Influence of Land Use on Travel Behavior: Empirical Strategies," by Reid Ewing and Robert Cervero, *Transportation Research, Policy and Practice* 35 (2001): 823-845.

"Location Efficiency: Neighborhood and Socio-Economic Characteristics Determine Auto Ownership and Use: Studies in Chicago, Los Angeles, and San Francisco," by John Holtzclaw et al., *Transportation Planning and Technology* 25 (2002).

The New Urbanism: Toward an Architecture of Community, by Peter Katz (McGraw Hill, 1993).

The Next American Metropolis, by Peter Calthorpe (Princeton Architectural Press, New York, 1993).

Retrofitting Suburbia: Urban Design Solutions for Redesigning Suburbs, by Ellen Dunham-Jones and June Williamson (John Wiley & Sons, 2008).

Suburban Nation: The Rise of Sprawl and the Decline of the American Dream, by Andres Duany et al. (North Point Press, 2000).

Sustainable Urbanism, by Douglas Farr (John Wiley & Sons, 2007).

CREDIT	TITLE	POINTS
NPD Prerequisite 1	Walkable Streets	Required
NPD Prerequisite 2	Compact Development	Required
NPD Prerequisite 3	Connected and Open Community	Required
NPD Credit 1	Walkable Streets	12 points
NPD Credit 2	Compact Development	6 points
NPD Credit 3	Mixed-Use Neighborhood Centers	4 points
NPD Credit 4	Mixed-Income Diverse Communities	7 points
NPD Credit 5	Reduced Parking Footprint	1 point
NPD Credit 6	Street Network	2 points
NPD Credit 7	Transit Facilities	1 point
NPD Credit 8	Transportation Demand Management	2 points
NPD Credit 9	Access to Civic and Public Space	1 point
NPD Credit 10	Access to Recreation Facilities	1 point
NPD Credit 11	Visitability and Universal Design	1 point
NPD Credit 12	Community Outreach and Involvement	2 points
NPD Credit 13	Local Food Production	1 point
NPD Credit 14	Tree-Lined and Shaded Streets	2 points
NPD Credit 15	Neighborhood Schools	1 point

	ND
Prerequisite	NPD Prerequisite 1
Points	Required

Intent

To promote transportation efficiency, including reduced *vehicle miles traveled* (VMT). To promote walking by providing safe, appealing, and comfortable *street* environments that support public health by reducing pedestrian injuries and encouraging daily physical activity.

Requirements

Design and build the *project* to achieve all of the following:

a. For 90% of new building frontage, a principal *functional entry* on the front façade faces a public space, such as a street, square, *park*, *paseo*, or *plaza*, but not a parking lot, and is connected to sidewalks or equivalent provisions for walking. The square, park, or plaza must be at least 50 feet wide at a point perpendicular to each entry.

b. At least 15% of *existing* and new street frontage within and bordering the project has a minimum building-height-to-street-width ratio of 1:3 (i.e., a minimum of 1 foot of building height for every 3 feet of street width).

  - Nonmotorized rights-of-way may be counted toward the 15% requirement, but 100% of such spaces must have a minimum building-height-to-street-width ratio of 1:1.

  - Projects with bordering street frontage must meet only their proportional share of the height-to-width ratio (i.e., only on the project side of the street).

  - Street frontage is measured in linear feet.

  - Building height is measured to eaves or the top of the roof for a flat-roof structure, and street width is measured façade to façade. For *block* frontages with multiple heights and/or widths, use average heights or widths weighted by each segment's linear share of the total block distance.

  - *Alleys* and driveways are excluded.

c. Continuous sidewalks or equivalent all-weather provisions for walking are provided along both sides of 90% of streets or frontage within the project, including the project side of streets bordering the project. New sidewalks, whether adjacent to streets or not, must be at least 8 feet wide on retail or mixed-use blocks and at least 4 feet wide on all other blocks. Equivalent provisions for walking include *woonerfs* and all-weather-surface footpaths. Alleys, driveways, and reconstructed existing sidewalks are excluded from these calculations.

d. No more than 20% of the street frontages within the project are faced directly by garage and service bay openings.

Projects in a designated *historic district* subject to review by a local historic preservation entity are exempt from (b), (c), and (d) if approval for compliance is not granted by the review body. Projects in historic districts listed in or eligible for listing in a state register or the National Register of Historic Places that are subject to review by a state historic preservation office or the National Park Service are exempt from (b), (c), and (d) if approval for compliance is not granted.

1. Benefits and Issues to Consider

Environmental Issues

Walkable streets are the foundation of projects that reduce carbon emissions and air pollution by creating a multimodal travel environment, with the pedestrian at the center. Pedestrian-scaled streets tend to be narrower than automobile-oriented arterials, requiring fewer materials. Pedestrians and bicyclists feel safe on streets with adequate spaces designed clearly for them, with plenty of visual interest and enclosure provided by buildings lining the street. Walkable streets also support the public health benefits of physical exercise by making it convenient and enjoyable to meet daily needs by walking. Streets designed for pedestrians offer protection from traffic, typically by including on-street parking as a buffer between pedestrians and traffic, and reduce collisions with vehicles.

The same features that make a street inviting for pedestrians support other sustainable design features. Walkable streets support a mix of uses, offer a comfortable environment to gather or wait for public transportation, and create a safe atmosphere for children traveling to school.

Economic and Social Issues

Walkable streets transform streetscapes into public amenities that are capable of attracting tenants and residents to the project. Limiting the number of garage doors and service bays reduces pedestrian-automobile collisions and increases the aesthetic appeal of the street. Placing functional entries directly on the street provides visual interest and draws in customers. Businesses are supported by the consistent foot traffic, and residents become loyal customers as they repeatedly pass businesses while walking to jobs and shops. Ensuring that walking is genuinely feasible is also inclusionary, allowing residents without cars to easily meet their daily needs.

2. Related Credits

Meeting or exceeding the Walkable Streets prerequisite may assist in earning the following related credits:

- SLL Credit 4, Bicycle Network and Storage
- NPD Credit 1, Walkable Streets
- NPD Credit 2, Compact Development
- NPD Credit 3, Mixed-Use Neighborhood Centers
- NPD Credit 5, Reduced Parking Footprint
- NPD Credit 15, Neighborhood Schools

3. Summary of Referenced Standards

There are no referenced standards for this credit.

4. Implementation

A street that is pleasant and safe for pedestrians encourages walking. If public spaces are "public rooms," buildings are the walls, and streets and sidewalks are the public room's interior.

Walkable streets are safe for pedestrians, are properly scaled, offer visual interest, and provide places to stop and rest. There are no physical barriers, such as busy roads without crossings or missing sidewalks. Buildings along walkable streets are integrated with the pedestrian and public realm. When a block is built one structure at a time and the buildings are designed to be self-contained, independent entities, the desirable integration with the public realm is often lacking.

Proximity to a diverse mix of uses, access to transit, real and perceived safety from crime, and high rates of existing foot traffic encourage more walking. Many of these issues are addressed in other credits within the rating system. The goal of this prerequisite is to achieve a baseline level of design for walkable streets; the related Walkable Streets credit encourages further amenities and design characteristics. Specific components of the prerequisite are described below.

Principal Functional Entries: Frontage

Buildings that can be accessed directly by pedestrians encourage walking and foster interaction between buildings and the pedestrian realm. In contrast, buildings that are entered through parking lots, driveways, or private gated areas feel isolated from passing pedestrians and may discourage them from walking or using alternative forms of transportation to access the building— or from using it altogether.

This prerequisite component involves measuring the length of qualifying building frontage. If a façade contains a principal functional entry from a public space, its length may be counted toward achieving the credit. If a façade does not contain a principal functional entry from a public space, its length is included in the denominator of the calculation and does not help the project achieve the credit. Since some buildings have multiple façades—for instance, a large building occupying an entire block—it is possible that one façade qualifies for the credit requirements (because it has an entry from a public space) and another does not (because it has no such entry). If a building has a corner entry connecting two façades, then both qualify, and their combined length counts toward the credit. If one enters a building from a square, park, or plaza, the amenity should be landscaped to prevent empty "dead" space in the front. The amenity must also be at least 50 feet wide at a point perpendicular to each entry (see Figure 1).

Figure 1. Principal functional entries on front façades facing public space that is a minimum 50 feet wide at a point perpendicular to each entry

Building-Height-to-Street-Width Ratios

On a walkable street, the building-height-to-street-width ratio should create a sense of enclosure and feel comfortable to pedestrians. Buildings can be too low for the width of the street. Buildings set far back from the street or separated from the sidewalk by a parking lot or a significant amount of landscaping also fail to create a pedestrian-friendly street wall, do not create the sense of enclosure at a pedestrian scale, and isolate the public realm.

The prerequisite requires that at least 15% of existing and new street frontages achieve a minimum building-height-to-street-width ratio of 1:3 (1 foot of building height for every 3 feet of street width, measured façade to façade), and 100% of existing and new nonmotorized rights-of-way included in the overall 1:3 calculation must achieve a ratio of 1:1.

There are two street frontages for each block inside a project, and one frontage for streets bordering a project. For simplicity, in both cases it is possible to express the ratio in equivalent building-height-to-street-centerline terms, measuring the street width from the façade to just the street centerline. When expressed as building-height-to-street-centerline, the minimum ratios become 1:1.5 for streets and 1:0.5 for nonmotorized rights-of-way.

Projects should identify each street frontage within and bordering its boundary, and measure the length of that frontage exclusive of alleys, driveways, parks, and similar dedicated public spaces. For the remaining lengths of each frontage, project teams must identify buildings facing the street, their heights, the widths of their façades facing the street, and the distances from the façades to the street or right-of-way centerline. Building height is measured to the eaves or, for a flat-roof structure, the top of the roof. For buildings with multiple heights and façade setbacks, use average values that represent the overall heights and setbacks.

Once those measurements are in hand, each building's building-height-to-street-centerline ratio is calculated using its height and façade distance to centerline. Those building frontages that meet or exceed minimum ratio requirements are summed and expressed as a percentage of total project street frontage length (after exclusions), which determines prerequisite achievement.

Continuous Sidewalks

The prerequisite requires projects to provide sidewalks, woonerfs, or all-weather-surface footpaths of a minimum width on both sides of the street (or on the project-side of streets bordering the project) for 90% of streets.

An internal street with sidewalks on only one side of the street does not meet the credit requirements; a bordering street with a sidewalk on only the project side of the street does. The sidewalk width requirement in the prerequisite, as well as in NPD Credit 1, Walkable Streets, applies to the walking surface, which may be pervious as long as it is all-weather. The width measurement includes any planting strip or other sidewalk buffer that is not designed as a walking surface.

Figure 2. New sidewalks minimum 8 feet wide on retail and mixed-use blocks (4 feet wide on all other blocks); width is inclusive of planter strips

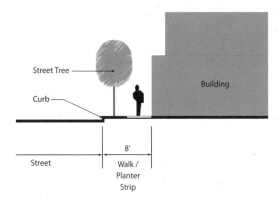

Although the prerequisite specifies minimum sidewalk widths, good sidewalks have other important design components. One is variety and diversity. Sidewalks may have varying widths, depending on the scale of surrounding neighborhood features, and different orientations. Sidewalks wider than the credit minimums may be desirable in high-pedestrian traffic areas and should include design features to keep the sidewalk interesting. A buffer zone, such as on-street parking or a planting strip between the sidewalk and the street, can also greatly enhance a sidewalk's walkability. A sidewalk's ideal setback from the street curb should be a function of street width, traffic speed, parking regulations, and building setbacks. Streetscape amenities—benches or other outdoor seating, planters, trash receptacles, telephone booths, bike racks, street lights, newsstands, drinking fountains—can make streets more walkable and inviting to pedestrians but should not impede pedestrian traffic. Ideally, sidewalk design should include necessary lighting, signage, ramps, and auditory signals for seniors and those with disabilities. Sidewalks may include street trees in wells or tree grates without reducing the measured sidewalk width, but trees should not obstruct the pedestrian path of travel.

Equivalent walking facilities, such as designated walking paths, trails, and woonerfs, can substitute for sidewalks. These should be finished with pervious or impervious pavement, gravel, or other material that is safe and passable in rain, snow, and ice.

Garage and Service Bay Openings

Garage openings and service bays are designed for automobiles and are often unpleasant to walk by. They also present a pedestrian safety hazard, since access to them usually crosses sidewalks or other pedestrian facilities. Thus, this prerequisite sets a maximum amount of street frontage, 20%, that may be dedicated to garage and service bay openings. Street frontage is measured in length and should include all streets within or bordering the project. Street frontage with existing buildings must be included in this calculation.

Figure 3. Maximum 20% of street frontage faced directly by garage or service bay openings

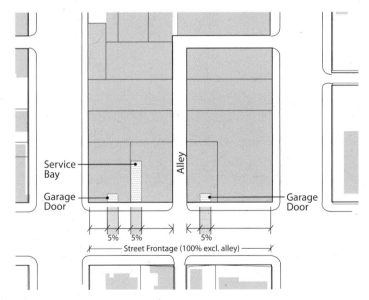

Historic Districts

The rating system accommodates historic districts where some requirements of this prerequisite may be unfeasible or inappropriate. Exemptions may apply to districts subject to review by a local historic preservation board and districts eligible for or listed in a state register or the National Register of Historic Places. Typically, the term "determined eligible" is used by state historic preservation offices to indicate historic districts that are eligible for listing but have not been designated because of opposition from the owners or some other reason.

If the project is wholly or partly in a designated or eligible historic district and the relevant historic preservation review body will not permit it to meet prerequisite requirements (b), (c), or (d), the project or its affected portion is exempt from these requirements.

5. Timeline and Team

The project's urban designers and architects should consider building-height-to-street-width ratios and appropriate pedestrian right-of-way widths during preliminary site planning and building massing, since changing building locations and street layouts later is difficult. In addition, the project's conceptual site plan should integrate plans for locating building entrances and minimizing garage and service bay locations. Although some walkable streets features may change as the project progresses, planning for them early in the design process makes them more likely to be successfully incorporated into the final project.

6. Calculations

Principal Functional Entries (a)

Step 1. Determine the total length of new building frontage.

Step 2. Measure the lengths of new building frontage that have principal functional entries from public space. Calculate their sum as the percentage of total length of building frontage, according to Equation 1. The result must be at least 90%.

Equation 1

$$\% \text{ principal functional entries} = \frac{\text{Length of building frontage with principal functional entrie}}{\text{Total building frontage length}}$$

Building-Height-to-Street-Width Ratio (b)

Some projects border only external streets and are therefore not responsible for the opposing block frontage. The following steps use the building-height-to-street-centerline ratio equivalent of the building-height-to-street-width ratio to accommodate such projects with single-side street frontages. Projects with internal streets that have two frontages should count each frontage individually.

Step 1. Identify all street frontages inside and bordering the project. Each street inside a project has two street frontages, one on either side of the street. Streets bordering a project have one street frontage. For each street frontage, measure its length exclusive of alleys, driveways, parks, and similar dedicated public spaces. Nonmotorized rights-of-way may be included as long as they do not exceed 15% of the total claimed frontage length of the entire project.

Step 2. For each street frontage, identify buildings facing the street and their height, façade width, and distance from façade to street centerline (see Figure 4). Use average height and façade setback for buildings with multiple heights and façade elements.

Figure 4. Building height-to-street-centerline (BH-SC) information for calculating BH-SC ratios for buildings on two street frontages

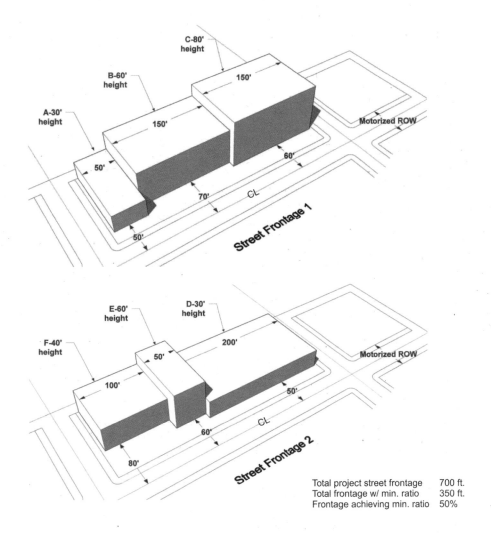

Total project street frontage   700 ft.
Total frontage w/ min. ratio   350 ft.
Frontage achieving min. ratio   50%

Street Frontage 1

Bldg	Height (ft)	Distance to CL (ft)	BH - CL Ratio	Frontage Counted (ft)
A	30	50	1:0.60	- - -
B	60	70	1:0.86	150
C	80	60	1:1.33	150
				300

Street Frontage 2

Bldg	Height (ft)	Distance to CL (ft)	BH - CL Ratio	Frontage Counted (ft)
D	30	50	1:0.60	- - -
E	60	60	1:1.00	50
F	40	80	1:0.50	- - -
				50

Step 3. For each street frontage, sum the building widths of those buildings that achieve the minimum ratios of 1:1.5 for streets and 1:0.5 for nonmotorized rights-of-way.

Step 4. Sum the street frontage subtotals of qualifying buildings and calculate the percentage of the total project street frontage that they represent to determine prerequisite compliance. In Figure 4, for example, the two street frontages have a total length of 700 feet, with 190 feet of building width meeting the minimum building-height-to-street-centerline ratio, or 27% of total frontage length.

Continuous Sidewalks (c)

Step 1. Determine the total length of streets within and bordering the project, using centerline feet.

Step 2. Determine the length of project streets that have sidewalks (or equivalent provisions for walking) on both sides; do the same for the project side of bordering streets. Calculate their sum as a percentage of total street centerline feet, according to Equation 3. The result must be at least 90%.

Equation 3

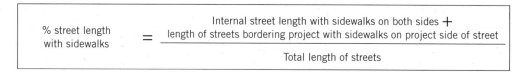

$$\text{\% street length with sidewalks} = \frac{\text{Internal street length with sidewalks on both sides} + \text{length of streets bordering project with sidewalks on project side of street}}{\text{Total length of streets}}$$

Garage Openings (d)

Step 1. Determine the total length of street frontages within and bordering the project.

Step 2. Determine the total length of garage doors and service bay openings on street frontages.

Step 3. Calculate the percentage of the total frontage represented by garage doors and service bays according to Equation 4. The result must be 20% or less.

Equation 4

$$\text{\% frontage with openings} = \frac{\text{Total length of garage door and service bay openings}}{\text{Total length of street frontage}}$$

7. Documentation Guidance

As a first step in preparing to complete the LEED-ND documentation requirements, work through the following measures. Refer to GBCI's website for the complete descriptions of all required documentation.

- Identify the principal functional entry or entries of every building in the project.

- Measure the lengths of all façades.

- Measure the length of every street within or bordering the project.

- Map the locations of all sidewalks and equivalent pedestrian provisions within and bordering the project.

- Map the locations of any garage doors or service bay openings.

- If the project is in a designated historic district, retain documents from the applicable review board if it did not grant approval for compliance with requirements (b), (c), or (d).

8. Examples

There are no examples for this prerequisite.

9. Exemplary Performance

This prerequisite is not eligible for exemplary performance under Innovation and Design Process.

10. Regional Variations

Local governments have different requirements for setbacks, sidewalk provision, and pedestrian and vehicle access. Some local requirements may be conducive to meeting the prerequisite requirements; others may make it more difficult. For instance, if a city requires both large setbacks and low densities, it may be difficult to achieve the minimum building-height-to-street-width ratios.

11. Resources

Websites

The Congress for the New Urbanism

www.cnu.org

The major group promoting New Urbanism in the United States hosts an annual conference, has information about design and development tools (including LEED-ND), grants awards for exemplary projects, indexes New Urbanist projects, and hosts networking events for New Urbanist practitioners through its chapters. The organization's charter contains many urban design strategies that promote walkable streets.

Local Government Commission

www.lgc.org

LGC provides information, technical assistance, and networking to local elected officials and developers about making more walkable and resource-efficient cities.

National Crime Prevention Council

www.ncpc.gov.sg/pdf/CPTED Guidebook.pdf

Principles of Crime Prevention through Environmental Design (2003) describes the design features of a built environment that can provide a sense of safety and discourage crime.

Pedestrian and Bicycle Information Center

www.bicyclinginfo.org/engineering/calming.cfm

This webpage provides information about bicycle and pedestrian design and infrastructure, as well as traffic-calming strategies.

Traditional Neighborhood Development Design Rating Standards

www.tndtownpaper.com/rating.htm

This formal set of standards for rating traditional neighborhood design is regularly updated and tested against new and existing projects.

Victoria Transportation Policy Institute

www.vtpi.org

This independent research organization provides consulting and publicly available research about solutions to emerging transportation issues, including walkability. It provides publications about transit cost-benefit analysis. A report titled "Valuing Transit Service Quality Improvements" explains the value transit users place on comfort and convenience.

Walkable Communities, Inc.

www.walkable.org

This nonprofit offers training courses, walk audits, and resources for creating walkable communities.

Print Media

Context Sensitive Solutions in Designing Major Urban Thoroughfares for Walkable Communities, by Institute of Transportation Engineers (ITE, 2006).

Form Based Codes: A Guide for Planners, Urban Designers, Municipalities, and Developers, by Dan G. Parolek, Karen Parolek, and Paul C. Crawford (John Wiley & Sons, 2008).

Great Streets, by Allan Jacobs (MIT Press, 1995).

Planning and Urban Design Standards, by American Planning Association (John Wiley & Sons, 2006).

Street Design for Healthy Neighborhoods, by Dan Burden, Michael Wallwork, P.E., Ken Sides, P.E., Ramon Trias, and Harrison Bright Rue (Local Government Commission, 2002).

Streets & Patterns, by Stephen Marshall (Spon Press, 2005).

Trees in Urban Design, by Henry Arnold (1992).

Urban Design: Street and Square, by J.C. Moughtin (Architectural Press, 2003).

Urban Design Handbook, by Urban Design Associates (Norton, 2003).

Urban Design Reclaimed: Tools, Techniques, and Strategies for Planners, by Emily Talen (American Planning Association, 2009).

12. Definitions

alley a publicly accessible right-of-way, generally located midblock, that can accommodate slow-speed motor vehicles, as well as bicycles and pedestrians. An alley provides access to the side or rear of abutting properties for loading, parking, and other service functions, minimizing the need for these functions to be located along streets. It may be publicly dedicated or privately owned and deeded in perpetuity for general public use.

block land bounded by the project boundary, transportation or utility rights-of-way that may be publicly dedicated or privately owned and deeded in perpetuity for general public use, waterfront, and/or comparable land division features.

existing present on the date of submission of LEED-ND certification documents; similarly, an element or condition that exists is present on the date that LEED-ND certification documents are submitted.

functional entry a building opening designed to be used by pedestrians and open during regular business hours. This does not include any door exclusively designated as an emergency exit, or a garage door not designed as a pedestrian entrance.

historic district a group of buildings, structures, objects, and sites, of varying sizes, that have been designated as historically and architecturally significant and categorized as either contributing or noncontributing.

park a publicly accessible area that is permanently maintained in a seminatural condition for human recreation and relaxation; it has soil, grass, water, flora, and/or recreation improvements.

paseo a publicly accessible pedestrian path, at least 4 feet wide and no more than 12 feet wide, that provides shortcuts between buildings and through the block, connecting street frontages to rear parking areas, midblock courtyards, alleys, or other streets. A paseo may be roofed for up to 50% of its length and may be privately owned or publicly dedicated.

plaza a publicly accessible gathering space that is integrated into the street network and allows vehicular, bicycle, and/or pedestrian travel. A plaza is generally paved, is spatially defined by building fronts paralleling at least two-thirds of its perimeter, and may be privately owned or publicly dedicated.

project the land, water, and construction that constitutes the project application. A project applicant does not have to own or control all land or water within a project boundary, but all the area within the project boundary must comply with prerequisites and attempted credits.

street a dedicated right-of-way that can accommodate one or more modes of travel, excluding alleys and paseos. A street is suitable for primary entrances and provides access to the front and/ or sides of buildings and lots. A street may be privately owned as long as it is deeded in perpetuity for general public use. A street must be an addressable thoroughfare (for mail purposes) under the standards of the applicable regulating authority.

woonerf a street, also known as a home zone, shared zone, or living street, where pedestrians have priority over vehicles and the posted speed limit is no greater than 10 miles per hour. Physical elements within the roadway, such as shared surfaces, plantings, street furniture, parking, and play areas, slow traffic and invite pedestrians to use the entire right-of-way.

vehicle miles traveled (VMT) the number of miles driven by motorists in a specified time period, such as a day or a year, in absolute or per capita terms.

	ND
Prerequisite	NPD Prerequisite 2
Points	Required

Intent

To conserve land. To promote livability, walkability, and transportation efficiency, including reduced *vehicle miles traveled* (VMT). To leverage and support transit investments. To reduce public health risks by encouraging daily physical activity associated with walking and bicycling.

Requirements

OPTION 1. Projects in Transit Corridors

For *projects* with *existing* and/or planned transit service (i.e., service with the funding commitments specified in SLL Prerequisite 1, Smart Location) that meets or exceeds the 2-point threshold in SLL Credit 3, Locations with Reduced Automobile Dependence, Option 1, build at the following densities, based on the *walk distances* to the transit service specified in SLL Credit 3:

   a. For residential components located within the walk distances: 12 or more *dwelling units* per acre of buildable land available for residential uses.

   b. For residential components falling outside the walk distances: 7 or more dwelling units per acre of buildable land available for residential uses.

   c. For nonresidential components located within the walk distances: 0.80 *floor-area ratio* (FAR) or greater of buildable land available for nonresidential uses.

   d. or nonresidential components falling outside the walk distances: 0.50 FAR or greater of buildable land available for nonresidential uses.

If the project location is served by a transit agency that has specified guidelines for minimum service densities that are greater than the densities required by this prerequisite, the project must achieve those service densities instead.

OR

OPTION 2. All Other Projects

Build any residential components of the project at a *density* of 7 dwelling units per acre of *buildable land* available for residential uses.

AND

Build any nonresidential components of the project at a density of 0.50 FAR or greater of buildable land available for nonresidential uses.

FOR ALL PROJECTS

Density calculations include all planned and existing buildings within the *project boundary*, excluding those portions of parking structures devoted exclusively to parking.

NPD PREREQUISITE 2

The specified density must be achieved within five years of the date that the first building of any type is occupied.

If one component of the project, residential or nonresidential, meets the minimum density requirement but the other component does not, include only the qualifying density. Use that component's dwelling units or nonresidential floor area in the numerator and the total buildable land area in the denominator. If the resulting density meets the minimum requirement, the prerequisite is achieved.

1. Benefits and Issues to Consider

Environmental Benefits

Building compactly makes efficient use of land and reduces the development footprint of the project. Less impervious surface may improve stormwater infiltration and free up land for additional development or as a park or conservation area. Compact development also makes more efficient use of infrastructure, such as water and sewer pipelines, gas pipelines, electrical cables, and telecommunications lines. In some cases, the development density may allow highly efficient alternative systems to be incorporated into the project, such as a district heating or cooling system.

Compact development can discourage automobile usage and reduce its associated negative environmental effects. A dense development pattern has the power to support existing public transportation and enable future public transportation. Other modes of transportation, such as walking and bicycling, also become more feasible and pleasant when destinations are closer together.

Economic Benefits

Building compactly can reduce up-front costs of infrastructure for the developer and the public. High-density development also makes it possible for small, pedestrian-friendly businesses occupying the commercial portions of mixed-use projects to succeed economically. Consider building near the top of the range of appropriate densities for the area. Consider how commercial corridors and transit can be supported by the strategic concentration of density, which gradually tapers off to lower densities in more exclusively residential areas.

2. Related Credits

Meeting or exceeding the Compact Development prerequisite may assist in earning the following related credits:

- SLL Prerequisite 1, Smart Location
- SLL Prerequisite 3, Wetland and Water Body Conservation
- SLL Credit 3, Locations with Reduced Automobile Dependence
- NPD Credit 1, Walkable Streets
- NPD Credit 2, Compact Development
- NPD Credit 3, Mixed-Use Neighborhood Centers
- GIB Credit 7, Minimized Site Disturbance in Design and Construction

3. Summary of Referenced Standards

There are no referenced standards for this credit.

4. Implementation

Maximize the project's density, especially if the site is near transit, while still integrating it with the character of the surrounding community and providing necessary amenities like public space and transportation facilities. To achieve high densities, build attached housing or multifamily residential housing and limit lot size for single-family homes. Build shops and restaurants below offices and apartments or in multistory nonresidential buildings. Identify locations on the site where higher-density development is most appropriate. Such areas may have a mix of residential and nonresidential uses (such as main streets, downtowns, mixed-use corridors, and retail areas) and locations served by transit. Densities are exclusive of parking structures and must be achieved within five years of the date that the first new building of any type is occupied.

Selecting the Appropriate Option

The first step in achieving this prerequisite is to determine whether the project is in a designated transit corridor, as defined in Option 1 of the requirements. Projects located in a transit corridor are required to meet a higher minimum density threshold than those that are not. This encourages transit-oriented development. Identify both existing and planned transit routes serving the site. Planned transit service is defined as transit with funding commitments, as described in the credit requirements for SLL Prerequisite 1, Smart Location, Option 3.

Once existing and planned transit service is identified, follow the requirements for SLL Credit 3, Locations with Reduced Automobile Dependence, Option 1, to determine the number of homes and nonresidential uses with building entrances within a specified distance of transit. If enough dwelling units and nonresidential use entrances (or all dwelling units and nonresidential use entrances) are reached by existing and planned transit and the project meets or exceeds the 2-point threshold in Option 1 of SLL Credit 3, then the project must pursue Option 1 (for projects in transit corridors) under NPD Prerequisite 2, Compact Development. This option specifies minimum densities for portions of the site in transit corridors and portions outside the transit corridors. In other words, areas within the specified walking distances to transit must have higher minimum levels of residential and nonresidential density than areas not near transit.

If the project has already earned 2 points under Option 1 (for existing transit service) of SLL Credit 3, Locations with Reduced Automobile Dependence, then additional calculations are not needed and the higher density threshold must be achieved for these areas. If the project has not earned 2 points under SLL Credit 3, the team must perform the assessment using both existing and planned transit service to determine whether the project is in a transit corridor and therefore must have higher densities. Figure 1 illustrates a project with portions in each density category.

Figure 1. Delineation of project areas meeting SLL Credit 3's 2-point threshold and therefore requiring higher minimum building densities

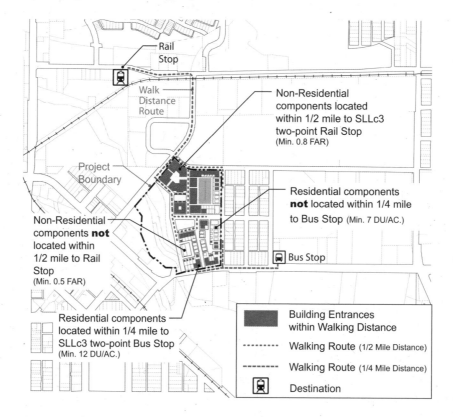

Also determine whether the transit agency serving the site has minimum density thresholds. Some transit agencies or local jurisdictions require minimum densities around existing or planned transit service to ensure support for the investment. Contact the appropriate agency to find out whether these density minimums apply. If the locally required minimum density requirement is higher than the density required by LEED-ND, the project must meet it to achieve this prerequisite.

Any project not within a transit corridor has a lower minimum density threshold for this prerequisite.

Determining Project Density

Regardless of the option used, calculate the density of the LEED-ND project site. In LEED-ND, density is defined as the total amount of new and existing development, expressed as a percentage of total "buildable land." Buildable land excludes public rights-of-way, like streets, as well as areas where development is not permitted by law or a LEED-ND prerequisite. As a result, the density may be different from what the project team has already calculated as "net density" or "gross density" for its approving jurisdiction. The method of determining residential and nonresidential buildable land is fully described in the Getting Started chapter of this reference guide.

Two types of density need to be calculated: (1) residential density, which is measured in dwelling units per buildable residential acre; and (2) nonresidential density, which is measured in floor-area ratio (FAR), the nonresidential building area divided by buildable nonresidential land area, in square feet. Any existing or new dwelling unit, whether in a single-use building or a mixed-use building, is included in the residential density calculation. All new and existing nonresidential uses—office, retail, industrial, civic, and so forth—are included in the nonresidential FAR calculation. Any nonresidential square footage, whether in a single-use or mixed-use building, is included in the nonresidential density calculation. The resulting residential and nonresidential density numbers will determine whether the project meets the applicable minimum residential and nonresidential density thresholds. Site area for parking structures must be included as buildable land, but parking structure floor area cannot be counted toward residential or nonresidential density, since parking structures are not habitable structures.

Projects Meeting the Density Threshold for Only One Component

In some projects, either the residential or the nonresidential component may not meet prerequisite requirements. For example, a predominantly residential project with high densities may include a small low-density commercial or civic space that makes up a very small percentage of the project. This does not automatically preclude the project from meeting the prerequisite. In the alternative calculation for overall density, the nonqualifying component is dropped and can be compensated for by higher density in the other component. For the alternative calculation, use either the total number of residential dwelling units or the total amount of nonresidential floor area in the numerator, and the total buildable land (the sum of both residential and nonresidential buildable land) in the denominator. If the resulting residential or nonresidential density is above the minimum threshold, then the prerequisite is achieved.

5. Timeline and Team

During the site planning process, the project team should determine the locations of existing and planned transit service and ensure that residential and nonresidential densities within the specified walk distances to the transit stops are high enough to meet the prerequisite requirements.

6. Calculations

Density of Project

Step 1. Determine the total number of residential dwelling units and the total nonresidential square footage in the project.

Step 2. Determine the total buildable land for residential and nonresidential development. Calculating buildable land and nonbuildable land is described in the Getting Started chapter.

Step 3. Calculate residential density in dwelling units per acre, according to Equation 1; the result must be at least 7 DU per acre, or if the project is served by transit, 12 DU per acre. Calculate nonresidential density in floor-area ratio, according to Equation 2; the result must be at least 0.50 FAR, or if the project is served by transit, 0.80 FAR.

Equation 1

$$\text{Residential density (DU/acre)} = \frac{\text{Total dwelling units}}{\text{Residential buildable land (acres)}}$$

Equation 2

$$\text{Nonresidential density (FAR)} = \frac{\text{Total nonresidential floor area}}{\text{Total nonresidential buildable land area (sf)}}$$

Density of Project Partially in Transit Corridor

Step 1. Determine the residential components and the nonresidential components that lie within the walking distances of transit as specified in SLL Credit 3, Locations with Reduced Automobile Dependence.

Step 2. Mark the remaining components as being outside walking distance of transit.

Step 3. Determine the density of project components within walking distance of transit, using the Density of Project calculation, above, and confirm that it exceeds the densities required for components with transit service.

Step 4. Determine the density of the remaining components and confirm that it exceeds the densities required for components outside walking distance of transit.

Density of Mixed-Use Building or Parcel

The project's overall residential and nonresidential density calculation must account for any mixed-use building space and buildable land. The method of determining residential and nonresidential land area is described in the Getting Started chapter.

Step 1. For a building or parcel with both residential and nonresidential components, first calculate the percentage of its total square footage that each component represents.

Step 2. Apply those percentages to the area of the mixed-use building or parcel to determine the proportionate share of buildable land for each component.

Step 3. Combine the proportionate residential share of the mixed-use buildable land with other single-use residential buildable land to determine total residential buildable land.

Step 4. Combine the proportionate nonresidential share of the mixed-use buildable land with other single-use nonresidential buildable land to determine total nonresidential buildable land.

7. Documentation Guidance

As a first step in preparing to complete the LEED-ND documentation requirements, work through the following measures. Refer to GBCI's website for the complete descriptions of all required documentation.

- Create a map showing buildable and nonbuildable areas. For buildable areas, show residential, nonresidential, and mixed-use areas.

- Create a development program table by block or parcel and track all necessary information to calculate density for the project, including site size and the square footage of existing and planned dwelling units and nonresidential buildings.

- If the project is in a transit corridor, maintain documents related to existing and planned transit service.

- If the project is in a transit corridor, maintain documentation about any minimum density requirements specified by a local transit agency.

8. Examples

Example 1. Density of Mixed-Use Building

A mixed-use building has ten dwellings, each 1,500 square feet, for a total of 15,000 square feet of residential space, plus 25,000 square feet of retail space, all on 1 acre (43,560 square feet) of buildable land. The project team calculates the residential density as 26 DU per acre and the nonresidential density as 0.92 FAR (Table 1, row 1).

Table 1. Example density for mixed-use building

	Buildable land (acres)		Dwelling units	Total area (sf)		Density	
Example	Residential	Nonresidential		Residential	Nonresidential	Residential (DU/acre)	Nonresidential (FAR)
1	0.38	0.62	10	15,000	25,000	26	0.92
2(a)	8	2	160	240,000	21,780	20	0.25
2(b)	10	—	160	640,000	21,780	16	—

Example 2. Density of Mixed-Use Project with One Qualifying Component

A project has 10 acres of total buildable land; 8 acres is residential, with a density of 20 DU per acre, and the remaining 2 acres has a density of 0.25 FAR (Table 1, row 2a). In this case, the residential component is the qualifying component. The prerequisite is achieved because even when the residential density is calculated over the entire 10 acres, the calculation still yields 16 DU per acre (row 2b), exceeding the required 7 DU per acre for a project not served by transit.

Example 3. Density of Project Partially in Transit Corridor

A 100-acre project with existing and planned transit service has earned only 1 point under SLL Credit 3, Locations with Reduced Automobile Dependence, Option 1, for its existing transit service. The planned transit service meets the funding requirements defined in SLL Prerequisite 1, Smart Location, Option 3. Using the methodology in SLL Credit 3, the team meets the 2-point threshold (inclusive of weekdays and weekends) for total transit (existing and planned). The project must therefore pursue Option 1 of this prerequisite. The team calculates that the area of the site within the prescribed walking distances of the transit service meeting at least the 2-point threshold is 20 acres; this is the "transit corridor." Of the 20-acre transit corridor, 15 acres is residential and 5 acres is nonresidential. Within the transit corridor, the residential density is 16.7 dwelling units per acre and the nonresidential density is 1.15 FAR. Once the 20-acre transit corridor has been netted out, the remainder of the site has a density of 7.3 dwelling units per acre and 0.54 FAR. The project achieves the prerequisite.

9. Exemplary Performance

This prerequisite is not eligible for exemplary performance under Innovation and Design Process.

10. Regional Variations

Density requirements vary significantly from jurisdiction to jurisdiction. These local requirements may affect a project's ability to achieve the prerequisite. Typically, high-density areas are located near transit and close to urban centers.

11. Resources

Websites

Reconnecting America
www.reconnectingamerica.org
Reconnecting America is a nonprofit organization seeking to integrate transportation systems and the communities they serve. It promotes awareness, conducts research, and supports legislation for transit-oriented compact development. The organization's publications include a transit technologies worksheet.

Smart Growth America
www.smartgrowth.org
This coalition of organizations from around the United States posts the latest smart growth news and supports smart growth initiatives, particularly related to historic preservation, the environment, farmland and open space preservation, and neighborhood revitalization. It helps states, communities, and other interested stakeholders adopt policies and legislation that support compact development.

Print Media

Creating Great Neighborhoods: Density in Your Community, by Local Government Commission (U.S. EPA, 2003).

Crossroads, Hamlets, Village, Town: Design Characteristics of Traditional Neighborhoods, Old and New, by Randall Arendt (American Planning Association, 1999).

Density by Design: New Directions in Residential Development, by Steven Fader (Urban Land Institute, 2000).

"Location Efficiency: Neighborhood and Socio-Economic Characteristics Determine Auto Ownership and Use: Studies in Chicago, Los Angeles, and San Francisco," by John Holtzclaw et al. *Transportation Planning and Technology* 25 (2002).

New Urban News, New Urbanism: Comprehensive Report & Best Practices Guide (New Urban Publications, 2003).

Place to Grow: Growth Plan for the Greater Golden Horsesho (Ministry of Public Infrastructure Renewal, Province of Ontario, 2006).

Planning and Urban Design Standards, by American Planning Association (John Wiley & Sons, 2006).

Public Transportation and Land Use Policy, by Pushkarev and Zupan (Indiana University Press, 1977).

Sustainability and Cities, by Peter Newman and Jeffrey Kenworthy (Island Press, 1999).

Urban Design Reclaimed: Tools, Techniques, and Strategies for Planners, by Emily Talen (American Planning Association, 2009).

Visualizing Density, by Julie Campoli and Alex S. MacLean (Lincoln Institute of Land Policy, 2007).

12. Definitions

buildable land the portion of the site where construction can occur, including land voluntarily set aside and not constructed upon. When used in density calculations, buildable land excludes public rights-of-way and land excluded from development by codified law or LEED for Neighborhood Development prerequisites. An applicant may exclude additional land not exceeding 15% of the buildable land base defined above, provided the following conditions are present:

    a. The land is protected from residential and nonresidential construction by easement, deed restriction, or other enforceable legal instrument.

AND

    b. Either 25% or more of the boundary of each contiguous parcel proposed for exclusion borders a water body or areas outside the project boundary that are protected by codified law; or ownership of, or management authority over, the exclusion area is transferred to a public entity.

density the amount of building structures constructed on the project site, measured for residential buildings as dwelling units per acre of buildable land available for residential uses, and for nonresidential buildings as the floor-area ratio of buildable land area available for nonresidential uses. In both cases, structured parking is excluded.

dwelling unit living quarters intended for long-term occupancy that provide facilities for cooking, sleeping, and sanitation. This does not include hotel rooms.

existing present on the date of submission of LEED-ND certification documents; similarly, an element or condition that exists is present on the date that LEED-ND certification documents are submitted.

floor-area ratio (**FAR**) the density of nonresidential land use, exclusive of parking, measured as the total nonresidential building floor area divided by the total buildable land area available for nonresidential structures. For example, on a site with 10,000 square feet of buildable land area, an FAR of 1.0 would be 10,000 square feet of building floor area. On the same site, an FAR of 1.5 would be 15,000 square feet of built floor area; an FAR of 2.0 would be 20,000 built square feet and an FAR of 0.5 would be 5,000 built square feet.

project the land, water, and construction that constitutes the project application. A project applicant does not have to own or control all land or water within a project boundary, but all the area within the project boundary must comply with prerequisites and attempted credits.

project boundary the platted property line of the project defining land and water within it. Projects located on publicly owned campuses that do not have internal property lines must delineate a sphere-of-influence line to be used instead. *Project site* is equivalent to the land and water inside the project boundary. The project must not contain noncontiguous parcels, but parcels can be separated by public rights-of-way. Projects may also have enclaves of nonproject properties that are not subject to the rating system, but such enclaves cannot exceed 2% of the total project area and cannot be described as certified.

walk distance the distance that a pedestrian must travel between origins and destinations without obstruction, in a safe and comfortable environment on a continuous network of sidewalks, all-weather-surface footpaths, crosswalks, woonerfs, or equivalent pedestrian facilities.

vehicle miles traveled (**VMT**) the number of miles driven by motorists in a specified time period, such as a day or a year, in absolute or per capita terms.

	ND
Prerequisite	NPD Prerequisite 3
Points	Required

Intent

To promote *projects* that have high levels of internal *connectivity* and are well connected to the community at large. To encourage development within *existing* communities that promote transportation efficiency through multimodal transportation. To improve public health by encouraging daily physical activity.

Requirements

OPTION 1. Projects with Internal Streets

Design and build the project such that its internal connectivity is at least 140 intersections per square mile. All *streets* and sidewalks that are counted toward the connectivity requirement must be available for general public use and not gated. Gated areas are not considered available for public use, with the exception of education and health care campuses and military bases where gates are used for security purposes.

AND

Design and build the project with at least one through-street and/or nonmotorized right-of-way intersecting or terminating at the *project boundary* at least every 800 feet, or at existing abutting street intervals and intersections, whichever is the shorter distance. Nonmotorized rights-of-way may count for no more than 20% of the total. This does not apply to portions of the boundary where connections cannot be made because of physical obstacles, such as prior platting of property, construction of existing buildings or other barriers, slopes over 15%, *wetlands* and *water bodies*, railroad and utility rights-of-way, existing limited-access motor vehicle rights-of-way, and parks and dedicated open space.

Figure 1. Project site design with 140 eligible intersections per square mile on streets that are not gated

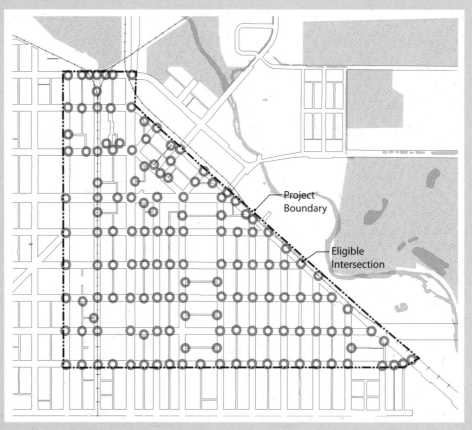

OR

OPTION 2. Projects without Internal Streets

Locate the project such that the connectivity of the existing streets within 1/4 mile of the project boundary is at least 90 intersections per square mile. All streets and sidewalks that are counted toward the connectivity requirement must be available for general public use and not gated. Gated areas are not considered available for public use, with the exception of education and health care campuses and military bases where gates are used for security purposes.

Figure 2. Project site with at least 90 eligible intersections per square mile within 1/4 mile of project boundary

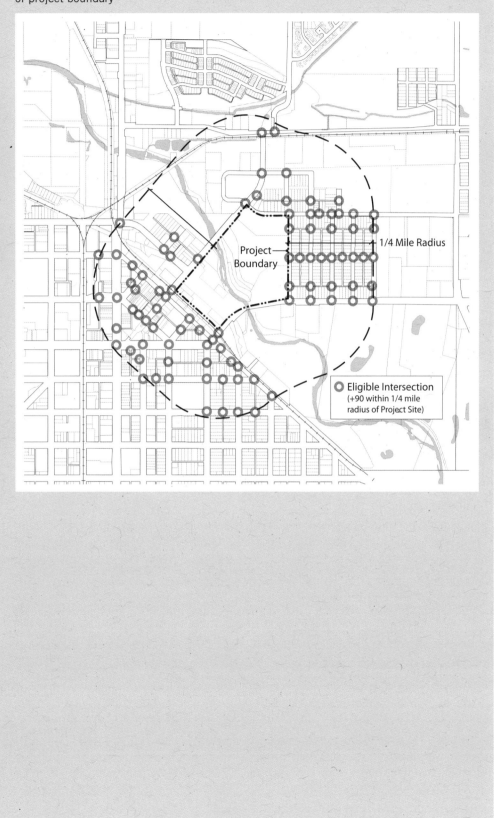

Project Boundary

1/4 Mile Radius

⊙ Eligible Intersection
(+90 within 1/4 mile radius of Project Site)

1. Benefits and Issues to Consider

Environmental Issues

Connectivity is the quality of accessibility in a community that allows residents, workers, and visitors to take full advantage of services, public spaces, and transportation options. Connectivity is measured in intersection density because this metric is most closely correlated with increased multimodal travel, particularly walking and bicycling. Projects designed with short blocks and frequent intersections make walking and bicycling more attractive and reduce carbon emissions from cars and other vehicles. A connected street network also relieves traffic congestion by increasing route options to a given destination, resulting in shorter trips.

Frequent connections from the project to the surrounding area mean that residents will have easy access to the services and amenities in surrounding communities. Integrating the project into the surrounding street network as much as possible is also a more efficient use of space than leaving a strip of undeveloped land between the project site and nearby development.

Economic and Social Issues

A permeable project boundary ensures that the businesses within are not limited to the client base inside the project. Investments made to attract customers and provide pleasing streetscapes and public spaces will realize greater returns if people have ample and efficient public access to the site.

Carefully consider whether gated enclaves are necessary. Gated areas hamper efficient travel and discourage an active and open community atmosphere.

2. Related Credits

Achieving this prerequisite may assist in earning the following related credits:

- SLL Credit 1, Preferred Locations
- NPD Credit 6, Street Network

3. Summary of Referenced Standards

There are no referenced standards for this credit.

4. Implementation

The goal of this prerequisite is to ensure that projects are either designed or located in areas that facilitate walking, bicycling, and reduced driving. Two options are available, one for large projects with internal streets, and one for small projects without streets.

Projects with Internal Streets

Projects that have internal streets must meet several criteria to achieve this prerequisite. They should be designed with a dense, interconnected, and publicly accessible street network. To meet the threshold, block lengths need to be relatively short. Intersection density must be measured in intersections per square mile, as described in the Getting Started chapter.

These projects must also have a minimum level of connectivity with surrounding neighborhoods. Specifically, the requirements call for at least one through-street or nonmotorized right-of-way intersecting or terminating at the project boundary at least every 800 feet (see Figure 11 in Getting Started). Avoid culs-de-sac wherever possible, since they discourage connectivity for pedestrians, bicycles, and vehicles. "Stub-outs"—streets that terminate at the project boundary and do not continue outside the boundary, are allowed. Keep in mind, however, that stub-outs are considered culs-de-sac under NPD Credit 6, Street Network, for purposes of calculating the percentage of culs-de-sac with pedestrian and bicycle through-connections.

Exceptions for connectivity along the project boundary are allowed if a travel right-of-way connection cannot be made because of a physical obstacle, such as a water body, a limited-access roadway, a park, or a hillside over 15% in grade. If a physical obstacle like this prevents an external connection, the documentation should identify its location and explain why no connection is possible. If a project shares a boundary with a previously developed parcel that does not have a through-street every 800 feet, an exemption is allowed: The project does not need to provide a through-connection because no connection can be made. However, if the project borders land without existing buildings and without physical obstacles, there is no exemption: A street must pass through or terminate at the project boundary at least every 800 feet, allowing for future connectivity.

Nonmotorized right-of-way may count for no more than 20% of the total through-streets for achieving this prerequisite.

Gated communities are not encouraged but are allowed for certain institutions, such as military bases, health care campuses, and educational facilities, that may need gates for security purposes. Even these types of facilities should be as publicly accessible as possible so that they are integrated with the surrounding community and subregional transportation patterns. Other types of gated communities are not prohibited inside the project boundary, but no streets within such gated enclaves can be counted toward the connectivity threshold. The gated area must be included in the calculation of the total project area.

Projects without Internal Streets

Projects that do not have internal streets should be located such that the area within 1/4-mile of the project boundary (inside and outside) has a minimum level of street connectivity. The street connectivity is measured in intersections per square mile, and the method of calculating street connectivity is described in the Getting Started chapter. Streets, sidewalks, and other routes of travel within this 1/4-mile area that are not accessible for public use may not be counted toward the minimum level of street connectivity. Thus, developments like gated subdivisions are not eligible to contribute toward the calculation of street connectivity. Parks, water bodies, wetlands, and other areas excluded from development by LEED-ND prerequisites should be excluded from the area calculations so that they do not negatively affect the connectivity calculation.

Information about the external street network should be available from local planning, public works, or transportation departments and usually shows street centerlines in GIS or CAD format. If digital information is not available, look at aerial photographs and manually count the intersections.

5. Timeline and Team

The project's urban designers and architects should address this prerequisite early, during the site selection and site design process. Projects without internal streets should locate in areas with a sufficiently high street connectivity. The architects or urban designers for projects with internal streets should design the site to meet the internal connectivity requirements.

6. Calculations

OPTION 1. Projects with Internal Streets

Step 1. Delineate any gated enclaves, calculate their land area, and subtract it from the total project area; the result is the net area.

Step 2. Count the qualifying intersections within the project. Omit intersections within gated enclaves, intersections where one must enter and exit an area through the same intersection, and intersections that lead only to culs-de-sac.

Step 3. Calculate the connectivity within the project according to Equation 1. The result must be at least 140 intersections per square mile.

Equation 1

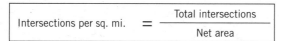

$$\text{Intersections per sq. mi.} = \frac{\text{Total intersections}}{\text{Net area}}$$

Step 4. After determining the intersections per square mile, count the through-streets and nonmotorized rights-of-way that intersect with or terminate at the project boundary. Nonmotorized rights-of-way cannot count for more than 20% of the total.

Equation 2

$$\%\text{ nonmotorized intersections} = \frac{\text{Total intersections} - \text{nonmotorized intersections}}{\text{Total intersections}}$$

OPTION 2. Projects without Internal Streets

Step 1. Determine the area within a 1/4-mile radius of the project boundary (inside and outside the boundary). Subtract any water bodies, steep slopes, rail yards, and other excludable areas; the result is the net area.

Step 2. Count the qualifying intersections within this buffer area. Omit intersections within gated enclaves, intersections where one must enter and exit an area through the same intersection, and intersections that lead only to culs-de-sac.

Step 3. Calculate the connectivity according to Equation 3. The result must be at least 90 intersections per square mile.

Equation 3

$$\text{Connectivity} = \frac{\text{Total qualifying intersections}}{\text{Net area}}$$

7. Documentation Guidance

As a first step in preparing to complete the LEED-ND documentation requirements, work through the following measures. Refer to GBCI's website for the complete descriptions of all required documentation.

- For projects with internal streets, map the intersections internal to the project and identify locations where streets are not available for public use.

- For projects without internal streets, map the street intersections external to the project and identify locations where streets are not available for public use; these are excluded from the calculations.

- When inventorying affected streets, identify ineligible intersections, such as culs-de-sac.

8. Examples

There are no examples for this prerequisite.

9. Exemplary Performance

This prerequisite is not eligible for exemplary performance under Innovation and Design Process.

10. Regional Variations

There are no regional variations associated with this prerequisite.

11. Resources

Websites

Victoria Transportation Policy Institute

www.vtpi.org

This independent research organization provides consulting and publicly available research about solutions to emerging transportation issues.

Print Media

Context Sensitive Solutions in Designing Major Urban Thoroughfares for Walkable Communities, by Institute of Transportation Engineers (ITE, 2006).

Streets & Patterns, by Stephen Marshall (Spon Press, 2005).

13. Definitions

connectivity the number of publicly accessible street intersections per square mile, including intersections of streets with dedicated alleys and transit rights-of-way, and intersections of streets with nonmotorized rights-of-way (up to 20% of total intersections). If one must both enter and exit an area through the same intersection, such an intersection and any intersections beyond that point are not counted; intersections leading only to culs-de-sac are also not counted. The calculation of square mileage excludes water bodies, parks larger than 1/2-acre, public facility campuses, airports, rail yards, slopes over 15%, and areas nonbuildable under codified law or the rating system. Street rights-of-way may not be excluded.

existing present on the date of submission of LEED-ND certification documents; similarly, an element or condition that exists is present on the date that LEED-ND certification documents are submitted.

project the land, water, and construction that constitutes the project application. A project applicant does not have to own or control all land or water within a project boundary, but all the area within the project boundary must comply with prerequisites and attempted credits.

project boundary the platted property line of the project defining land and water within it. Projects located on publicly owned campuses that do not have internal property lines must delineate a sphere-of-influence line to be used instead. *Project site* is equivalent to the land and water inside the project boundary. The project must not contain noncontiguous parcels, but parcels can be separated by public rights-of-way. Projects may also have enclaves of nonproject properties that are not subject to the rating system, but such enclaves cannot exceed 2% of the total project area and cannot be described as certified.

street a dedicated right-of-way that can accommodate one or more modes of travel, excluding alleys and paseos. A street is suitable for primary entrances and provides access to the front and/or sides of buildings and lots. A street may be privately owned as long as it is deeded in perpetuity for general public use. A street must be an addressable thoroughfare (for mail purposes) under the standards of the applicable regulating authority.

water body the surface water of a stream (first-order and higher, including intermittent streams), arroyo, river, canal, lake, estuary, bay, or ocean, excluding irrigation ditches.

NPD	
ND	Prerequisite 3

wetland an area that is inundated or saturated by surface or ground water at a frequency and duration sufficient to support, and that under normal circumstances do support, a prevalence of vegetation typically adapted for life in saturated soil conditions. Wetlands generally include swamps, marshes, bogs, and similar areas, but exclude irrigation ditches unless delineated as part of an adjacent wetland.

WALKABLE STREETS

	ND
Credit	NPD Credit 1
Points	1-12 points

Intent

To promote transportation efficiency, including reduced *vehicle miles traveled* (VMT). To promote walking by providing safe, appealing, and comfortable *street* environments that support public health by reducing pedestrian injuries and encouraging daily physical activity.

Requirements

A *project* may earn a maximum of 12 points according to the schedule in Table 1:

Table 1. Points for walkable street features

Items achieved	Points
2–3	1
4–5	2
6–7	3
8–9	4
10	7
11	8
12	9
13	10
14	11
15–16	12

Façades and Entries

    a. At least 80% of the total linear feet of street-facing building façades in the project is no more than 25 feet from the property line.

    b. At least 50% of the total linear feet of street-facing building façades in the project is no more than 18 feet from the property line.

Figure 1. Minimal street-facing building façade setbacks

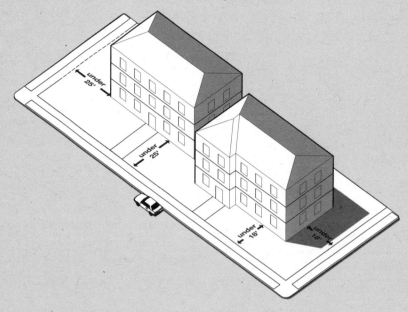

    c. At least 50% of the total linear feet of mixed-use and nonresidential street-facing building façades in the project is within 1 foot of a sidewalk or equivalent provision for walking.

    d. *Functional entries* to the building occur at an average of 75 feet or less along nonresidential or mixed-use buildings or *blocks*.

Figure 2. Functional building entries at minimum average distances along blocks

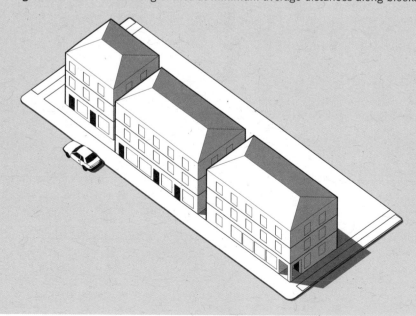

e. Functional entries to the building occur at an average of 30 feet or less along nonresidential or mixed-use buildings or blocks (items d and e are cumulative).

Ground-Level Use and Parking

f. All ground-level retail, service, and trade uses that face a public space have clear glass on at least 60% of their façades between 3 and 8 feet above grade.

Figure 3. Ground-level retail and service uses with minimum amounts of clear glass façades

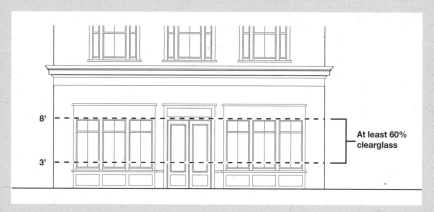

g. If a façade extends along a sidewalk, no more than 40% of its length or 50 feet, whichever is less, is blank (without doors or windows).

Figure 4. Limits on length of blank walls along sidewalks

h. Any ground-level retail, service, or trade windows must be kept visible (unshuttered) at night; this must be stipulated in *covenants, conditions, and restrictions* (CC&R) or other binding documents.

i. On-street parking is provided on a minimum of 70% of both sides of all new and *existing* streets, including the project side of bordering streets. The percentage of on-street parking is calculated by dividing the length of street designated for parking by the total length of the curb along each street, including curb cuts, driveways, and intersection radii. Space within the parking lane that is occupied by corner bulb-outs (within 24 feet of an intersection), transit stops, and motorcycle or bicycle parking may be counted as designated for parking in this calculation. *Woonerfs* are not considered streets for this subsection.

Figure 5. On-street parking requirements

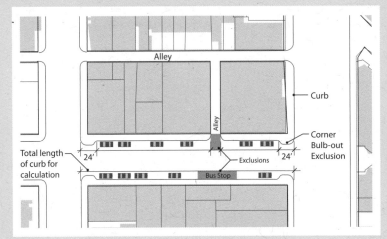

j. Continuous sidewalks or equivalent provisions for walking are available along both sides of all streets within the project, including the project side of streets bordering the project. New sidewalks, whether adjacent to streets or not, must be at least 10 feet wide on retail or mixed-use blocks and at least 5 feet wide on all other blocks. Equivalent provisions for walking include woonerfs and all-weather-surface footpaths at least 5 feet wide. Note that these requirements specify wider sidewalks than required by NPD Prerequisite 1, Walkable Streets.

k. If the project has ground-floor *dwelling units*, the principal floor of at least 50% of those units must have an elevated finished floor no less than 24 inches above the sidewalk grade. Below-grade basement spaces and/or *accessory dwelling units* are exempt from this requirement.

Figure 6. Minimal above-grade entrance requirements

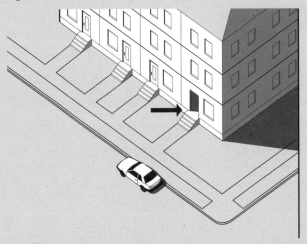

l. In nonresidential or mixed-use projects, 50% or more of the total number of office buildings include ground-floor retail along 60% of the length of the street-level façade; 100% of mixed-use buildings include ground-floor retail, live-work spaces, and/or ground-floor dwelling units along at least 60% of the street-level façade; and all businesses and/or other community services on the ground floor are accessible directly from sidewalks along a public space, such as a street, square, paseo, or plaza, but not a parking lot.

m. At least 40% of all street frontage within the project has a minimum building-height-to-street-width ratio of 1:3 (i.e., a minimum of 1 foot of building height for every 3 feet of street width).

   ▪ Nonmotorized rights-of-way may be counted toward the 40% requirement, but 100% of such spaces must have a minimum 1:1 ratio of building height to street width.

   ▪ Projects with bordering street frontage must meet only their proportional share of the height-to-width ratio (i.e., only on the project side of the street).

   ▪ Street frontage is measured in linear feet.

   ▪ Building height is measured to eaves or the top of the roof for a flat-roof structure, and street width is measured façade to façade. For block frontages with multiple heights and/or widths, use average heights or widths weighted by each segment's linear share of the total block distance.

   ▪ *Alleys* and driveways are excluded.

Design Speeds for Safe Pedestrian and Bicycle Travel

n. 75% of new residential-only streets within the project are designed for a target speed of no more than 20 mph.

o. 70% of new nonresidential and/or mixed-use streets within the project are designed for a target speed of no more than 25 mph. A multiway boulevard, with travel lanes separated from access lanes by medians, may apply this requirement to its outer access lanes only (through-lanes are exempt), provided pedestrian crosswalks are installed across the boulevard at intervals no greater than 800 feet.

Sidewalk Intrusions

p. At-grade crossings with driveways account for no more than 10% of the length of sidewalks within the project.

NPD	
ND	Credit 1

1. Benefits and Issues to Consider

For a summary of the primary benefits of walkable streets, please see NPD Prerequisite 1, Walkable Streets. Additional benefits provided by the requirements of this credit are noted below.

Environmental Issues

Slow street speeds and sidewalks largely uninterrupted by driveways downplay automobile use, making other travel modes more attractive. Reducing building setbacks conserves land and places storefronts where pedestrians can easily see and enter them, increasing the aesthetic appeal of the street.

Economic and Social Issues

An effective way to encourage walking is to create lively streetscapes with visual interest by designing well-fenestrated storefronts at ground level and providing frequent entrances into establishments. Pedestrians feel safe when on-street parking and street trees separate them from traffic. Residents in ground-level units feel safer if the first floor is elevated to provide more privacy.

Careful planning is necessary to ensure that the elements of the streetscape fit together in a modest space. Weigh the importance of desirable features that may widen the streets, such as street trees, bicycle lanes, or benches, against the cost of building taller buildings to achieve the building-height-to-street-ratio required by NPD Prerequisite 1, Walkable Streets.

2. Related Credits

Meeting or exceeding the requirements for the Walkable Streets credit may assist in earning the following related credits:

- NPD Prerequisite 1, Walkable Streets
- NPD Credit 2, Compact Development
- NPD Credit 5, Reduced Parking Footprint

The following credits include measures that can enhance streets' appeal and utility for pedestrians:

- SLL Credit 3, Locations with Reduced Automobile Dependence
- NPD Credit 3, Mixed-Use Neighborhood Centers
- NPD Credit 11, Visitability and Universal Design
- NPD Credit 14, Tree-Lined and Shaded Streets
- GIB Credit 9, Heat Island Reduction

3. Summary of Referenced Standards

There are no referenced standards for this credit.

4. Implementation

The Implementation section of NPD Prerequisite 1, Walkable Streets, describes basic strategies for enhancing walkability. NPD Credit 1, Walkable Streets, includes additional standards for walkability, each of which is discussed below. The provisions apply to planned and existing buildings and features within the project boundary, except for street design speeds (n, o), which apply only to new streets. Unlike NPD Prerequisite 1, Walkable Streets, this credit does not include a historic district exemption.

Façades and Entries: Setbacks (a, b, c)

Buildings set back from the street reduce a pedestrian's sense of enclosure and comfort. The requirements for façades encourage building close to the street or sidewalk to create a street wall. Projects are evaluated in terms of linear feet of building frontage that does not exceed the maximum setback specified in the credit component (a and b). Linear feet of building frontage up to the maximum can be counted toward the credit, but linear feet that exceeds the maximum cannot be counted. This means that some portions of a building's frontage may contribute toward the credit while other portions do not. If, on the other hand, an entire building frontage meets the minimum ratio, all its linear feet of frontage can be counted toward the credit.

For the mixed-use and nonresidential setback from sidewalks requirement (c), the distance of setback should be measured from the property line.

Functional Entries (d, e)

Frequent building entries from streets and sidewalks, rather than blank walls, create a more interesting, varied, and safer pedestrian environment. Qualifying entrances are functional entries for pedestrians that encourage residents, employees, or visitors to enter and exit the building from a street or other public space. Entrances not normally used by pedestrians, such as service entries, emergency exits, nonfunctioning doors, and secondary or side doors, cannot be counted as principal functional entries. Only frontages facing public spaces, such as a street, park, paseo, or plaza, should be included in this calculation. Frontages facing alleys, parking lots, or other nonpublic spaces are excluded from the requirement.

This component of the credit is only for nonresidential and mixed-use buildings or blocks (mixed-use buildings or blocks have both residential and nonresidential uses within or along them); projects that have only residential components may not pursue this portion of the credit. Project teams may choose to measure along buildings or along blocks but must measure consistently throughout the site. Thus, if the team chooses to measure buildings instead of blocks, the same block may have both included and excluded buildings. If the team chooses to measure by block, any block with a mix of uses must include all entrances along the block, regardless of use.

The measurement of average distance between functional building entries is a cumulative average over the whole project, not an absolute minimum. This means that even if one segment between functional building entries exceeds the maximum distance—75 and 30 feet, respectively, for (d) and (e)—the project can still qualify if the overall average distance between building entries is below the maximum. The project team may choose to measure distances between building entrances along individual buildings or along entire blocks (not differentiating between buildings), as long as this is done consistently for the entire project site. In other words, if there are two blocks in a project, each with more than one building, the project team may not measure along buildings on one but along the entire block on the other.

Ground-Level Use and Parking: Clear Glass (f)

A view through glass into shops and other nonresidential ground-floor building space makes walking more interesting and can provide a sense of comfort and safety. It also encourages interaction between pedestrians and ground-floor uses.

The requirements of this credit component call for all ground-level retail, service, and trade uses to have clear glass covering 60% of the façade between 3 and 8 feet above grade. If the project team intends to achieve the credit component, it should ensure that this design consideration is applied consistently to all retail, service, and trade space. When determining whether each use's façade meets the 60% requirement, measure the façade and clear glass area in square feet.

	NPD
ND	Credit 1

The advantages of clear ground-floor windows can conflict with the energy savings of low-emissivity ("low E" or "tinted") glass, which is generally less clear or has a lower level of visible light transmittance (VLT). Low-E glass with at least 60% VLT qualifies as clear glass; although tinted, it provides a sufficiently clear view that it meets the requirements.

Ground-Level Use and Parking: Blank Walls (g)

Blank walls may cause pedestrians to feel uncomfortable or unsafe and do not add to the character of a community. To achieve this component of the credit, discourage blank walls throughout the project site by including building entrances and windows along all building frontages with sidewalks. Building frontages that occur along parking lots or alleys or immediately adjacent other buildings are not included in the calculation. No single blank wall may be longer than 50 feet or longer than 40% of a building's frontage, regardless of its location. That is, a single noncompliant blank wall disqualifies a project from achieving this component of the credit. Landscaping, murals, street furniture, and similar points of interest are other design concepts for avoiding blank walls on building frontages; however, they do not assist with achieving this requirement.

Ground-Level Use and Parking: Unshuttered Windows (h)

Visible, unshuttered windows make walking more interesting and can provide a sense of comfort and safety, especially at night. As with the clear glass component of the credit, 100% of retail, service, and trade uses in the project must comply with this requirement, which must be implemented with CC&Rs. Security bars over windows that allow a view of interior spaces are allowed.

Ground-Level Use and Parking: On-Street Parking (i)

On-street parking creates a buffer between vehicles on the street and pedestrians on the sidewalk. It can also reduce the need for off-street parking, which consumes buildable land, necessitates driveways, and interrupts sidewalks. Some projects may need to provide on-street parking on all streets to achieve this credit component, since curb cuts, driveways, and intersection radii count as places where on-street parking is not allowed. On the other hand, transit stops, on-street motorcycle and bicycle parking, and curb bulb-outs may be counted as areas where on-street parking is allowed if they are within 24 feet of an intersection, so including these facilities will increase a project's likelihood of achieving the required minimum. Woonerfs are exempted from on-street parking requirements because their unique design circumstances warrant greater flexibility, and they have a traffic-calming effect similar to that of on-street parking.

Ground-Level Use and Parking: Sidewalks (j)

This credit measure requires wider sidewalks than NPD Prerequisite 1, Walkable Streets—at least 10 feet (rather than 8 feet) on retail or mixed-use blocks, and at least 5 feet (rather than 4 feet) on all other blocks. Refer to the Implementation section of NPD Prerequisite 1 for more information about sidewalks.

Ground-Level Use and Parking: Elevated Ground Floors (k)

Elevated ground floors provide increased privacy for residents in ground-floor housing. The credit threshold requires 50% of ground-floor units to have elevated floors, excluding basement spaces (since they are below the main living floor) and accessory dwellings (since they are ancillary to the main dwelling). Thus, if the team chooses, the other half of the project's ground-floor units may be designed to be accessible at grade. This makes it possible to achieve both this requirement and NPD Credit 11, Visitability and Universal Design, within the same project.

Ground-Level Use and Parking: Office Uses (l)

Office uses at the street level tend to have less appeal to pedestrians than retail space. To support pedestrian traffic, therefore, this credit component requires office buildings to include ground-floor retail along 60% of the façade in at least half of the buildings. In addition, all mixed-use buildings must include retail, live-work, or residential uses on the ground floor along 60% of the façade. The 60% façade length calculation for both office and mixed-use buildings must include all street frontages and driveways, entryways, service entries and similar areas. All businesses and community services must be directly accessible from sidewalks along a public space, such as a square or street.

Ground-Level Use and Parking: Building-Height-to-Street-Width Ratios (m)

This credit measure requires more street frontage with a 1:3 building-height-to-street-width ratio than NPD Prerequisite 1, Walkable Streets—at least 40% (rather than 15%). Refer to the Implementation section of the prerequisite for more information about building-height-to-street-width ratios.

Design Speeds for Safe Pedestrian and Bicycle Travel (n, o)

This component of the credit can be achieved by designing new streets for multiple users—pedestrians, bicycles, transit vehicles, trucks, and cars. Techniques for designing slower streets include narrow rights-of-way, narrow lane widths, and on-street parking. Streets should be designed for slow target speeds (20 mph for residential streets, 25 mph for nonresidential and mixed-use streets). A target speed is the speed at which vehicles are intended to travel for a given stretch of street. Determine the specified percentage after measuring the length of all new streets. Existing streets are exempt from this credit, and projects with no internal streets are not eligible. A multiway boulevard with travel lanes separated from access lanes by medians may apply the requirements to its outer lanes only.

The design speed of a street depends on its functional classification, its geometric design, and the maximum speed posted by the local jurisdiction. If the local jurisdiction's speed limits do not meet the credit requirements, provide evidence of the policy or the denial of a request to post lower speed limits, plus evidence that the proposed street meets the listed design and engineering criteria for the intended target speed. Project teams should document that the following design and engineering criteria are in place and verify that the street is designed for an appropriate target speed:

- The presence of on-street parking (parallel or angled) on 70% or more of both sides of the street, for the length of the street.

- Intersections spaced no more than 800 feet apart.

- Paving materials with texture.

- Presence of medians and median landscaping.

- Roadside and curb treatments, including bulb-outs, street furniture, and other landscaping elements.

- Travel lane widths no greater than 11 feet and parallel parking lane widths no greater than 8 feet.

Consult the technical standards of the Institute of Transportation Engineers for additional design speed information (see Resources, below).

	NPD
ND	Credit 1

Sidewalk Intrusions (p)

Driveways that cross sidewalks make walking less pleasant and are a safety hazard. Reducing the amount of off-street parking or using shared driveway designs reduces the amount of sidewalk intrusions from driveways.

5. Timeline and Team

During preliminary site planning and building massing, the project's urban designers and architects should consider setbacks, building-height-to-street-width ratios, and appropriate pedestrian right-of-way widths, since changing building locations and street layouts later is difficult. In addition, the project's conceptual site plan should integrate plans for building entrances, ground-level building design, potential ground-level building uses, and sidewalk intrusions. Although some walkable streets features may change as the project progresses, planning for them early in the design process makes them more likely to be successfully incorporated into the final project.

6. Calculations

Façades and Entries: Street Setbacks (a, b)

Step 1. Sum the linear feet (lf) of street-facing building frontage in the project.

Step 2. Measure the distance from each façade to the property line it faces. Subtract from the total the lengths of any façade segments that are more than 25 feet (a) or 18 feet (b) from the property line.

Step 3. Determine the percentage of linear feet of building façade that is no greater than 25 feet (a) or 18 feet (b) from the property line, according to Equation 1. The result must be at least 80% (a) or 50% (b).

Equation 1

$$\text{\% building façade within maximum setback} = \frac{\text{Street-facing façade (lf) within maximum setback}}{\text{Total building façade (lf)}}$$

Façades and Entries: Sidewalk Setbacks (c)

Step 1. Sum the linear feet (lf) of frontage of all nonresidential and mixed-use buildings in the project.

Step 2. Measure the distance from the nonresidential and mixed-use building façades to the sidewalk or other pedestrian walkway. Subtract from the total the lengths of any façade segments that are more than 1 foot from the sidewalk.

Step 3. Determine the percentage of qualifying façades according to Equation 2. The result must be at least 50%.

Equation 2

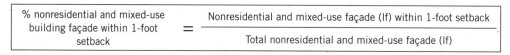

$$\text{\% nonresidential and mixed-use building façade within 1-foot setback} = \frac{\text{Nonresidential and mixed-use façade (lf) within 1-foot setback}}{\text{Total nonresidential and mixed-use façade (lf)}}$$

Façades and Entries: Functional Entries, Building Measurement Option (d, e)

	NPD
ND	Credit 1

Step 1. Sum the linear feet (lf) of frontage of all nonresidential or mixed-use buildings in the project.

Step 2. Count the principal functional entries along these façades.

Step 3. Calculate the average distance between principal functional entries, in feet, according to Equation 3. The result must be 75 feet or less.

Equation 3

$$\text{Average distance between entries} = \frac{\text{Entries in nonresidential and mixed-use buildings}}{\text{Total nonresidential or mixed-use building frontage (lf)}}$$

Façades and Entries: Functional Entries, Block Measurement Option (d, e)

Step 1. Identify blocks in the project with any nonresidential use and sum the linear feet of these blocks' frontage (including residential, nonresidential, and mixed-use buildings). This is the total length of the façades for nonresidential or mixed-use blocks.

Step 2. Count the principal functional entries (including residential, nonresidential, and mixed-use buildings) along the nonresidential or mixed-use blocks identified in Step 1.

Step 3. Calculate the average distance between principal functional entries along nonresidential or mixed-use blocks, in feet, according to Equation 3, above. The result must be 30 feet or less.

Ground-Level Use and Parking: Clear Glass (f)

Step 1. For all retail, trade, and service uses in the project, calculate the total area of the façades between 3 and 8 feet above grade, in square feet (sf).

Step 2. Calculate the square footage of clear glass within that area and express this as a percentage of the total square footage of façade, according to Equation 4. The result must be 60% or more.

Equation 4

$$\% \text{ clear glass} = \frac{\text{Façade with clear glass area 3–8 feet high (sf)}}{\text{Total façade area 3–8 feet high (sf)}}$$

On-Street Parking (i)

Step 1. Sum the curb lengths on both sides of all streets in the project.

Step 2. Measure the curb lengths designated for parking (exclusive of bulb-outs and transit stops) and express this sum as a percentage of total curb length, according to Equation 5. The result must be 70% or more.

Equation 5

$$\% \text{ on-street parking} = \frac{\text{urb length with parking}}{\text{Total curb length}}$$

Ground-Level Use and Parking: Elevated Ground Floors (k)

Step 1. Count all ground-floor dwelling units.

Step 2. Count the ground-floor dwelling units with a finished floor elevation of 24 inches or higher and express this number as a percentage of the total, according to Equation 6. The result should be 50% or more.

Equation 6

$$\% \text{ elevated ground-floor units above 24 inches} = \frac{\text{Ground floor units above 24 inches}}{\text{Total ground floor units}}$$

Ground-Level Use and Parking: Office Uses (l)

Step 1. Count all office buildings.

Step 2. Count the office buildings that have ground-floor retail along 60% of the street façade and express this number as a percentage of the total, according to Equation 7. The result must be 50% or more.

Equation 7

$$\begin{array}{c}\% \text{ office buildings with 60\% or more of street} \\ \text{façade containing ground-floor retail}\end{array} = \frac{\text{Qualifying office buildings}}{\text{Total office buildings}}$$

Ground-Level Use and Parking: Mixed Uses (l)

Step 1. Count all mixed-use buildings.

Step 2. Count the mixed-use buildings that have ground-floor retail along 60% of the street façade and express this number as a percentage of the total. The result must be 100%.

Ground-Level Use and Parking: Building-Height-to-Street-Width Ratio (m)

Step 1. Determine the total length of street frontage within and bordering the project, exclusive of any alleys and driveways, and the building heights and street widths, in linear feet (lf).

Step 2. For each street frontage, identify buildings facing the street and their height, façade width, and distance from façade to street centerline. Use average height and façade setback for buildings with multiple heights and façade elements.

Step 3. Calculate the percentage of street frontage that has a building-height-to-street-width ratio of at least 1:3, according to Equation 8. The result must be at least 40%.

Equation 8

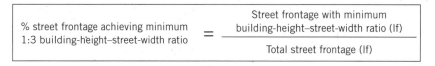

$$\begin{array}{c}\% \text{ street frontage achieving minimum} \\ \text{1:3 building-height–street-width ratio}\end{array} = \frac{\begin{array}{c}\text{Street frontage with minimum} \\ \text{building-height–street-width ratio (lf)}\end{array}}{\text{Total street frontage (lf)}}$$

In addition, 100% of existing and new nonmotorized rights-of-way included in the overall 1:3 calculation must achieve a ratio of 1:1.

Design Speeds for Safe Pedestrian and Bicycle Travel: Residential Streets (n)

Step 1. Sum the length of new residential streets within the project, using their centerlines, in linear feet (lf).

Step 2. Determine the length of new residential streets that have a target speed of 20 mph and express this as a percentage of the total, according to Equation 9. The result must be 75% or more.

Equation 9

$$\text{\% of residential streets with 20 mph target speed} = \frac{\text{Total length (lf) of new residential streets with 20 mph target speed}}{\text{Total length (lf) of new residential streets}}$$

Design Speeds for Safe Pedestrian and Bicycle Travel: Nonresidential and Mixed-Use Streets (o)

For new nonresidential and mixed-use streets within the project, follow the same steps as for new residential streets, using the length of streets that have a target speed of 25 mph; the result must be 70% or more.

Sidewalk Intrusions (p)

Step 1. Sum the lengths of all sidewalks in the project.

Step 2. Sum the widths of driveways that cross sidewalks and express the total as a percentage of total sidewalk length, according to Equation 10. The result must be less than 10%.

Equation 10

$$\text{\% sidewalk intrusions} = \frac{\text{Total driveway widths}}{\text{Total length of sidewalks}}$$

7. Documentation Guidance

As a first step in preparing to complete the LEED-ND documentation requirements, work through the following measures. Refer to GBCI's website for the complete descriptions of all required documentation.

- Determine the setbacks of all building frontage.
- Map the principal functional entry or entries of every building in the project.
- Determine the location of ground-level retail, service, and trade uses and determine the area of their façades that will be clear glass.
- Map the locations of on-street parking.
- Map the locations of all sidewalks and other pedestrian provisions within and bordering the project. Map all driveways and other intrusions that cross sidewalks.
- Determine which ground-floor units have a finished floor elevation 24 inches or more above grade.
- Determine the locations of ground-floor office uses.

- Retain information about target street speeds for all new residential, nonresidential, and mixed-use streets.

- Measure the length of every street within or bordering the project.

8. Examples

See Figures 1-6 in the Rating System for illustrations of façade setbacks, distances between building entries, ground-level design features, and on-street parking requirements..

9. Exemplary Performance

Projects may be eligible for an exemplary performance credit under Innovation and Design by achieving at least 7 points and meeting a 95% threshold for (n) and a 90% threshold for (o).

10. Regional Variations

Local governments have different requirements for setbacks, ground-level building design and uses, on-street parking, street speeds, sidewalk design, and pedestrian and vehicle access. Some local requirements may be conducive to meeting the prerequisite requirements; others may make it more difficult.

11. Resources

City of Davis, California, parking lot shading
www.city.davis.ca.us/pb/pdfs/planning/forms/Parking_Lot_Shading_Guidelines.pdf
www.city.davis.ca.us/pcs/trees/master.cfm
This website provides an example ordinance to make streets more walkable by providing at least 50% shading.

The Congress for the New Urbanism
www.cnu.org
The major group promoting New Urbanism in the United States hosts an annual conference, has information about design and development tools (including LEED-ND), grants awards for exemplary projects, indexes New Urbanist projects, and hosts networking events for New Urbanist practitioners through its chapters. The organization's charter contains many urban design strategies that promote walkable streets.

Institute of Transportation Engineers, traffic calming
www.ite.org/traffic/
This webpage includes descriptions of traffic-calming strategies, a searchable library of reports (such as *Trip Generation* and *Parking Generation*), articles about traffic calming, and other resources related to traffic engineering.

Local Government Commission
www.lgc.org
LGC provides information, technical assistance, and networking to local elected officials and developers about making more walkable and resource-efficient cities.

National Crime Prevention Council
www.ncpc.gov.sg/pdf/CPTED Guidebook.pdf
Principles of Crime Prevention through Environmental Design (2003) describes the design features of a built environment that can provide a sense of safety and discourage crime.

Pedestrian and Bicycle Information Center
www.bicyclinginfo.org/engineering/calming.cfm

This webpage provides information about bicycle and pedestrian design and infrastructure, as well as traffic-calming strategies.

Victoria Transportation Policy Institute
www.vtpi.org
This independent research organization provides consulting and publicly available research about solutions to emerging transportation issues, including walkability.

Walkable Communities, Inc.
www.walkable.org
This nonprofit offers training courses, walk audits, and resources for creating walkable communities.

Print Media

Context Sensitive Solutions in Designing Major Urban Thoroughfares for Walkable Communities, by Institute of Transportation Engineers (ITE, 2006).

Form Based Codes: A Guide for Planners, Urban Designers, Municipalities, and Developers, by Dan G. Parolek, Karen Parolek, and Paul C. Crawford (John Wiley & Sons, 2008).

Great Streets, by Allan Jacobs (MIT Press, 1995).

Planning and Urban Design Standards, by American Planning Association (John Wiley & Sons, 2006).

Street Design for Healthy Neighborhoods, by Dan Burden, Michael Wallwork, P.E., Ken Sides, P.E., Ramon Trias, and Harrison Bright Rue (Local Government Commission, 2002).

Streets & Patterns, by Stephen Marshall (Spon Press, 2005).

Streets and Sidewalks, People and Cars: The Citizens' Guide to Traffic Calming, by Dan Burden (Local Government Commission Center for Livable Communities, 2000).

Trees in Urban Design, 2nd edition, by Henry F. Arnold (Van Nostrand Reinhold, 1992).

Urban Design: Street and Square, by J.C. Moughtin (Architectural Press, 2003).

Urban Design Reclaimed: Tools, Techniques, and Strategies for Planners, by Emily Talen (American Planning Association, 2009).

12. Definitions

accessory dwelling unit a subordinate dwelling unit that is attached to a principal building or contained in a separate structure on the same property as the principal unit.

block land bounded by the project boundary, transportation or utility rights-of-way that may be publicly dedicated or privately owned and deeded in perpetuity for general public use, waterfront, and/or comparable land division features.

covenants, conditions, and restrictions limitations that may be placed on a property and its use and are made a condition of holding title or lease.

dwelling unit living quarters intended for long-term occupancy that provide facilities for cooking, sleeping, and sanitation. This does not include hotel rooms.

existing present on the date of submission of LEED-ND certification documents; similarly, an element or condition that **exists** is present on the date that LEED-ND certification documents are submitted.

functional entry a building opening designed to be used by pedestrians and open during regular business hours. This does not include any door exclusively designated as an emergency exit, or a garage door not designed as a pedestrian entrance.

project the land, water, and construction that constitutes the project application. A project applicant does not have to own or control all land or water within a project boundary, but all the area within the project boundary must comply with prerequisites and attempted credits.

street a dedicated right-of-way that can accommodate one or more modes of travel, excluding alleys and paseos. A street is suitable for primary entrances and provides access to the front and/ or sides of buildings and lots. A street may be privately owned as long as it is deeded in perpetuity for general public use. A street must be an addressable thoroughfare (for mail purposes) under the standards of the applicable regulating authority.

vehicle miles traveled (VMT) the number of miles driven by motorists in a specified time period, such as a day or a year, in absolute or per capita terms.

woonerf a street, also known as a home zone, shared zone, or living street, where pedestrians have priority over vehicles and the posted speed limit is no greater than 10 miles per hour. Physical elements within the roadway, such as shared surfaces, plantings, street furniture, parking, and play areas, slow traffic and invite pedestrians to use the entire right-of-way.

COMPACT DEVELOPMENT

	ND
Credit	NPD Credit 2
Points	1-6 points

Intent

To encourage development in *existing* areas to conserve land and protect farmland and wildlife habitat. To promote livability, walkability, and transportation efficiency, including reduced *vehicle miles traveled* (VMT). To improve public health encouraging daily physical activity associated with alternative modes of transportation and compact development.

Requirements

Design and build the *project* such that residential and nonresidential components achieve the *densities* per acre of *buildable land* listed in Table 1 (excluding those portions of parking structures devoted to parking).

Table 1. Points for density per acre of buildable land

Residential density (DU/acre)	Nonresidential density (FAR)	Points
> 10 and ≤ 13	> 0.75 and ≤ 1.0	1
> 13 and ≤ 18	> 1.0 and ≤ 1.25	2
> 18 and ≤ 25	> 1.25 and ≤ 1.75	3
> 25 and ≤ 38	> 1.75 and ≤ 2.25	4
> 38 and ≤ 63	> 2.25 and ≤ 3.0	5
> 63	> 3.0	6
DU = dwelling unit; FAR = floor-area ratio.		

The specified densities must be achieved within five years of the date that the first building of any type is occupied.

The scoring of a mixed-use project is calculated with a weighted average, according to the following steps.

1. Determine the total square footage of all residential and nonresidential uses.

2. Calculate the percentage residential and percentage nonresidential of the total square footage.

3. Determine the density of each component as measured in *dwelling units* per acre and *floor-area ratio*, respectively.

4. Referring to Table 1, find the appropriate points for the densities of the residential and nonresidential components.

5. If the points are different, multiply the point value of the residential component by its percentage of the total square footage and multiply the point value of the nonresidential component by its percentage.

6. Add the two scores.

1. Benefits and Issues to Consider

For a summary of the benefits of building compactly, see the Benefits and Issues section under NPD Prerequisite 2, Compact Development.

2. Related Credits

Meeting or exceeding the requirements for Compact Development may assist in earning the following related credits:

- SLL Prerequisite 1, Smart Locations
- SLL Prerequisite 3, Wetland and Water Body Conservation
- SLL Credit 3, Locations with Reduced Automobile Dependence
- NPD Prerequisite 2, Compact Development
- NPD Credit 3, Mixed-Use Neighborhood Centers

3. Summary of Referenced Standards

There are no referenced standards for this credit.

4. Implementation

Strategies for implementing compact development can be found in the Implementation section of NPD Prerequisite 2, Compact Development. This credit differs from the corresponding prerequisite in that it does not allow one component's density to qualify when divided by all buildable land.

5. Timeline and Team

See the Timeline and Team section of NPD Prerequisite 2, Compact Development.

6. Calculations

See the Calculations section of NPD Prerequisite 2, Compact Development, for guidance on completing the residential and nonresidential density calculations. See the Getting Started chapter for guidance on determining residential and nonresidential buildable land.

The NPD Credit 2 requirements describe the process for scoring a mixed-use project using a weighted average. This is shown in the corresponding prerequisite and demonstrated in the Examples section, below. It is necessary to calculate the weighted average only if the residential and nonresidential components of the project earn different numbers of points based on the density threshold table (i.e., if residential density achieves the 3-point threshold but nonresidential achieves only the 1-point threshold). As described in the rating system, the weighted score for residential or nonresidential is proportionate to each component's percentage of the total square footage. The results of Equation 1 should be rounded to the nearest whole number (decimals of .50 and higher round up, and decimals of .49 and lower round down). Projects may have densities of less than 10 dwelling units per acre or 0.75 FAR, provided the final mixed-use weighted score, calculated according to Equation 1, meets the minimum.

7. Documentation Guidance

See the Documentation Guidance section of NPD Prerequisite 2, Compact Development.

Equation 1

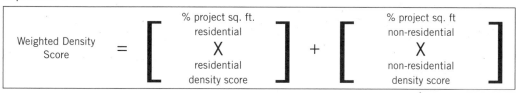

$$\text{Weighted Density Score} = \left[\frac{\text{\% project sq. ft. residential}}{\text{X}}\ \text{residential density score} \right] + \left[\frac{\text{\% project sq. ft non-residential}}{\text{X}}\ \text{non-residential density score} \right]$$

8. Examples

For an example of calculating project density, see the Examples section of NPD Prerequisite 2, Compact Development. The example below illustrates the weighted scoring average calculation.

Example 1. Mixed-Use Project with Two Qualifying Components, Weighted Score

A project contains a mix of uses, with 75% of project square footage residential and 25% nonresidential. The residential component has a density of 65 DU per acre, which exceeds the 6-point threshold; the nonresidential component has a density of 0.80 FAR, which exceeds the 1-point threshold (see Table 1). Since the scores are different, the team calculates the weighted score of residential and nonresidential, respectively: (0.75 x 6) + (0.25 x 1) = 4.75. The weighted result, 4.75, rounds up, and the project scores 5 points.

Example 2. Mixed-Use Project with One Qualifying Component, Weighted Score

A project contains a mix of uses, with 80% of project square footage residential and 20% nonresidential. The residential component has a density of 20 DU per acre and scores 3 points; the nonresidential component has a density of 0.50 FAR, which does not achieve the minimum threshold (see Table 1). Since the scores are different, the project calculates the weighted score of residential and nonresidential, respectively: (0.8 x 3) + (0.2 x 0) = 2.4. The weighted result, 2.4, rounds down, and the project scores 2 points.

9. Exemplary Performance

This credit is not eligible for exemplary performance under Innovation and Design Process.

10. Regional Variations

See the Regional Variations section under NPD Prerequisite 2, Compact Development.

11. Resources

See the Resources section under NPD Prerequisite 2, Compact Development.

12. Definitions

buildable land the portion of the site where construction can occur, including land voluntarily set aside and not constructed upon. When used in density calculations, buildable land excludes public rights-of-way and land excluded from development by codified law or LEED for Neighborhood Development prerequisites. An applicant may exclude additional land not exceeding 15% of the buildable land base defined above, provided the following conditions are present:

    a. The land is protected from residential and nonresidential construction by easement, deed restriction, or other enforceable legal instrument.

AND

    b. Either 25% or more of the boundary of each contiguous parcel proposed for exclusion borders a water body or areas outside the project boundary that are protected by codified law; or ownership of, or management authority over, the exclusion area is transferred to a public entity.

density the amount of building structures constructed on the project site, measured for residential buildings as dwelling units per acre of buildable land available for residential uses, and for nonresidential buildings as the floor-area ratio of buildable land area available for nonresidential uses. In both cases, structured parking is excluded.

dwelling unit living quarters intended for long-term occupancy that provide facilities for cooking, sleeping, and sanitation. This does not include hotel rooms.

existing present on the date of submission of LEED-ND certification documents; similarly, an element or condition that exists is present on the date that LEED-ND certification documents are submitted.

floor-area ratio (FAR) the density of nonresidential land use, exclusive of parking, measured as the total nonresidential building floor area divided by the total buildable land area available for nonresidential structures. For example, on a site with 10,000 square feet of buildable land area, an FAR of 1.0 would be 10,000 square feet of building floor area. On the same site, an FAR of 1.5 would be 15,000 square feet of built floor area; an FAR of 2.0 would be 20,000 built square feet and an FAR of 0.5 would be 5,000 built square feet.

project the land, water, and construction that constitutes the project application. A project applicant does not have to own or control all land or water within a project boundary, but all the area within the project boundary must comply with prerequisites and attempted credits.

vehicle miles traveled (VMT) the number of miles driven by motorists in a specified time period, such as a day or a year, in absolute or per capita terms.

MIXED-USE NEIGHBORHOOD CENTERS

	ND
Credit	NPD Credit 3
Points	1-4 points

Intent

To cluster diverse land uses in accessible neighborhood and regional centers to encourage daily walking, biking, and transit use, reduce *vehicle miles traveled* (VMT) and automobile dependence, and support car-free living.

Requirements

FOR ALL PROJECTS

Locate and/or design the *project* such that 50% of its *dwelling units* are within a 1/4-mile *walk distance* of the number of diverse uses (see Appendix) in Table 1, including at least one use from each of the four categories. For projects with no dwellings, 50% of dwelling units within 1/4 mile of the *project boundary* must be within a 1/4-mile walk distance of the number of diverse uses specified in Table 1, including at least one food retail store and at least one establishment from each of two other categories. Establishments may be inside or outside the project and may be *existing* or *planned diverse uses*.

The specified number of diverse uses must be in place by the time of occupancy according to the percentages indicated in Table 1 (exclusive of portions of parking structures devoted to parking):

Table 1. Points for diverse uses within 1/4-mile walk distance, by time of occupancy

Diverse uses	Percentage occupancy of total square footage	Points
4–6	20%	1
7–10	30%	2
11–18	40%	3
≥ 19	50%	4

Per neighborhood center, the following restrictions apply:

a. A single establishment may not be counted in two categories (e.g., a place of worship may be counted only once even if it also contains a daycare facility, and a retail store may be counted only once even if it sells products in several categories).

b. Establishments in a mixed-use building may each count if they are distinctly operated enterprises with separate exterior entrances, but no more than half of the minimum number of diverse uses can be situated in a single building or under a common roof.

c. Only two establishments in a single category may be counted (e.g., if five restaurants are within the required distance, only two may be counted).

FOR PROJECTS 40 ACRES OR GREATER

Cluster diverse uses into neighborhood centers as follows:

Table 2. Points for clustering of diverse uses

Diverse uses	Minimum uses per neighborhood center	Points
4–6	3	1
7–10	5	2
11–18	7	3
≥ 19.	9	4

Within each neighborhood center, the principal entries of the establishments must be within a 300-foot walk distance from a single common point that represents the center of the cluster (1 or 2 points) or within a 400-foot walk distance (3 or 4 points).

Also, projects with multiple centers must determine points earned based on the number of uses in the centers weighted by the percentage of total dwelling units within a 1/4-mile walk distance from each center's common point.

AND

FOR PROJECTS WITH REGIONAL-SERVING RETAIL OF 150,000 OR MORE SQUARE FEET

Projects with retail uses totaling 150,000 or more square feet, if they have at least one retail establishment totaling 75,000 or more square feet, must also earn a minimum of 1 point under SLL Credit 3, Reduced Automobile Dependence, Option 1, Transit-Served Location (planned transit service can be counted), and for every additional 50,000 square feet of retail above 150,000 square feet, must earn 1 additional point under SLL Credit 3.

If transit service is planned but not yet operational, the project must demonstrate one of the following:

a. The relevant transit agency has a signed full funding grant agreement with the Federal Transit Administration that includes a revenue operations date for the start of transit service. The revenue operations date must be no later than the occupancy date of 50% of the project's total building square footage.

b. For bus, streetcar, *bus rapid transit*, or ferry service, the transit agency must certify that it has an approved budget that includes specifically allocated funds sufficient to provide the planned service at the levels listed above and that service at these levels will commence no later than occupancy of 50% of the project's total building square footage.

c. For rail service other than streetcars, the transit agency must certify that preliminary engineering for a rail line has commenced. In addition, the service must meet either of these two requirements:

   ▪ A state legislature or local subdivision of the state has authorized the transit agency to expend funds to establish rail transit service that will commence no later than occupancy of 50% of the project's total building square footage.

OR

- A municipality has dedicated funding or reimbursement commitments from future tax revenue for the development of stations, platforms, or other rail transit infrastructure that will service the project no later than occupancy of 50% of the project's total building square footage.

1. Benefits and Issues to Consider

Environmental Issues

Developments located within walking distance of existing or planned basic services limit urban sprawl and reduce air pollution and greenhouse gas emissions from transportation. Residents and visitors can walk, bike, or drive and park once to fulfill multiple needs. Facilitating walkable access to basic services may improve workers' productivity by reducing the time spent driving and finding a parking space when running errands or eating lunch.

Economic and Social Issues

Providing walkable access to basic services saves money for project occupants who do not own cars. Even occupants who own vehicles may welcome not having to drive to meet daily needs. Additionally, daily physical activity has important public health benefits.

Including a significant amount of retail can result in increased tax revenue for a jurisdiction. If served by transit, large retail centers will have much less negative environmental impact than is typically associated with such facilities.

It may be feasible to include services and amenities beyond those that meet basic daily needs, particularly if the project is in an existing area that already has some of these uses in place. The project should consider how to capitalize on existing uses by providing additional, complementary uses (see Appendix, Diverse Uses).

2. Related Credits

The following credits require or count diverse uses that can also contribute to achieving Mixed-Use Neighborhood Centers:

- SLL Prerequisite 1, Smart Location
- SLL Credit 5, Housing and Jobs Proximity
- NPD Credit 9, Access to Civic and Public Space
- NPD Credit 10, Access to Recreation Facilities
- NPD Credit 13, Local Food Production
- NPD Credit 15, Neighborhood Schools

Achieving the following credits, which encourage infill, connected, and compact development, often increases a project's chances of being near diverse uses:

- SLL Credit 1, Preferred Locations
- NPD Credit 2, Compact Development

3. Summary of Referenced Standards

There are no referenced standards for this credit.

4. Implementation

The purpose of this credit is to encourage projects to provide access to a wide range of retail, service, and civic facilities, as illustrated in Figure 1. This includes existing and planned uses outside the project boundary as well as uses that are part of the project. Projects that locate in compact, infill areas may already have access to many existing diverse uses. Other projects may be able to earn points based primarily on the uses provided as part of the project. The credit also encourages clustering diverse uses in neighborhood centers so that shops and services are within easy walking distance.

Figure 1. Project site with single diverse use, cluster of diverse uses, and diverse uses in regional retail center

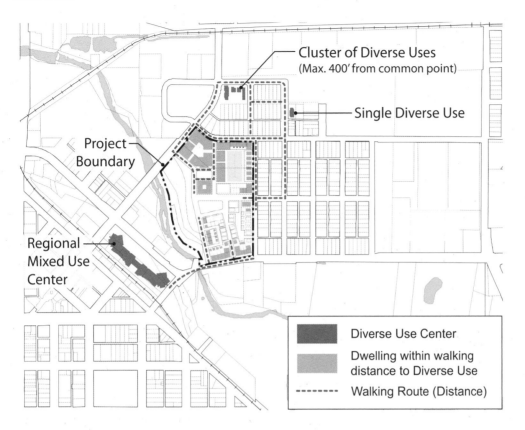

All Projects

All projects, regardless of size or type, must meet minimum performance thresholds for proximity between dwelling units and a diversity of uses, with a maximum of 4 points possible for increasing levels of performance. The rating system Appendix lists the categories and types of diverse uses that contribute toward the credit.

To determine the number of points achieved, first identify any existing diverse uses near the project. Second, identify any planned diverse uses near the project—that is, uses that are outside the project boundary, have building permits, and are under construction. Finally, identify any diverse uses, existing or planned, that are part of the project. Once all of these diverse uses have been located, identify which project dwelling units are within 1/4-mile walk distance of which diverse uses. Different dwelling units or buildings may be within 1/4-mile walk distance of several diverse uses, depending on their location. The project's score is based on the 50% of dwellings with the highest level of access. As long as 50% of the dwelling units meet or exceed a certain scoring threshold, the project may contain other dwelling units that do not.

Projects that contain no dwelling units can still achieve this credit. For such projects, identify the area within 1/4-mile of the project boundary, identify all dwelling units in this area, and then count the diverse uses within a 1/4-mile walk distance of at least 50% of the dwelling units. There is no minimum number of dwelling units in the 1/4-mile area that is needed to achieve this credit. If there are no dwelling units in the 1/4-mile area or as part of the project, the project is not eligible for this credit.

A wide range of shops and services enables residents and employees in the project to meet a high percentage of their daily needs within walking distance. For all types of projects, regardless of size or amount of retail, uses must meet certain levels of diversity to count toward the credit. First, if the project contains dwelling units, it must provide access to at least one use from each of the four diverse use categories listed in the Appendix. If the project does not contain dwelling units and is counting dwelling units within a 1/4-mile area of the project boundary, it must provide a food retail use and a use from at least two of the other three use categories. Second, a single use may not be counted in more than one category, and a single retail store may only be counted once even if it sells a wide diversity of products and services. For example, a single big-box store that contains a grocery store, retail, pharmacy, and optometrist may be counted only once, in only one category; the category selected is at the project team's discretion. Third, a single type of diverse use, such as a restaurant, maybe counted only two times per neighborhood center. For example, if there are two restaurants in one neighborhood center and three in another, only four may be counted. Finally, a single building may contain more than one use, but no more than half the minimum number of diverse uses in each point category may be under a common roof.

The last part of the requirement is that a certain percentage of the total project square footage must be in place for the diverse uses to be counted. The number of points increases as the percentage of occupancy rises. For example, for 2 points, all of the diverse uses that are counted toward credit achievement must be in place when the project occupancy is at 30% of total building square footage.

Projects 40 Acres or More

For projects 40 acres or more, all of the above requirements apply. In addition, these projects must also cluster a minimum number of their diverse uses in one or more neighborhood centers for these uses to count toward the credit. Neighborhood centers provide a central gathering place for neighborhoods and create synergies between the diverse uses, and they prevent the haphazard spread of establishments throughout a neighborhood. Neighborhood centers, which can be inside or outside the project boundary and still contribute to the credit, are defined as places that have three to ten uses within 300 feet walking distance of a single common point, or more than seven uses within 400 feet walking distance of a single common point. For projects 40 acres or more, the point scale per use is the same as for all other projects. However, a minimum number of uses must be present per neighborhood center, depending on whether the project is seeking 1, 2, 3, or 4 points. Restrictions on the eligibility of diverse uses may be applied per neighborhood center if a project has more than one center; see the All Projects section, above.

For projects with numerous neighborhood centers, the number of points achieved is a weighted average of the uses found in each neighborhood center. The weighting is based on the number of dwelling units within a 1/4-mile walk of each neighborhood center. The results of the weighting should be rounded to the nearest whole number, with decimals of 0.50 and higher rounding up, and lower values rounding down.

Projects with Regional-Serving Retail of 150,000 Square Feet or More

Projects that include more than 150,000 square feet of retail space, if they have at least one retail establishment totaling 75,000 or more square feet (e.g., a large department store), must identify both existing and planned transit routes serving the site. This additional requirement applies even if a project is smaller than 40 acres. If no retail establishment of greater than 75,000 square feet is present, this section does not apply. The intent of this requirement is to ensure that large retailers are accessible by transit, since they will likely be visited by customers from outside the immediate neighborhood. Projects with less than 150,000 square feet of retail space, on the other hand, are more likely to provide neighborhood-serving retail, which can be reached on foot from surrounding neighborhoods and create less demand for transit.

Planned transit service is defined as transit with funding commitments, as described in the credit requirements. The project must then measure both existing and planned transit according to the requirements in SLL Credit 3, Locations with Reduced Automobile Dependence, Option 1, Transit-Served Location. If the project is able to earn 1 point when counting both existing and planned transit, it can earn points under this credit, too. If it does not meet the threshold in SLL Credit 3, Option 1, it cannot earn any points under this credit. In addition, for each 50,000 square feet of retail space on the site, projects must earn an additional point on the SLL Credit 3, Option 1, scale. This means that a project with 280,000 square feet of retail must meet the 4-point threshold.

5. Timeline and Team

The project developer should choose a location that is near a wide range of existing and planned uses. The urban designer and architect should design a site plan that contains a diversity of uses clustered into neighborhood centers.

6. Calculations

Weighted Average of Uses for Multiple Neighborhood Centers

Step 1. Identify all clusters of diverse uses that qualify as neighborhood centers. Count the uses in each such center.

Step 2. Identify the percentage of project dwelling units within a 1/4-mile walk distance of each neighborhood center. Some dwelling units may be within walking distance of more than one center, so the percentage may exceed 100%.

Step 3. Calculate a weighted average of uses in neighborhood centers by dwelling unit, according to Equation 1. The equation can include more neighborhood centers, as necessary.

Equation 1

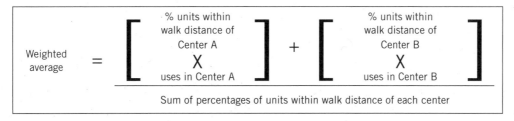

$$\text{Weighted average} = \frac{\left[\begin{array}{c} \text{\% units within} \\ \text{walk distance of} \\ \text{Center A} \\ \times \\ \text{uses in Center A} \end{array}\right] + \left[\begin{array}{c} \text{\% units within} \\ \text{walk distance of} \\ \text{Center B} \\ \times \\ \text{uses in Center B} \end{array}\right]}{\text{Sum of percentages of units within walk distance of each center}}$$

Step 4. Round the results of Equation 1 to the nearest whole number. This is the weighted average of uses that determines the points earned, according to Table 1.

7. Documentation Guidance

As a first step in preparing to complete the LEED-ND documentation requirements, work through the following measures. Refer to GBCI's website for the complete descriptions of all required documentation.

- Identify the locations of all existing and planned diverse uses within and near the project.

- Identify the locations of neighborhood centers and for each, identify a single common point that represents the center of the cluster.

- If the project contains more than 150,000 square feet of retail space, identify nearby existing and planned transit, according to the requirements in SLL Credit 3, Locations with Reduced Automobile Dependence, Option 1, Transit-Served Location.

8. Examples

Example 1

A large project with more than 40 acres counts seven uses, five of which are in a single neighborhood center, all within a 1/4-mile walk distance of 50% of the dwelling units. Based on Table 2, this project earns 2 points.

Example 2

A 10-acre project has five uses in one neighborhood center and three uses in another neighborhood center, all within a 1/4-mile walk distance of 50% of the dwelling units. The uses will be in place by the time that 30% of the project's total square footage is occupied. Based on Table 2, this project earns 2 points for providing a total of eight uses. Since the project is smaller than 40 acres, the uses do not need to be clustered in neighborhood centers of a certain size to count toward the credit.

Example 3

A large project with more than 40 acres has 32 uses—five uses in one neighborhood center, 25 uses in another neighborhood center, and two uses not in a neighborhood center—all within a 1/4-mile walk distance of at least 50% of the dwelling units. Of the 500 dwelling units in the project, 400 (80%) are within the required walking distance of the large center, and 200 (40%) are within the required walking distance of the small center. Some uses are within walking distance of both centers, which is why the percentages total more than 100. The number of uses that count toward the credit is a weighted average of the number of uses in the two centers, as follows: $(0.8 \times 25) + (0.4 \times 5) / (0.8 + 0.4) = 18$. Therefore, 32 total uses, with a weighted average of 18 uses per center, earns 3 points (Table 2), provided the project also meets the percentage occupancy threshold of 50%. The two uses not in a neighborhood center do not factor into the weighted average calculation but do count toward total number of uses because they are within the specified walking distance of 50% of the dwelling units.

9. Exemplary Performance

Projects may earn an Innovation and Design Process credit for exemplary performance as follows:

- For projects smaller than 40 acres, at least 30 diverse uses must be available within a 1/4-mile walk distance of 50% of the dwelling units.

- For projects larger than 40 acres, at least 30 diverse uses must be available within a 1/4-mile walk distance of 50% of the dwelling units, and at least 11 uses must be clustered in a neighborhood center.

10. Regional Variations

There are no regional variations associated with this credit.

11. Resources

Websites
Project for Public Spaces
www.pps.org/mixed_use/
This site provides examples and links to services related to creating mixed-use development.

Smart Growth Network

www.smartgrowth.org

This network of nonprofit organizations and government agencies promotes smart growth practices. The website outlines smart growth principles, provides a guide to smart growth terms and technical concepts, and hosts a searchable catalogue of reports, websites, tools, and case studies dating from 1997.

Print Media

Mixed-Use Development Handbook, by Dean Schwanke et al. (Urban Land Institute, 2003).

"Mixed Use in Theory and Practice," by Jill Grant, *Journal of the American Planning Association* 68(1) (2002): 71-84.

Retrofitting Suburbia, by Ellen Dunham-Jones et al. (Urban Land Institute, 2009).

Sustainable Urbanism, by Douglas Farr (John Wiley & Sons, 2007).

12. Definitions

bus rapid transit an enhanced bus system that operates on exclusive bus lanes or other transit rights-of-way; it is designed to combine the flexibility of buses with the efficiency of rail.

dwelling unit living quarters intended for long-term occupancy that provide facilities for cooking, sleeping, and sanitation. This does not include hotel rooms.

existing present on the date of submission of LEED-ND certification documents; similarly, an element or condition that exists is present on the date that LEED-ND certification documents are submitted.

planned diverse use a shop, service, or facility outside the project boundary that has received a building permit and is under construction at the time of the first certificate of occupancy is issued for any building in the LEED-ND project.

project the land, water, and construction that constitutes the project application. A project applicant does not have to own or control all land or water within a project boundary, but all the area within the project boundary must comply with prerequisites and attempted credits.

project boundary the platted property line of the project defining land and water within it. Projects located on publicly owned campuses that do not have internal property lines must delineate a sphere-of-influence line to be used instead. *Project site* is equivalent to the land and water inside the project boundary. The project must not contain noncontiguous parcels, but parcels can be separated by public rights-of-way. Projects may also have enclaves of nonproject properties that are not subject to the rating system, but such enclaves cannot exceed 2% of the total project area and cannot be described as certified.

walk distance the distance that a pedestrian must travel between origins and destinations without obstruction, in a safe and comfortable environment on a continuous network of sidewalks, all-weather-surface footpaths, crosswalks, woonerfs, or equivalent pedestrian facilities.

vehicle miles traveled (**VMT**) the number of miles driven by motorists in a specified time period, such as a day or a year, in absolute or per capita terms.

MIXED-INCOME DIVERSE COMMUNITIES

	ND
Credit	NPD Credit 4
Points	1-7 points

Intent

To promote socially equitable and engaging communities by enabling residents from a wide range of economic levels, household sizes, and age groups to live in a community.

Requirements

Meet the requirements of one or more options below.

OPTION 1. Diversity of Housing Types

Include a sufficient variety of housing sizes and types in the *project* such that the total variety of planned and *existing* housing within the project achieves a Simpson Diversity Index score greater than 0.5, using the housing categories below. Projects of less than 125 acres may calculate the Simpson Diversity Index for the area within 1/4 mile of the project's geographic center. The Simpson Diversity Index calculates the probability that any two randomly selected *dwelling unit*s in a project will be of a different type.

$$Score = 1 - \sum (n/N)^2$$

where n = the total number of dwelling units in a single category, and N = the total number of dwelling units in all categories.

Table 1. Points for housing diversity

Simpson Diversity Index score	Points
> 0.5 to < 0.6	1
≥ 0.6 to < 0.7	2
≥ 0.7	3

Housing categories are defined according to the dwelling unit's net square footage, exclusive of any garage, as listed in Table 2.

Table 2. Housing categories

Type	Square feet
Detached residential, large	> 1,250
Detached residential, small	≤ 1,250
Duplex or townhouse, large	> 1,250
Duplex or townhouse, small	≤ 1,250
Dwelling unit in multiunit building with no elevator, large	> 1,250
Dwelling unit in multiunit building with no elevator, medium	> 750 to ≤ 1,250
Dwelling unit in multiunit building with no elevator, small	≤ 750
Dwelling unit in multiunit building with elevator, 4 stories or fewer, large	> 1,250
Dwelling unit in multiunit building with elevator, 4 stories or fewer, medium	> 750 to ≤ 1,250
Dwelling unit in multiunit building with elevator, 4 stories or fewer, small	≤ 750
Dwelling unit in multiunit building with elevator, 5 to 8 stories, large	> 1,250
Dwelling unit in multiunit building with elevator, 5 to 8 stories, medium	> 750 to ≤ 1,250
Dwelling unit in multiunit building with elevator, 5 to 8 stories, small	≤ 750
Dwelling unit in multiunit building with elevator, 9 stories or more, large	> 1,250
Dwelling unit in multiunit building with elevator, 9 stories or more, medium	> 750 to ≤ 1,250
Dwelling unit in multiunit building with elevator, 9 stories or more, small	≤ 750
Live-work space, large	> 1,250
Live-work space, small	≤ 1,250
Accessory dwelling unit, large	> 1,250
Accessory dwelling unit, small	≤ 1,250

For the purposes of this credit, townhouse and live-work units may have individual ground-level entrances and/or be within a multiunit or mixed-use building. Double counting is prohibited; each dwelling may be classified in only one category. The number of stories in a building is inclusive of the ground floor regardless of its use.

AND/OR

OPTION 2. Affordable Housing

Include a proportion of new rental and/or for-sale dwelling units priced for households earning below the *area median income* (AMI). Rental units must be maintained at affordable levels for a minimum of 15 years. Existing dwelling units are exempt from requirement calculations. A maximum of 3 points may be earned by meeting any combination of thresholds in Table 3.

Table 3. Points for affordable housing

Rental dwelling units				For-sale dwelling units			
Priced up to 60% AMI		Priced up to 80% AMI		Priced up to 100% AMI		Priced up to 120% AMI	
Percentage of total rental units	Points	Percentage of total rental units	Points	Percentage of total for-sale units	Points	Percentage of total for-sale units	Points
5	1	10	1	5	1	8	1
10	2	15	2	10	2	12	2
15	3	25	3	15	3	--	--
AMI = area median income.							

AND/OR

OPTION 3. Mixed-Income Diverse Communities

A project may earn 1 additional point by earning at least 2 points in Option 1 and at least 2 points in Option 2 (at least one of which must be for providing housing at or below 100% AMI).

1. Benefits and Issues to Consider

Environmental Issues

Providing a range of housing types within a project can help maximize available space and limit the development footprint. Projects with attached or multiunit housing support a compact development strategy. Consider the potential efficiencies in materials use and infrastructure from building multiunit housing.

Economic and Social Issues

Varied housing types and multiple price points are mutually reinforcing strategies that help create a complete, equitable community serving households of differing incomes. Projects that provide a range of housing options enable residents to stay in the community as their circumstances change, be it through age, a growing family, or income fluctuations.

Daily routines typically vary by demographic categories. Businesses may be able to use these patterns to their benefit, drawing retired customers during the day, families in the evening, and young professionals or students at night. Consider also that a project with diverse housing options may be better able to withstand a volatile housing market than one containing a single housing type.

2. Related Credits

Inclusion of a diversity of dwelling unit types and affordable housing may assist in earning the following related credits:

- SLL Credit 1, Preferred Locations
- SLL Credit 5, Housing and Jobs Proximity
- NPD Credit 2, Compact Development

3. Summary of Referenced Standards

There are no referenced standards for this credit. The Simpson Diversity Index application for housing diversity comes from the Traditional Neighborhood Development Design Rating Standards, Version 2.2, developed by Laurence Aurbach.

4. Implementation

The purpose of this credit is to promote a diversity of housing types for different household sizes, age groups, and income levels. It is organized in two parts: diversity of physical housing types and presence of affordable units. To identify an appropriate diversity of housing types for a project, consider conducting a market analysis of the feasibility of incorporating the various housing categories identified in the requirements.

To find out about existing housing types in the area, ask the local planning or the tax assessor's office for information on the size of residential units within 1/4-mile of the project's center, including building square footage for single-family residences and multiunit residential buildings.

Identify the area median income and the resulting rental and for-sale unit price points. Many cities have housing departments and staff who specialize in affordable housing and may already have data on affordable housing price points. Consider subsidizing affordable housing through tax credits, if available, from the local, state or federal government. In California, for example, projects that provide affordable housing may increase their density or size beyond what the zoning code allows. Consider partnerships with local nonprofit developers or organizations that have expertise in creating affordable housing projects.

5. Timeline and Team

Project developers may choose to conduct a market analysis of the viability of various housing categories during preliminary planning stages. Early in the entitlement and financing processes, developers should engage with local government, nonprofit organizations that specialize in affordable housing, and other entities (see the Resources section of this credit) to identify any local and state regulations and incentives for affordable housing, such as inclusionary zoning or tax and fiscal policies. During conceptual design, project designers should incorporate a variety of dwelling unit types and affordable housing units.

6. Calculations

OPTION 1. Diversity of Housing Types

The Simpson Diversity Index calculates the probability that two dwellings randomly selected will be in different categories.

Step 1. Classify all dwelling units according to the 20 housing types listed in the requirements. If using the 1/4-mile radius option, measure from the geographic center of the project.

Step 2. Calculate the Simpson Diversity Index (Equation 1). Use the result to determine the number of points earned.

Equation 1

$$\text{Housing diversity score} = 1 - \sum (n/N)^2$$

$$\text{where } n = \text{total dwelling units in a single category}$$

$$\text{and } N = \text{total dwelling units in all categories}$$

OPTION 2. Affordable Housing

Step 1. Determine the area median income (AMI) of a four-person household for the area in which the project is located.

Step 2. Multiply the AMI by the household income percentages from Table 1—rental, 60% or 80%, and for-sale, 100% or 120%—to determine the target income (Equation 2).

Equation 2

$$\text{Target income} = \text{AMI} \times \text{household income percentage}$$

Step 3. For each size of dwelling unit in the project, adjust the target income for family size by multiplying by the appropriate bedroom factor (Table 4, Equation 3):

Table 4. Bedroom (BR) factors for adjusting target income

Unit	Factor
Studio	0.70
1 BR	0.75
2 BRs	0.90
3 BRs	1.04
4 BRs	1.16

Equation 3

$$\text{Adjusted target income} = \text{Target income} \times \text{BR factor}$$

Step 4. For each size of rental unit, multiply by 30% to determine the maximum amount of income for housing (annual rental price). Divide by 12 to determine the maximum monthly gross rent for the unit (Equation 4).

Equation 4

$$\text{Maximum monthly gross rent} = \frac{\text{Adjusted target income} \times .30}{12}$$

For each category of for-sale unit, multiply by 28% to determine the maximum amount of income available to pay principal, interest, taxes, and insurance (PITI). Divide by 12 to determine the maximum monthly PITI that the household can afford (Equation 5).

Equation 5

$$\text{Maximum monthly PITI} = \frac{\text{Adjusted target income} \times .28}{12}$$

Step 5. Calculate the percentage of rental and/or for-sale units that meet at least one of the requirement thresholds. At least one of the requirements' thresholds for affordably priced housing must be achieved.

7. Documentation Guidance

As a first step in preparing to complete the LEED-ND documentation requirements, work through the following measures. Refer to GBCI's website for the complete descriptions of all required documentation.

- For projects that include a diversity of housing types, note the locations of different types of housing within the project and include them in the site map.

- For projects of less than 125 acres, calculate the Simpson Diversity Index for the area within 1/4-mile of the project's geographic center.

- For projects that include a diversity of housing types, track the number and size of dwelling units in each category defined in the requirement, as well as the total number of dwelling units.

- For projects that include affordable housing, maintain HUD data for the area median income and the resulting maximum monthly rents and PITI.

- For projects that include affordable housing, track the number of affordable and market-rate housing units, the rental and sale prices of any affordable units, and the percentage of rental and for-sale units that are priced within the specified range.

- For projects that include affordable rental units, maintain a regulatory and operating agreement, deed restrictions, or other recorded document ensuring that the units will be maintained at the specified affordable levels for a minimum of 15 years.

8. Examples

OPTION 1. Diversity of Housing Types

Referring to Table 2, the team of a project with 2,358 total residential units classifies its dwelling units according to type:

- 238 — Detached residential, large
- 239 — Detached residential, small
- 378 — Townhouses, small
- 513 — Apartments in multiunit building with elevator, four stories or fewer, medium
- 909 — Apartments in multiunit building with elevator, nine stories or more, large
- 45 — Live-work, large
- 36 — Accessory dwellings, small

Using Equation 1, the team calculates the Simpson Diversity Index:

1. $(238 \div 2,358)^2$	=	.01
2. Add to $(239 \div 2,358)^2$	=	0.02
3. Add to $(378 \div 2,358)^2$	=	0.046
4. Add to $(513 \div 2,358)^2$	=	0.092
5. Add to $(909 \div 2,358)^2$	=	0.239
6. Add to $(45 \div 2,358)^2$	=	0.2394
7. Add to $(36 \div 2,358)^2$	=	0.2396
$1 - 0.2396$	=	0.76

The index score exceeds 0.70, so the project earns 3 points.

OPTION 2. Affordable Housing

A project with 350 rental units will include a yet-to-be-determined number of units priced for households up to 60% of the area median income. The team wants to earn 3 points and must calculate the necessary number of units and maximum monthly rent for each unit size.

According to HUD data, the local AMI for a four-person household is $99,000. The team's target renter has an income of 60% AMI: $99,999 x 0.6 = $59,400. The team next adjusts that income for studio and two-bedroom rental units, using Table 4 and Equation 3:

- For studios, $59,400 x .7 = $41,580.
- For two-bedroom units, $59,400 x .9 = $53,460.

The team then determines the monthly gross rent for each type of dwelling unit, first multiplying the adjusted incomes by 30% to find the annual rental price and then dividing by 12 (Equation 4):

- For studios, ($41,580 x .30) / 12 = $1,039.50.
- For two-bedroom units, ($53,460 x .30) / 12 = $1,336.50.

To earn 3 points, the project must price a minimum 15% of the 350 rental units for the target income level (Table 3): 350 x .15 = 53.

The project could also earn 3 points by pricing 10% of the rentals at 60% AMI (2 points) and 5% of its for-sale units at 100% AMI (1 point); see Table 3.

9. Exemplary Performance

Options 1 and 3 are not eligible for exemplary performance under Innovation and Design Process.

Projects that use Option 2, Affordable Housing, may earn an Innovation and Design Process credit for exemplary performance by demonstrating either of the following significant improvements over the baseline thresholds:

- 30% or more of rental units are priced up to 60% of the AMI.
- 50% or more of rental units are priced up to 80% of the AMI.

10. Regional Variations

Regulations on dwelling unit types vary by jurisdiction, and some types, such as accessory dwelling units, may be prohibited outright. Area median income is determined using consistent methodology by the U.S. Department of Housing and Urban Development; the results vary widely by region. State and local regulations and programs for affordable housing vary.

11. Resources

Websites

Enterprise Community Partners
www.enterprisecommunity.org/
Enterprise Community Partners, formerly the Enterprise Foundation, provides assistance in determining maximum rents and sales prices.

Enterprise Community Partners, Green Communities
www.greencommunitiesonline.org
Green Communities is a national green building program, administered by Enterprise Community Partners, focused entirely on affordable housing. It offers "green grants," loans, tax credit equity, training, and technical assistance.

Fannie Mae
www.efanniemae.com/sf/refmaterials/hudmedinc/
This website contains searchable and easy-to-use database for median family incomes (MFI) based on area median incomes (AMI) in metropolitan and nonmetropolitan areas.

NeighborWorks America
www.nw.org
The NeighborWorks website has various resources, including reports and training programs, on affordable housing and low-income housing tax credits; the guidance is geared toward nonprofit developers and for-profit developers of affordable housing.

U.S. Department of Housing and Urban Development, affordable housing
www.hud.gov
HUD provides information to help increase access to affordable housing, promote homeownership, and support community development.

U.S. Department of Housing and Urban Development, HUD user
www.huduser.org/datasets/il.html
This website contains datasets with median family incomes (MFI) based on area median incomes (AMI) in metropolitan and nonmetropolitan areas as well as the detailed method of calculating the AMI.

U.S. Department of Housing and Urban Development, low-income housing tax credit
www.hud.gov/offices/cpd/affordablehousing/training/web/lihtc/basics/
This HUD website offers information on how to apply for the Low-Income Housing Tax Credit Program. In addition to background information and eligibility requirements, the site explains how developers can syndicate tax credits to obtain up-front equity capital.

Print Media

"Best Practices in the Production of Affordable Housing," ULI Community Catalyst Report (Urban Land Institute, 2005), available at www.uli.org/ResearchAndPublications/Reports.

Best Practices in Workforce Housing Development, by J. Ronald Terwilliger Center for Workforce Housing (Urban Land Institute, 2009).

Developing Affordable Housing: A Practical Guide for Nonprofit Organizations, by Bennett L. Hecht (Wiley Nonprofit Law, Finance and Management Series, 2006).

Developing Housing for the Workforce: A Tool Kit, by Richard Haughey (Urban Land Institute, 2007).

12. Definitions

area median income the median income of a county as determined by the U.S. Department of Housing and Urban Development.

dwelling unit living quarters intended for long-term occupancy that provide facilities for cooking, sleeping, and sanitation. This does not include hotel rooms.

existing present on the date of submission of LEED-ND certification documents; similarly, an element or condition that exists is present on the date that LEED-ND certification documents are submitted.

project the land, water, and construction that constitutes the project application. A project applicant does not have to own or control all land or water within a project boundary, but all the area within the project boundary must comply with prerequisites and attempted credits.

REDUCED PARKING FOOTPRINT

	ND
Credit	NPD Credit 5
Points	1 point

Intent

To design parking to increase the pedestrian orientation of *projects* and minimize the adverse environmental effects of parking facilities. To reduce public health risks by encouraging daily physical activity associated with walking and bicycling.

Requirements

For new nonresidential buildings and *multiunit residential* buildings, either do not build new off-street parking lots, or locate all new off-street surface parking lots at the side or rear of buildings, leaving building frontages facing streets free of surface parking lots.

AND

Use no more than 20% of the total *development footprint* area for all new off-street surface parking facilities, with no individual surface parking lot larger than 2 acres. For the purposes of this credit, surface parking facilities include ground-level garages unless they are under *habitable building* space. Underground or multistory parking facilities can be used to provide additional capacity, and on-street parking spaces are exempt from this limitation.

AND

Provide bicycle parking and storage capacity to new buildings as follows:

a. **Multiunit residential.** Provide at least one secure, enclosed bicycle storage space per occupant for 30% of the *planned occupancy* but no fewer than one per unit. Provide secure visitor bicycle racks on-site, with at least one bicycle space per ten *dwelling units* but no fewer than four spaces per project site.

b. **Retail.** Provide at least one secure, enclosed bicycle storage space per new retail worker for 10% of retail worker planned occupancy. Provide visitor or customer bicycle racks on-site, with at least one bicycle space per 5,000 square feet of retail space, but no fewer than one bicycle space per business or four bicycle spaces per project site, whichever is greater. Provide at least one on-site shower with changing facility for any development with 100 or more new workers and at least one additional on-site shower with changing facility for every 150 new workers thereafter.

c. **Nonresidential other than retail.** Provide at least one secure, enclosed bicycle storage space per new occupant for 10% of planned occupancy. Provide visitor bicycle racks on-site with at least one bicycle space per 10,000 square feet of new commercial nonretail space but not fewer than four bicycle spaces per building. Provide at least one on-site shower with changing facility for any development with 100 or more new workers and at least one additional on-site shower with changing facility for every 150 new workers thereafter.

Secure, enclosed bicycle storage areas must be locked and easily accessible to residents and/or workers. Provide informational signage on using the storage facilities.

Visitors' and customers' bicycle racks must be clearly visible from a main entry, located within 100 feet of the door, served with night lighting, and protected from damage from nearby vehicles. If the building has multiple main entries, bicycle racks must be proportionally dispersed within 100 feet of each.

Shower and changing facility requirements may be met by providing the equivalent of free access to on-site health club shower facilities, if the health club can be accessed without going outside. Provide informational signage on using the shower facilities.

AND

Provide carpool and/or shared-use vehicle parking spaces equivalent to 10% of the total automobile parking for each nonresidential and mixed-use building on the site. Signage indicating such parking spots must be provided, and the parking spots must be within 200 feet of entrances to the buildings served.

1. Benefits and Issues to Consider

Limiting the construction of parking infrastructure conserves valuable land and discourages dependence on automobiles, which in turn limits the harmful effects of transportation-related carbon emissions and air pollution. Surface parking lots also fragment the streetscape and make it less inviting for pedestrians. If surface parking is needed, locating it behind or at the side of buildings maintains an engaging and safer pedestrian environment and promotes the public health benefits of walking. Designating preferred parking spaces for carpool and shared-use vehicles encourages employees to think about alternative ways to commute.

For a summary of the benefits of bicycle use, please see SLL Credit 4, Bicycle Network and Storage.

2. Related Credits

Reducing the project's parking footprint may assist in earning the following related credits by improving walkability, increasing density, supporting alternative transportation, and reducing runoff and the heat island effect:

- SLL Credit 4, Bicycle Network and Storage
- NPD Credit 1, Walkable Streets
- NPD Credit 2, Compact Development
- NPD Credit 8, Transportation Demand Management
- GIB Credit 8, Stormwater Management
- GIB Credit 9, Heat Island Reduction

3. Summary of Referenced Standards

There are no referenced standards for this credit.

4. Implementation

Surface parking lots create heat islands, produce stormwater runoff, and often fragment urban neighborhoods. Excessive amounts of off-street parking consume building and land space that could otherwise be used for habitation, open space, and other purposes. Providing bicycle parking and car-sharing spaces helps reduce the use of single-occupant automobiles by making alternatives more convenient. This credit pertains to off-street surface parking only, not on-street parking.

Location of Surface Parking

Parking lots adjacent to streets and sidewalks create an inhospitable environment for pedestrians and discourage walking. For all new nonresidential and multiunit residential buildings, surface parking lots should be at the rear or side of the buildings. Any off-street parking for these buildings that is located between the building frontage and the street will disqualify the project for the credit. This credit applies to all building frontage facing streets; if a building fronts more than one street, then all frontages must be free of surface parking lots. This component of the requirement applies only to off-street surface parking, not on-street parking. Providing no off-street parking lots or providing only covered or structured off-street parking will meet the requirement. If the economics of the project allow, put as much nonresidential, mixed-use, and multiunit parking in structured or underground parking. The local jurisdiction may already have exemptions from parking space requirements if a project uses transportation demand management strategies or is near transit stops. Alternatively, during any site plan review, request a parking ratio below the minimum standards.

	NPD
ND	Credit 5

Reduced Surface Parking Footprint

The credit is intended to ensure that no off-street surface parking lots exceed 2 acres or constitute more than 20% of the development footprint. The 20% requirement applies to the project as a whole, not to individual building sites. This means that a parking lot for an individual building can exceed 20% of that building's development footprint as long as the project total is below 20%. A habitable building is defined as a structure intended for living, working, or other types of occupancy; it does not mean garage or utility space. For the purposes of this credit, ground-level garages are considered surface parking unless habitable building space is located above the parking lot. Multistory structured parking is exempt from the credit requirements.

Bicycle Storage

The bicycle storage specifications for this credit are equivalent to those for SLL Credit 4, Bicycle Network and Storage. A detailed description of bicycle storage minimum ratios and design considerations, showers and changing facilities, and planned occupancy can be found in the Implementation section under SLL Credit 4.

Shared-Vehicle Parking

The credit encourages project teams to designate parking spaces for carpool and shared-use vehicles. In many places, companies or nonprofit organizations run car-sharing programs; ask the local transportation department whether any operators exist or are planned for the jurisdiction. Shared-use refers to both vehicles used by multiple people within an organization and vehicles shared by residents of multiple dwelling units. Carpool and shared-use vehicle parking must be located within 200 feet of building entrances so that the location is convenient and creates an incentive to use such vehicles. This portion of the requirement applies only to nonresidential buildings and mixed-use buildings; multiunit residential buildings are exempt from this portion of the requirement. The designated spaces must amount to 10% of each nonresidential and mixed-use building's parking; that is, the 10% is not an average for the project's total spaces.

5. Timeline and Team

During the design phase, the project's urban designers, architects, and transportation consultants should identify the demand for off-street parking facilities and determine their location. The project team should contract with design or transportation professionals that have experience designing bicycle storage facilities and car-sharing parking. Often, these facilities are not considered until the very end of a design process, but planning them early can improve their overall quality.

6. Calculations

Reduced Surface Parking Footprint

Step 1. Calculate the project's total development footprint.

Step 2. Sum the area of all off-street surface parking lots on the project site. Include ground-level garages unless they are under habitable building space. Do not include on-street parking.

Step 3. Calculate the percentage of the project's development footprint occupied by off-street surface parking, according to Equation 1.

Equation 1

$$\% \text{ off-street surface parking} = \frac{\text{Off-street surface parking area}}{\text{Total development footprint}}$$

Bicycle Storage

See the Calculations section of SLL Credit 4, Bicycle Network and Storage.

7. Documentation Guidance

As a first step in preparing to complete the LEED-ND documentation requirements, work through the following measures. Refer to GBCI's website for the complete descriptions of all required documentation.

- Identify and map the locations and sizes of all surface parking lots.
- Determine the total amount of parking that will be provided per building.

8. Examples

There are no examples for this credit.

9. Exemplary Performance

This credit is not eligible for exemplary performance under Innovation and Design Process.

10. Regional Variations

There are no regional variations associated with this credit.

11. Resources

In addition to the resources listed below, refer to the Resources section under SLL Credit 4.

Websites

Best Workplaces for Commuters
www.bestworkplaces.org/index.htm
This program, established by the U.S. Environmental Protection Agency and U.S. Department of Transportation, publicly recognizes employers for exemplary commuter benefits programs, including carpooling schemes. It provides tools, guidance and promotions to help employers incorporate commuter benefits into their employee benefits plan, reap financial benefits, and gain national recognition.

Metropolitan Transportation Commission, parking policies
www.mtc.ca.gov/planning/smart_growth/parking_study.htm
This commission, the transportation planning, coordinating, and financing agency for the nine-county San Francisco Bay Area, has many resources on innovative parking policies and strategies, including a report on smart growth parking best practices from across the country and videos from research seminars.

Print Media

The Aesthetics of Parking, by Thomas P. Smith (American Planning Association, 1988).

The High Cost of Free Parking, by Donald Shoup (American Planning Association, 2005).

Parking Cash Out, by Donald Shoup (American Planning Association, 2005).

12. Definitions

development footprint the total land area of a project site covered by buildings, streets, parking areas, and other typically impermeable surfaces constructed as part of the project.

dwelling unit living quarters intended for long-term occupancy that provide facilities for cooking, sleeping, and sanitation. This does not include hotel rooms.

	NPD
ND	Credit 5

habitable building a structure intended for living, working, or other types of occupancy. Habitable structures do not include stand-alone garages and utility structures such as pump stations.

multiunit residential consisting of four or more residential units sharing a common entry.

planned occupancy the highest estimate of building occupants based on planned use(s) and industry standards for square foot requirements per employee. The minimum planned occupancy for multiunit residential buildings is 1 person for a studio unit, 1.5 persons for a one-bedroom unit, and 1.25 persons per bedroom for a two-bedroom or larger unit.

project the land, water, and construction that constitutes the project application. A project applicant does not have to own or control all land or water within a project boundary, but all the area within the project boundary must comply with prerequisites and attempted credits.

	ND
Credit	NPD Credit 6
Points	1-2 points

Intent

To promote *projects* that have high levels of internal connectivity and are well connected to the community at large. To encourage development within *existing* communities, thereby conserving land and promoting multimodal transportation. To improve public health by encouraging daily physical activity and reducing the negative effects of motor vehicle emissions.

Requirements

Design and/or locate the project such that a through-street and/or nonmotorized right-of-way intersects or terminates at the *project boundary* at least every 400 feet or at existing abutting street intervals and intersections, whichever is the shorter distance. Include a pedestrian or bicycle through-connection in at least 90% of any new *culs-de-sac*. This does not apply to portions of the boundary where connections cannot be made because of physical obstacles, such as prior platting of property, construction of existing buildings or other barriers, slopes over 15%, *wetlands* and *water bodies*, railroad and utility rights-of-way, existing limited-access motor vehicle rights-of-way, and parks and dedicated open space.

Figure 1. Project site with right-of-way intersects on project boundary at least every 400 feet

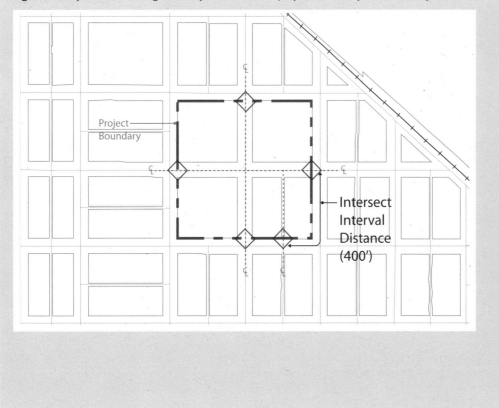

AND

Locate and/or design the project such that its internal *connectivity* and/or the connectivity within a 1/4-mile distance of the project boundary falls within one of the ranges listed in Table 1.

Table 1. Points for connectivity

Street intersections per square mile	Points
> 300 and ≤ 400	1
> 400	2

All streets and sidewalks that are counted toward the connectivity requirement must be available for general public use and not gated. Gated areas are not considered available for public use, with the exception of education and health care campuses, and military bases where gates are used for security purposes.

1. Benefits and Issues to Consider

For a summary of the benefits of a connected, multimodal street network, please see NPD Prerequisite 3, Connected and Open Community.

2. Related Credits

Meeting or exceeding this credit may assist in earning the following related credits:

- SLL Credit 1, Preferred Locations
- NPD Prerequisite 3, Connected and Open Community

3. Summary of Referenced Standards

There are no referenced standards for this credit.

4. Implementation

The goal of this credit is to promote projects that are designed or located in areas that facilitate walking, biking, and shortest-path vehicular travels. NPD Credit 6 is similar to NPD Prerequisite 3, Connected and Open Community, in that it encourages a fine-grained street network and multiple connections across the project boundary. There are two requirements for this credit: that projects have regular and frequent connections to surrounding areas, and that projects have a high street network density within and/or outside the site.

External Connections

Connections on the perimeter of the project help create a well-connected community by allowing pedestrians and bicyclists to reach their destinations via the shortest possible path; the multiple connections also disperse traffic, thereby reducing traffic delays for motorists.

Projects must have a through-street or nonmotorized right-of-way at least every 400 feet. Ideally, the internal streets should connect with existing, abutting streets outside the project, to create a more efficient transportation system. Culs-de-sac are allowed but should be avoided to achieve a high level of vehicle connectivity. Where culs-de-sac are used, at least 90% of them must have a pedestrian or bicycle through-connection.

Exceptions are allowed if a connection cannot be made because of a physical obstacle, such as a water body, a limited-access roadway, a park, or a hillside over 15% in grade. If a physical obstacle like this prevents an external connection, the documentation should identify its location and explain why no connection is possible. If a project shares a boundary with a previously developed parcel that does not have a through-street every 400 feet, an exemption is allowed: The project does not need to provide a through-connection because no connection can be made. However, if the project borders land without existing buildings and without physical obstacles, there is no exemption: A street or nonmotorized right-of-way must pass through or terminate at the project boundary at least every 400 feet. Any street that terminates at the project boundary without intersecting an existing external street segment is a cul-de-sac and subject to the 10% limitation on culs-de-sac without pedestrian or bicycle through-connections.

Projects without internal streets or rights-of-way are required to meet only the following connectivity requirement.

Street Network Connectivity

Projects must calculate their connectivity, measured in intersections per square mile. The method is described in the Getting Started chapter.

Street connectivity may be measured inside the project boundary, within 1/4-mile outside the project boundary, or both. Parks, water bodies, wetlands, and areas excluded from development by

LEED-ND prerequisites should be excluded from the connectivity calculations (see Equation 1) so that they do not negatively affect the connectivity calculation.

Large projects may meet this street connectivity standard if the site is designed with relatively small block lengths, creating a high intersection density within the project. Street design features such as culs-de-sac generally reduce the street network density but may be appropriate to accommodate certain topographic features, such as steep slopes, protected habitat, or water bodies. Small projects can meet the standard if the site is designed with a high intersection density or located in an area with a high intersection density. Areas with the highest intersection density are often found in downtowns and inner-ring suburbs of metropolitan areas.

As with NPD Prerequisite 3, Connected and Open Community, streets, sidewalks, and other routes of travel that are within the 1/4-mile area but not accessible for public use may not be counted toward the minimum level of street connectivity. Thus, developments like gated subdivisions are not eligible to contribute toward street connectivity; exemptions apply only to military bases, health care campuses, educational facilities, and other institutions that need gates for security purposes.

Information about the external street network should be available from local planning, public works, or transportation departments and usually shows street centerlines in GIS or CAD format. If digital information is not available, look at aerial photographs and manually count the intersections.

5. Timeline and Team
The project's urban designers and architects should address this prerequisite early in the site selection and site design process.

6. Calculations
Step 1. Determine the area of the project (or the area within a 1/4-mile radius of the project boundary, or both), exclusive of water bodies, parks larger than 1/2-acre, public facility campuses, airports, rail yards, slopes over 15%, and areas nonbuildable under codified law or the rating system. This is the net area.

Step 2. Calculate the percentage of any new culs-de-sac containing pedestrian or bicycle through-connections. The result must be at least 90%.

Step 3. Count the qualifying intersections within the project and/or within 1/4-mile of the project boundary. Omit intersections within gated enclaves, intersections where one must enter and exit an area through the same intersection, and intersections that lead only to culs-de-sac.

Step 4. Calculate the connectivity according to Equation 1. The resulting number of intersections per square mile must be at least 300 (1 point) or 400 (2 points).

Equation 1

$$\text{Intersections per sq. mi.} = \frac{\text{Total intersections}}{\text{Net area}}$$

7. Documentation Guidance

As a first step in preparing to complete the LEED-ND documentation requirements, work through the following measures. Refer to GBCI's website for the complete descriptions of all required documentation.

- Map the existing street network and nonmotorized rights-of-way surrounding the project site.

- Map the streets and nonmotorized rights-of-way that intersect or terminate at the project boundary.

- Map the intersections internal to the project and the intersections within 1/4-mile of the project boundary and identify locations where streets are not available for public use.

8. Examples

There are no examples for this credit.

9. Exemplary Performance

This credit is not eligible for exemplary performance under Innovation and Design Process.

10. Regional Variations

There are no regional variations associated with this prerequisite.

11. Resources

Websites
Victoria Transportation Policy Institute
www.vtpi.org
This independent research organization provides consulting and publicly available research about solutions to emerging transportation issues.

Print Media
Context Sensitive Solutions in Designing Major Urban Thoroughfares for Walkable Communities, by Institute of Transportation Engineers (ITE, 2006).

Streets & Patterns, by Stephen Marshall (Spon Press, 2005).

Urban Design: Street and Square, by J.C. Moughtin (Architectural Press, 2003).

12. Definitions

connectivity the number of publicly accessible street intersections per square mile, including intersections of streets with dedicated alleys and transit rights-of-way, and intersections of streets with nonmotorized rights-of-way (up to 20% of total intersections). If one must both enter and exit an area through the same intersection, such an intersection and any intersections beyond that point are not counted; intersections leading only to culs-de-sac are also not counted. The calculation of square mileage excludes water bodies, parks larger than 1/2-acre, public facility campuses, airports, rail yards, slopes over 15%, and areas nonbuildable under codified law or the rating system. Street rights-of-way may not be excluded.

cul-de-sac a street segment that terminates without intersecting another street segment.

existing present on the date of submission of LEED-ND certification documents; similarly, an element or condition that exists is present on the date that LEED-ND certification documents are submitted.

project the land, water, and construction that constitutes the project application. A project applicant does not have to own or control all land or water within a project boundary, but all the area within the project boundary must comply with prerequisites and attempted credits.

project boundary the platted property line of the project defining land and water within it. Projects located on publicly owned campuses that do not have internal property lines must delineate a sphere-of-influence line to be used instead. *Project site* is equivalent to the land and water inside the project boundary. The project must not contain noncontiguous parcels, but parcels can be separated by public rights-of-way. Projects may also have enclaves of nonproject properties that are not subject to the rating system, but such enclaves cannot exceed 2% of the total project area and cannot be described as certified.

water body the surface water of a stream (first-order and higher, including intermittent streams), arroyo, river, canal, lake, estuary, bay, or ocean, excluding irrigation ditches.

wetland an area that is inundated or saturated by surface or ground water at a frequency and duration sufficient to support, and that under normal circumstances do support, a prevalence of vegetation typically adapted for life in saturated soil conditions. Wetlands generally include swamps, marshes, bogs, and similar areas, but exclude irrigation ditches unless delineated as part of an adjacent wetland.

TRANSIT FACILITIES

	ND
Credit	NPD Credit 7
Points	1 point

Intent

To encourage transit use and reduce driving by providing safe, convenient, and comfortable transit waiting areas and safe and secure bicycle storage facilities for transit users.

Requirements

Work with the transit agency or agencies serving the *project* to identify transit stop locations within and/or bordering the *project boundary* where transit agency-approved shelters and any other agency-required improvements, including bicycle racks, will be installed no later than construction of 50% of total project square footage. At those locations, install approved shelters and any required improvements, or provide funding to the transit agency for their installation. Shelters must be covered, be at least partially enclosed to buffer wind and rain, and have seating and illumination. Any required bicycle racks must have a two-point support system for locking the frame and wheels and be securely affixed to the ground or a building.

AND

Work with the transit agency or agencies serving the project to identify locations within and bordering the project boundary where the agency determines that transit stops will be warranted within two years of project completion, either because of increased ridership on *existing* service resulting from the project or because of planned future transit. At those locations, reserve space for transit shelters and any required improvements, including bicycle racks. In lieu of or in addition to new stops, this requirement can be satisfied with a commitment from the transit agency to provide increased service to the transit stops that will have been installed at the time of 50% *build-out*.

AND

Work with the transit agency or agencies serving the project to provide kiosks, bulletin boards, and/or signs that display transit schedules and route information at each public transit stop within and bordering the project.

1. Benefits and Issues to Consider

Environmental Issues

Public transportation has great potential to reduce carbon emissions, decrease the need for road infrastructure, and encourage walking and bicycling. Proper support of public transportation must involve the provision of facilities to make services comfortable and convenient.

Economic and Social Issues

Modern, attractive transit facilities may help combat negative assumptions that public transportation is uncomfortable or inconvenient. Such facilities also bring dignity to the transit riding experience for all riders but especially those who cannot afford cars and rely on transit. Working with the local transit agency to identify the locations of future facilities will limit the developer's redesign and additional construction costs. Knowing where transit demand is likely to increase may also help the project team make design choices, such as where to locate higher densities.

2. Related Credits

Provision of safe, convenient, and comfortable transit facilities may assist in earning the following related credits:

- SLL Credit 3, Locations with Reduced Automobile Dependence

- NPD Credit 5, Reduced Parking Footprint

- NPD Credit 8, Transportation Demand Management

3. Summary of Referenced Standards

There are no referenced standards for this credit.

4. Implementation

Collaborate with the transit agency or agencies serving the project so that adequate transit stop facilities will be provided within the specified timeframe. The facilities must meet the credit requirements as well as any additional criteria stipulated by the transit agency. In some cases, transit agencies may provide some or all of the required facilities.

Determine whether the agency has standards or guidelines for the type or location of facilities and for any specific brands for benches, shelters, bicycle racks, or information signs. Posted transit information should include a map and schedule of the routes that serve the project and information regarding fares and how tickets, tokens, or passes can be purchased. Work with the transit agency to provide improvements if facilities provided by the agency do not meet the credit requirements for shelter enclosure, seating, illumination, bicycle racks, and signage. Work with the transit agency to determine whether additional transit stops or service will be warranted within two years of project completion and either reserve space for the required facilities or plan for increased service at existing transit stops.

5. Timeline and Team

During the site selection process, the developer should determine whether any transit service is planned for the area around the project site. During preliminary site planning, the developer should work with the transit agency or agencies serving the project in identifying planned transit stop locations within or bordering the project boundary for 50% build-out of total project square footage and for two years after project completion. The developer should collaborate with transit agencies to ensure that the facilities will be installed or spaces reserved within the specified timeframes.

6. Calculations

There are no calculations for this credit.

7. Documentation Guidance

As a first step in preparing to complete the LEED-ND documentation requirements, work through the following measures. Refer to GBCI's website for the complete descriptions of all required documentation.

- Maintain a map of transit stops and facilities within and bordering the project.

- Record transit service start and/or expansion dates for each transit stop.

- Retain any correspondence from the transit agency confirming its collaboration with the project team on meeting the credit requirements.

8. Examples

The following examples illustrate several scenarios that may satisfy credit requirements.

Example 1

After consulting with the transit agency, the developer installs approved shelters at all transit stop locations that will serve the project. These improvements are completed before 50% construction of the project. Bicycle racks are not required by the transit agency but are installed at some locations. The transit agency confirms that ten new transit stops for the project will be added within two years of project completion. The developer reserves space for the additional facilities.

Example 2

After consulting with the transit agency, the developer installs approved shelters at all transit stop locations that will serve the project. These improvements are completed before 50% construction of the project. Bicycle racks are required by the transit agency, so the developer installs two-point support system racks at all the transit stop locations. The transit agency agrees to provide increased frequency of service to the transit stop serving the project.

Example 3

After consulting with the transit agency, the developer installs approved shelters at all transit stop locations that will serve the project. These improvements are completed before 50% construction of the project. Bicycle racks are required by the transit agency, so the developer installs two-point support system racks at all transit stop locations that were identified. The transit agency determines that no new transit stops will be warranted within two years of project completion, so no additional space is reserved by the developer.

9. Exemplary Performance

This credit is not eligible for exemplary performance under Innovation and Design Process.

10. Regional Variations

There are no regional variations associated with this credit.

11. Resources

Websites

American Public Transit Association

www.apta.com

This website describes best practices, contains comprehensive rail and bus information, lists transit facility standards and guidelines, announces conferences and reports, and provides news about public transportation in the United States.

Reconnecting America

www.reconnectingamerica.org

Reconnecting America is a nonprofit organization seeking to integrate transportation systems and the communities they serve. It promotes awareness, conducts research, and supports legislation for transit-oriented compact development. The organization's publications include a transit technologies worksheet.

Victoria Transportation Policy Institute

www.vtpi.org

This independent research organization provides consulting and publicly available research about solutions to emerging transportation issues, including transit. It provides publications about transit cost-benefit analysis. A report titled "Valuing Transit Service Quality Improvements" explains the value transit users place on comfort and convenience.

Print Media

The New Transit Town: Best Practices in Transit-Oriented Development, by Hank Dittmar and Gloria Ohland (Island Press, 2004).

12. Definitions

build-out the time at which all habitable buildings on the project are complete and ready for occupancy.

existing present on the date of submission of LEED-ND certification documents; similarly, an element or condition that exists is present on the date that LEED-ND certification documents are submitted.

project the land, water, and construction that constitutes the project application. A project applicant does not have to own or control all land or water within a project boundary, but all the area within the project boundary must comply with prerequisites and attempted credits.

project boundary the platted property line of the project defining land and water within it. Projects located on publicly owned campuses that do not have internal property lines must delineate a sphere-of-influence line to be used instead. *Project site* is equivalent to the land and water inside the project boundary. The project must not contain noncontiguous parcels, but parcels can be separated by public rights-of-way. Projects may also have enclaves of nonproject properties that are not subject to the rating system, but such enclaves cannot exceed 2% of the total project area and cannot be described as certified.

	ND
Credit	NPD Credit 8
Points	1-2 points

Intent

To reduce energy consumption, pollution from motor vehicles, and adverse public health effects by encouraging multimodal travel.

Requirements

FOR ALL PROJECTS

Earn one point for every two options achieved below, for a maximum of two points. For the purposes of this credit, *existing* buildings and their occupants are exempt from the requirements.

OPTION 1. TDM Program

Create and implement a comprehensive transportation demand management (TDM) program for the *project* that reduces weekday peak-period motor vehicle trips by at least 20% compared with a baseline case, and fund the program for a minimum of three years following *build-out* of the project. The TDM program must be prepared by a qualified transportation professional. Any trip reduction effects of Options 2, 3, 4, or 5 may not be included in calculating the 20% threshold.

OR

OPTION 2. Transit Passes

Provide transit passes valid for at least one year, subsidized to be half of regular price or cheaper, to each occupant locating within the project during the first three years of project occupancy (or longer). Publicize the availability of subsidized transit passes are available to project occupants;

OR

OPTION 3. Developer-Sponsored Transit

Provide year-round, *developer*-sponsored private transit service (with vans, shuttles, buses) from at least one central point in the project to other major transit facilities, and/ or other destinations such as a retail or *employment center*, with service no less frequent than 45 daily weekday trips and 30 daily weekend trips. The service must begin by the time the project total square footage is 20% occupied and must be guaranteed for at least three years beyond project build-out. Twenty percent occupancy is defined as residents living in 20% of the *dwelling units* and/or employees working in 20% of the total nonresidential square footage.

Provide transit stop shelters and bicycle racks adequate to meet projected demand but no less than one shelter and one bicycle rack at each transit stop. Shelters must be covered, be at least partially enclosed to buffer wind and rain, and have seating and illumination.

Bicycle racks must have a two-point support system for locking the frame and wheels and must be securely affixed to the ground or a building.

OR

OPTION 4. Vehicle Sharing

Locate the project such that 50% of the dwelling units and nonresidential building entrances are within a 1/4 mile *walk distance* of at least one vehicle in a vehicle-sharing program. For each vehicle, dedicate one parking space accessible to vehicle-sharing members. Through signage and other means, publicize to project occupants the availability and benefits of the vehicle-sharing program. If the project has more than 100 dwelling units and/or employees and has a minimum transit service of 60 daily weekday trips and 40 daily weekend trips, at least one additional vehicle and parking space for every 100 dwelling units and/or employees must be available. If the project has more than 100 dwelling units and/or employees but does not have transit service at the frequencies specified above, at least one additional vehicle and parking space for every 200 dwelling units and/or employees must be available. Where new vehicle locations are created, a vehicle sharing program must begin by the time the project total square footage is 20% occupied; commit to providing vehicles to the locations for at least two years. Twenty percent occupancy is defined as residents living in 20% of the project dwelling units and/or employees working in 20% of the total nonresidential square footage of the project.

OR

OPTION 5. Unbundling of Parking

For 90% of *multiunit residential* units and/or nonresidential square footage, the associated parking spaces are sold or rented separately from the dwelling units and/or nonresidential square footage.

1. Benefits and Issues to Consider

For a summary of the benefits of reducing automobile trips, please see SLL Credit 3, Location with Reduced Automobile Dependence, and NPD Credit 5, Reduced Parking Footprint.

2. Related Credits

There may be synergies between transportation demand management programs, transit passes, developer-sponsored transit, vehicle sharing, or unbundled parking and the following credits:

- SLL Credit 3, Locations with Reduced Automobile Dependence

- SLL Credit 4, Bicycle Network and Storage

- NPD Credit 5, Reduced Parking Footprint

- NPD Credit 7, Transit Facilities

3. Summary of Referenced Standards

There are no referenced standards for this credit.

4. Implementation

The goal of this credit is to reduce the number of automobile trips generated by new development. The credit can be earned by providing transit passes or developer-sponsored transit (such as shuttles, vehicle sharing, and unbundled parking) or implementing a combination of measures in a transportation demand management (TDM) program. One point may be earned for every two options achieved. Each strategy is discussed below.

Transportation Demand Management Program

A TDM program comprises strategies that result in more efficient use of transportation infrastructure. For LEED-ND, the efficacy of a TDM program is measured by its ability to reduce motor vehicle trips during a weekday peak period, the time of day with the most traffic. Many design provisions, facilities improvements, incentives, and services can be considered TDM strategies, but for this credit option, the project team can count only those strategies that do not contribute to another option under this credit. In other words, the same strategy cannot be double-counted for multiple options within the credit.

A TDM program should have a budget, be implemented by designated individuals, and be prepared by a transportation professional with TDM experience. Ideally, it will be funded in perpetuity, but it must be funded for at least three years after project build-out. If the project team plans to sell all or part of the project before three years after build-out, set up an escrow account or other dedicated financial mechanism to pay for the program as required by the credit. The program's strategies should be complementary, applicable to local conditions, and coordinated for maximum effectiveness. Common TDM strategies include the following:

- Parking cash out. Commuters or residents who are eligible for a free parking space are also offered the cash equivalent when they use alternative transportation modes.

- Flextime. The employer allows employees to work nontraditional hours to avoid driving during peak commute times.

- Ride sharing. Commuters travel together in carpools or vanpools.

- Ride matching. An organized system matches residents or workers to facilitate ride sharing. For example, rosters with contact information for those interested in ride sharing are established and regularly updated.

- **Pedestrian and bicycle promotion.** A project can support and promote nonmotorized transportation by providing preferred bicycle parking, showers, or reimbursement for employees' cycling or pedestrian mileage.

- **Guaranteed ride home.** The employer offers an occasional subsidized ride—via taxi, company vehicle, or rental car—to carpoolers, cyclists, ride-share commuters, or transit users who miss a ride after working late, are commuting to an irregular location, or must attend to an emergency at home. Guaranteed ride home programs address a common objection to the use of alternative modes of transportation.

- **Car-free programs.** Schools, campuses, office buildings, civic facilities, or other large nonresidential facilities can establish policies that discourage or prohibit unnecessary driving.

- **Reduced parking.** Reducing the number of parking spaces within a project can discourage automobile use.

Trip reductions from TDM strategies can be calculated based on future traffic models. First, identify the baseline trip rates for the project using the Institute for Transportation Engineers' standard rates or comparable references used by the regional transportation agency or state department of transportation. Second, to determine potential reductions from TDM strategies, contact the state department of transportation, local metropolitan planning organization, or regional air quality management district. These agencies often have standard trip reductions that can be applied to different strategies. If regional or state standards do not exist, use the trip reductions developed for California's URBEMIS transportation model (www.urbemis.com). The Institute for Transportation Engineers may also provide information about trip reduction assumptions. Many transportation professionals have experience preparing estimates of trip reductions from TDM for developers and local governments. Determine whether the local jurisdiction has any ordinances or incentives to encourage TDM strategies.

Transit Passes

In addition to reducing vehicle use, subsidized transit passes can attract new tenants or property owners to the project. Some transit agencies may offer discounts for bulk purchases of transit passes. "Occupants" are full-time residents or employees, not visitors. If the project team plans to sell all or part of the project before or during the first three years of occupancy, set up an escrow account or other dedicated financial mechanism to pay for transit passes, as required by the credit.

Developer-Sponsored Transit

Developer-sponsored transit, provided as part of the project, is distinguished from existing public transit provided by a local or regional transit agency. Existing public transit should be documented under SLL Credit 3, Locations with Reduced Automobile Dependence. Examples of developer-sponsored transit include shuttles from housing to workplaces, regular or on-demand bus service from the project to a transit stop, or shuttles for project residents to destinations like a university, shopping center, or recreational facility. "Developer-sponsored" means that the transit is sponsored and paid for solely by the developer or in partnership with any entity other than the local public transit agency. Developer-sponsored transit can also be paid for by the LEED-ND applicant if the developer is not the applicant.

Vehicle Sharing

Vehicle sharing is a model of car rental in which users rent cars for a short period, often by the hour. It enables people to avoid the high fixed costs of car ownership while still having access to a car when needed. Most successful vehicle-sharing programs make payment and reservation easy, distribute vehicles widely in easily accessible locations, and provide real-time web-based information about where and when vehicles are available. The number of private sector or nonprofit vehicle-sharing providers is increasing. If the project team is considering pursuing this credit option, identify which providers are active in the project area and contact them. If no provider exists, the team can create a private vehicle-sharing program specifically for the project.

Projects with up to 100 dwellings and/or employees must provide at least one shared vehicle. Projects with more than 100 dwellings and/or employees must furnish additional shared vehicles at the rates specified in the credit requirements.

Projects with frequent transit service are required to provide a higher ratio of car-sharing spaces to dwelling units or employees than projects with infrequent transit service, as specified in the credit requirements. This encourages the clustering of vehicle-sharing facilities around transit. Either new or existing car-share locations can contribute to achieving the option. If the project creates new vehicle-sharing locations, either new or used vehicles may be used at the new locations.

Unbundling of Parking

Off-street parking, especially parking garages and underground parking, is expensive to build. Conventionally, the cost of parking spaces is internalized into the cost of residential units or nonresidential spaces and recouped when they are sold. However, selling parking spaces separately from dwelling units or nonresidential space provides a strong financial incentive for building occupants not to use a parking space. This can both make housing more affordable and decrease the amount of parking necessary for some projects, potentially reducing building costs and trip generation. Unbundled parking is most effective as a TDM strategy when it enables a project to provide less parking altogether, although a project's ability to reduce parking often depends on local zoning. Unbundling of parking is particularly useful when local parking requirements or allowances are already low.

5. Timeline and Team

Some TDM strategies rely on integrated project design; others, such as providing transit passes to incoming occupants, can be deployed at a later date. However, identifying potential TDM strategies early, in the conceptual design phase, will enable the project's urban designers and architects to incorporate any necessary design provisions into the site and building plans. These could include shuttle routes and stops, vehicle-sharing spaces, fewer parking spaces, bicycle parking, and other TDM components. A qualified transportation professional should create, implement, and estimate the effects of any TDM program instituted as part of the project.

6. Calculations

OPTION 1. TDM Program

Step 1. Count the baseline trips (i.e., without TDM) using data from the Institute for Transportation Engineers or comparable references.

Step 2. Determine the number of trips with TDM measures and calculate the percentage reduction based on implementing the TDM program, using Equation 1.

Equation 1

$$\% \text{ trip reduction} = \frac{\text{Baseline trips} - \text{trips with TDM}}{\text{Baseline trips}}$$

OPTION 4. Vehicle Sharing

High-Frequency Transit

If the project site is served by transit with at least 60 daily weekday trips and 40 daily weekend trips, calculate the number of required vehicle-sharing spaces according to Equation 2. The project team may round down the result to the nearest whole number, as long as it is no less than 1.

Equation 2

$$\text{Required vehicle-sharing spaces} = \frac{\text{Dwelling units and/or employees}}{100}$$

Low-Frequency Transit

If the project site has transit service that provides fewer than 60 daily weekday trips and 40 daily weekend trips, calculate the number of required vehicle-sharing spaces according to Equation 3. The project team may round down the result to the nearest whole number, as long as it is no less than 1.

Equation 3

$$\text{Required vehicle sharing spaces} = \frac{\text{Dwelling units and/or employees}}{200}$$

OPTION 5. Unbundling of Parking

Step 1. Count the parking spaces associated with multiunit residential units and nonresidential areas, and count those that are not sold or rented along with the unit.

Step 2. Calculate the percentage of unbundled spaces according to Equation 2. The result must be 90% or more.

Equation 4

$$\% \text{ unbundled parking} = \frac{\text{Unbundled parking spaces}}{\text{Total parking spaces}}$$

7. Documentation Guidance

As a first step in preparing to complete the LEED-ND documentation requirements, work through the following measures. Refer to GBCI's website for the complete descriptions of all required documentation.

- For TDM programs, maintain a list of any TDM strategies planned for the project.

- For transit passes, document the regular price of transit passes and the reduced price of transit passes.

- For developer-sponsored transit, document the route and schedule information for any planned service.

- For vehicle sharing, document any agreements with existing vehicle-sharing programs.

- For unbundling of parking, retain sales, rental, or leasing information indicating that the cost of parking is separate.

- Find out whether the local jurisdiction has any ordinances or programs to encourage TDM strategies.

8. Examples

There are no examples for this credit.

9. Exemplary Performance

This credit is not eligible for exemplary performance under Innovation and Design Process.

10. Regional Variations

Transit, minimum parking requirements, vehicle-sharing programs, and the applicability of TDM strategies vary by region. A project team's ability to deploy different strategies will depend on what is regionally available or feasible.

11. Resources

Websites

American Public Transit Association

www.apta.com

This website describes best practices, contains comprehensive rail and bus information, lists transit facility standards and guidelines, announces conferences and reports, and provides news about public transportation in the United States.

CarSharing.net

www.carsharing.net

CarSharing.net is a nonprofit, privately maintained informational resource intended to support the car sharing industry in the United States. It provides news about car sharing, lists of car sharing organizations, and references for industry providers of technology and consulting services.

Institute of Transportation Engineers

www.ite.org/traffic/

This webpage includes descriptions of traffic-calming strategies, a searchable library of reports (such as *Trip Generation* and *Parking Generation*), articles about traffic calming, and other resources related to traffic engineering.

Metropolitan Transportation Commission, parking policies

www.mtc.ca.gov/planning/smart_growth/parking_study.htm

This commission, the transportation planning, coordinating, and financing agency for the nine-county San Francisco Bay Area, has many resources on innovative parking policies and strategies, including a report on smart growth parking best practices from across the country and videos from research seminars.

URBEMIS Environmental Management Software, transportation demand management

www.urbemis.com

This website contains standard trip reduction coefficients for transportation demand management measures, locations, and building types, used to estimate trip reductions from TDM policies.

Victoria Transportation Policy Institute

www.vtpi.org

This independent research organization provides consulting and publicly available research about solutions to emerging transportation issues, including transportation demand management. It publishes a regularly updated encyclopedia of TDM strategies, programs, organizations and stakeholder groups, and planning and evaluation techniques. The encyclopedia also contains reference information about terminology, transportation costs, transportations statistics, and standard trip reduction effects.

Print Media

The High Cost of Free Parking, by Donald Shoup (American Planning Association, 2004)

Parking Cash Out, by Donald Shoup (American Planning Association, 2005).

Transportation Demand Management, by Erik Ferguson (American Planning Association, 1998).

12. Definitions

build-out the time at which all habitable buildings on the project are complete and ready for occupancy.

developer a public and/or private entity that controls a majority of the project's buildable land and is committed to making a majority of the investments required for the project implementation described in the LEED-ND submission.

dwelling unit living quarters intended for long-term occupancy that provide facilities for cooking, sleeping, and sanitation. This does not include hotel rooms.

existing present on the date of submission of LEED-ND certification documents; similarly, an element or condition that exists is present on the date that LEED-ND certification documents are submitted.

multiunit residential consisting of four or more residential units sharing a common entry.

project the land, water, and construction that constitutes the project application. A project applicant does not have to own or control all land or water within a project boundary, but all the area within the project boundary must comply with prerequisites and attempted credits.

walk distance the distance that a pedestrian must travel between origins and destinations without obstruction, in a safe and comfortable environment on a continuous network of sidewalks, all-weather-surface footpaths, crosswalks, woonerfs, or equivalent pedestrian facilities.

	ND
Credit	NPD Credit 9
Points	1 point

Intent

To improve physical and mental health and social capital by providing a variety of open spaces close to work and home to facilitate social networking, civic engagement, physical activity, and time spent outdoors.

Requirements

Locate and/or design the *project* such that a civic or passive-use space, such as a square, *park*, *paseo*, or *plaza*, at least 1/6 acre in area lies within a 1/4-mile *walk distance* of 90% of planned and *existing dwelling units* and nonresidential building entrances. Spaces less than 1 acre must have a proportion no narrower than 1 unit of width to 4 units of length.

AND

For projects larger than 7 acres, locate and/or design the project such that the median size of civic or passive-use spaces within and/or contiguous to the project is at least 1/2 acre.

1. Benefits and Issues to Consider

Environmental Issues

Vegetated open spaces may provide valuable habitat for plants and wildlife. Parks left in a more natural state can also serve as important buffers around wetlands, creeks, streams, and other water bodies. Plants that support insects and other pollinators can help sustain populations higher up the food chain. Open space also reduces the urban heat island effect and increases stormwater infiltration. Green, open spaces near schools can be an excellent resource for teaching about natural systems, biodiversity, and other ecological and natural science subjects.

Economic and Social Issues

As multipurpose neighborhood amenities, public spaces can knit together a community and provide a place for contemplation or socializing. Outdoor public gathering places, if strategically located throughout or near the project, offer an incentive to walk instead of drive. Parks offer additional public health benefits by encouraging passive and active recreation. Consider providing a variety of public space types to meet a variety of community needs, from pocket parks to more formal civic spaces. Especially in urban settings, parks are a place for people to connect with nature. Even where land costs are high and the incentive to build out to the property line is strong, well-designed open space can significantly increase property values. Parks and civic spaces are often attractive amenities for existing neighbors, so explore the need for parks during any community outreach efforts.

2. Related Credits

Projects designed or located within a short walking distance of civic and passive use spaces are more likely to have other diverse uses nearby. They are also more likely to have interconnected street networks, which result in shorter walking distances. For these reasons, this credit is related to the following credits:

- NPD Credit 3, Mixed-Use Neighborhood Centers
- NPD Credit 6, Street Network
- NPD Credit 10, Access to Recreation Facilities

3. Summary of Referenced Standards

There are no referenced standards for this credit.

4. Implementation

Design a pedestrian network that efficiently connects dwellings and businesses with nearby public spaces. Both new and existing public spaces count toward meeting the requirement. If the project incorporates civic and passive use space, design the public spaces to attract residents and occupants of all ages whenever possible. During the design charrette or other public participation process, ask nearby residents and workers about the type of civic or passive use spaces best suited to the community. Design the civic or public spaces to attract different groups of users during different times of the day and seasons of the year. Passive civic and public spaces can be located as stand-alone open areas, but they are often paired with recreation facilities. If a project team attempts to achieve both NPD Credit 9 and NPD Credit 10, the land area of civic and public space can count toward Credit 9, and the land area of recreational facilities counts toward Credit 10, even if both are in the same park. Each, however, must be within the specified walking distance of new and existing dwelling units.

The local planning or parks department has information on existing nearby civic and passive use spaces, such as squares or plazas. These departments may also have minimum standards for the creation of new parks within the jurisdiction.

5. Timeline and Team

In the site selection phase, the urban planner and developer should determine which candidate locations will best provide access to public spaces. Once a site has been selected, beginning in the conceptual design phase for the project, the design team and the developer should ensure that the project is designed so that people can easily and safely reach civic and passive spaces.

6. Calculations

Step 1. Identify qualifying squares, parks, paseos, and plazas planned or existing within the project and near the site.

Step 2. Use shortest path analysis to create a table of walking distances from each of the project's dwelling units and nonresidential building entrances to the closest qualifying civic or passive use space. See the Getting Started chapter for guidance on shortest path analysis.

Alternative Step 2. Use shortest path analysis to determine the walking distance from the farthest entrance to a civic or passive use space. If a site or vicinity map clearly shows that other entrances are closer to the civic or passive use space than the measured entrance, the team may count the closer entrances without measuring their walk distances.

Step 3. Using the shortest path results, count the dwelling units and business entrances within a 1/4-mile walk of a qualifying civic or passive use space.

Step 4. Calculate the percentage of dwelling units and nonresidential building entrances within a 1/4-mile walk distance by dividing the number of entrances within a 1/4-mile walk by the total number of entrances, then multiplying by 100 (Equation 1). The result must be 90% or more.

Equation 1

$$\% \text{ qualifying entrances} = \frac{\sum \text{qualifying entrances}}{\text{Total entrances}} \times 100$$

7. Documentation Guidance

As a first step in preparing to complete the LEED-ND documentation requirements, work through the following measures. Refer to GBCI's website for the complete descriptions of all required documentation.

- Obtain information on the size and dimensions of nearby civic and passive use spaces.

- Find out whether the local jurisdiction has plans for parks on or near the site.

- Identify dwelling units and nonresidential business entrances within a 1/4-mile walk distance from parks.

8. Examples

An 18-acre project is designed with a 1-acre plaza outside a light rail station, a 0.07-acre pocket park, a 3-acre park, and a 1/2-acre public square. The pocket park does not qualify as a civic or passive use space because it is less than 1/6 acre. To determine whether the remaining public spaces are within walking distance of 90% of the project building entrances, the team constructs the following table.

Table 1. Example walking distances to public spaces

Building	Dwelling units and nonresidential uses per entry	Closest qualifying public space	Walking distance to closest qualifying public space (miles)	Entrances within 1/4-mile of closest qualifying public space
Detached Residential A	1	Park	.31	—
Detached Residential B	1	Park	.29	—
Detached Residential C	1	Park	.25	1
Detached Residential D	1	Park	.23	1
Detached Residential E	1	Park	.21	1
Detached Residential F	1	Park	.19	1
Duplex A	2	Metro plaza	.32	—
Duplex B	2	Metro plaza	.25	2
Duplex C	2	Metro plaza	.23	2
Duplex D	2	Metro plaza	.20	2
Multifamily Dwelling A	64	Public square	.02	64
Multifamily Dwelling B	46	Public square	.02	46
Multifamily Dwelling C	52	Public square	.11	52
Office-Retail A	3	Metro plaza	.08	3
Office-Retail B	4	Metro plaza	.14	4
Total	183			179

Using Equation 1, the team determines that 98% of the 183 dwelling units and nonresidential uses entrances are within a 1/4-mile walk distance of a qualifying civic or passive use space: (179 / 183) x 100 = 98%.

Because the project is larger than 7 acres, the team must also calculate the median size of the civic and public use spaces. The pocket park is too small to be included in the calculations; the median size of the three remaining public spaces (1/2-acre, 1 acre, 3 acres) is 1 acre. Therefore, this project meets the credit requirements because the median size is greater than 1/2-acre.

9. Exemplary Performance

This credit is not eligible for exemplary performance under Innovation and Design Process.

10. Regional Variations

There are no regional variations associated with this credit.

11. Resources

Websites

Municipal Research Services Center of Washington, park planning and design
www.mrsc.org/Subjects/Parks/parkplanpg.aspx
This website provides an overview of park planning, design, and open space programs. The "comprehensive plan—park and recreation element" is an example of Washington state's guidelines for local governments.

National Recreation and Park Association
www.nrpa.org
NRPA provides educational resources, holds conferences, recommends accreditation programs, describes community initiatives, and lists published research about parks.

Project for Public Spaces

www.pps.org

The PPS website contains guidelines for and examples of successful civic and passive spaces, including squares, plazas, and parks.

Print Media

Designing Small Parks: A Manual for Addressing Social and Ecological Concerns, by Ann Forsyth and Laura Musacchio (Wiley, 2005).

Green Infrastructure: Linking Landscapes and Communities, by Mark Benedict and Edward T. McMahon (Island Press, 2006).

Green Infrastructure/Urban Parks Info Packet, by Urban Land Institute (ULI, 2007).

Park, Recreation, Open Space and Greenway Guidelines, by J. Mertes et al. (National Recreation and Park Association, 1995).

Parks, Recreation, and Open Space: *A Twenty-First Century Agenda,* by Alexander Garvin (American Planning Association, 2001).

Public Places—Urban Spaces, by Matthew Carmona, Tim Heath, Taner Oc, and Steve Tiesdell (Architectural Press, 2003).

Rethinking Urban Parks: Public Space and Cultural Diversity, by Setha Low, Dana Taplin, and Suzanne Scheld (University of Texas Press, 2005).

Urban Open Space: Designing for User Needs, by Mark Francis (Island Press, 2003).

12. Definitions

dwelling unit living quarters intended for long-term occupancy that provide facilities for cooking, sleeping, and sanitation. This does not include hotel rooms.

existing present on the date of submission of LEED-ND certification documents; similarly, an element or condition that exists is present on the date that LEED-ND certification documents are submitted.

park a publicly accessible area that is permanently maintained in a seminatural condition for human recreation and relaxation; it has soil, grass, water, flora, and/or recreation improvements.

paseo a publicly accessible pedestrian path, at least 4 feet wide and no more than 12 feet wide, that provides shortcuts between buildings and through the block, connecting street frontages to rear parking areas, midblock courtyards, alleys, or other streets. A paseo may be roofed for up to 50% of its length and may be privately owned or publicly dedicated.

plaza a publicly accessible gathering space that is integrated into the street network and allows vehicular, bicycle, and/or pedestrian travel. A plaza is generally paved, is spatially defined by building fronts paralleling at least two-thirds of its perimeter, and may be privately owned or publicly dedicated.

project the land, water, and construction that constitutes the project application. A project applicant does not have to own or control all land or water within a project boundary, but all the area within the project boundary must comply with prerequisites and attempted credits.

walk distance the distance that a pedestrian must travel between origins and destinations without obstruction, in a safe and comfortable environment on a continuous network of sidewalks, all-weather-surface footpaths, crosswalks, woonerfs, or equivalent pedestrian facilities.

ACCESS TO RECREATION FACILITIES

	ND
Credit	NPD Credit 10
Points	1 point

Intent

To improve physical and mental health and social capital by providing a variety of recreational facilities close to work and home to facilitate physical activity and social networking.

Requirements

Locate and/or design the *project* so that a publicly accessible outdoor recreation facility at least 1 acre in area, or a publicly accessible indoor recreational facility of at least 25,000 square feet, lies within a 1/2-mile *walk distance* of 90% of new and *existing dwelling units* and nonresidential building entrances. Outdoor recreation facilities must consist of physical improvements and may include "tot lots," swimming pools, and sports fields, such as baseball diamonds.

1. Benefits and Issues to Consider

Depending on the type of recreation facilities provided, many of the social networking and habitat benefits they offer are similar to those found in parks; see the Benefits and Issues section under NPD Credit 9, Access to Civic and Public Space.

Additionally, recreation facilities encourage physical activity as part of daily life. Consider including a variety of indoor and outdoor facilities to appeal to a broad range of ages, ability levels, and interests. Recreation facilities are excellent venues for community groups and sports leagues, whose activities enhance quality of life within a community.

2. Related Credits

Because civic and passive use spaces are closely related to the project's recreation facilities, it may be appropriate to locate them near each other. A neighborhood school, for example, may have recreation facilities that are open to the general public. Outdoor recreation facilities can reduce potable water use by irrigating with treated wastewater. For these reasons, this credit is related to the following credits:

- NPD Credit 9, Access to Civic and Public Space

- NPD Credit 15, Neighborhood Schools

- GIB Credit 4, Water-Efficient Landscaping

- GIB Credit 14, Wastewater Management

3. Summary of Referenced Standards

There are no referenced standards for this credit.

4. Implementation

This credit applies to planned and existing recreation facilities. For planned recreation facilities, consider using a design charrette or otherwise soliciting early public input to identify the recreation facilities most desired by the community. Recreation facilities are more successful when they combine multiple activities and attract many demographic groups. For example, playgrounds or sports fields could be combined to work synergistically with picnic areas, lakes, seating areas, gardens, trails, and other amenities. Design the facilities to attract different groups of users during different times of the day and seasons of the year.

People should be able to reach the recreation facility easily and safely using a variety of transportation modes. For outdoor areas, consider using native or adapted species for turf and landscaping, to reduce the need for irrigation and chemical fertilizers and pesticides. Consider water efficiency and the use of graywater and treated wastewater for irrigation.

Contact the city parks and recreation department to determine the location of existing recreation facilities in the jurisdiction. This information is often available in a parks and recreation master plan. Geographic information on parks is often also available from the local planning department. Map these resources in relation to the project site.

Passive civic and public spaces can be located as stand-alone open areas, but they are often paired with recreation facilities. If a project team attempts to achieve both NPD Credit 9 and NPD Credit 10, the land area of civic and public space can count toward Credit 9, and the land area of recreational facilities counts toward Credit 10, even if both are in the same park. Each, however, must be within the specified walking distance of new and existing dwelling units.

A trail may not be used for this credit if it occurs by itself (i.e., is apart from adjoining recreation facilities that, combined with the trail, are at least 1 acre). A school's recreation facilities are eligible but must be open to the public during and after school hours. A recreation facility that requires a fee for entrance is eligible as long as it is open to the general public. Private gyms, swimming pools, and other recreation facilities for members only are not eligible. A recreation facility that offers memberships can be used for this credit, provided it is accessible to nonmembers who are not accompanied by members.

5. Timeline and Team

In the site selection phase, the developer can consult the jurisdiction's parks and recreation master plan and identify publicly accessible recreation facilities. In the conceptual design phase, the urban planner and civil and environmental engineers should use an environmental site assessment to identify the most appropriate places for outdoor recreation facilities. The developer should consider working with an urban planner to gather public input on outdoor or indoor recreation facilities desired by the existing community. Starting in conceptual design phase, the developer should also work with the urban planner and landscape architect to design the street network and streetscape so that people can safely and easily reach the recreation facilities using multiple transportation modes.

6. Calculations

Step 1. Identify qualifying recreation facilities existing in or near the site and planned facilities within the project.

Step 2. Use shortest path analysis to create a table of walk distances from each of the project's dwelling units and nonresidential use building entrances to the closest qualifying recreation facility. For an entry point to the recreation facility, use either the principal entrance of the indoor recreation facility or the closest point at which someone can enter the outdoor recreation facility. See the Getting Started chapter for guidance on shortest path analysis.

Alternative Step 2. Use shortest path analysis to determine the walk distance from the farthest entrance to a recreation facility. If a site or vicinity map clearly shows that other entrances are closer to the recreation facility than the measured entrance, the team may count the closer entrances without measuring their walk distances.

Step 3. Using the shortest path results, count the dwelling units and nonresidential uses building entrances within a 1/2-mile walk distance of at least one qualifying recreation facility.

Step 4. Calculate the percentage of dwelling units and nonresidential uses building entrances within a 1/2-mile walk distance by dividing the number of dwellings and nonresidential uses within a 1/2-mile walk by the total number of dwellings and nonresidential uses, then multiplying by 100 (Equation 1). Building entrances that serve multiple dwellings and nonresidential uses should be considered the common starting point for the walk distance for all dwelling units and nonresidential uses sharing an entry.

Equation 1

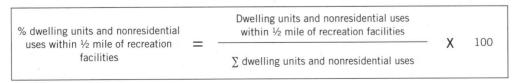

$$\text{\% dwelling units and nonresidential uses within ½ mile of recreation facilities} = \frac{\text{Dwelling units and nonresidential uses within ½ mile of recreation facilities}}{\Sigma \text{ dwelling units and nonresidential uses}} \times 100$$

7. Documentation Guidance

As a first step in preparing to complete the LEED-ND documentation requirements, work through the following measures. Refer to GBCI's website for the complete descriptions of all required documentation.

- Review the jurisdiction's master plan for planned parks and recreation facilities.
- Obtain information on the size and public accessibility of nearby recreation facilities.
- Identify any existing indoor or outdoor facilities on or near the site.

8. Examples

A 6-acre area with fields used for soccer and football lies near a 5-acre project. The team measures the walking distances from the project building entrances to the fields.

Table 1. Example walking distances to recreation facilities

	Walk distance to playing fields (feet)	Less than 2,640 feet
Office A Main Entrance	2,670	N
Office A Retail 1	2,648	N
Office B Main Entrance	2,487	Y
Office B Retail 1	2,526	Y
Office B Retail 2	2,456	Y
Residential A Main Entrance	2,632	Y
Residential A Retail 1	2,597	Y
Residential B Main Entrance	2,544	Y
Townhouse A	2,450	Y
Townhouse B	2,406	Y
Townhouse C	2,361	Y
Townhouse D	2,310	Y
Townhouse E	2,267	Y
Townhouse F	2,219	Y

In this example, two of the 14 dwellings and nonresidential uses are more than a 1/2-mile walk distance from the playing fields. The percentage of entrances that do comply is (12/14) x 100= 86%. This project does not meet the credit requirement that 90% of entrances be within a 1/2-mile walk distance.

9. Exemplary Performance

This credit is not eligible for exemplary performance under Innovation and Design Process.

10. Regional Variations

There are no regional variations associated with this credit.

11. Resources

Websites

Trust for Public Land

www.tpl.org/tier2_pa.cfm?folder_id=3208

The Trust for Public Land's Center for City Park Excellence provides information on the importance of city parks and success stories of city park establishment.

Print Media

Green Infrastructure/Urban Parks Info Packet, by Urban Land Institute (ULI, 2007).

Rethinking Urban Parks: Public Space and Cultural Diversity, by Setha Low, Dana Taplin, and Suzanne Scheld (University of Texas Press, 2005).

Park, Recreation, Open Space and Greenway Guidelines, by J. Mertes et al. (National Recreation and Park Association, 1995).

Parks, Recreation, and Open Space: A *Twenty-First Century Agenda,* by Alexander Garvin (American Planning Association, 2001).

Recreation Facility Management: Design, Development, Operation, and Utilization, by Richard F. Mull, Brent A. Beggs, and Mick Renneisen (Human Kinetics Publishers, 2009).

Urban Open Space: Designing for User Needs, by Mark Francis (Island Press, 2003).

12. Definitions

dwelling unit living quarters intended for long-term occupancy that provide facilities for cooking, sleeping, and sanitation. This does not include hotel rooms.

existing present on the date of submission of LEED-ND certification documents; similarly, an element or condition that exists is present on the date that LEED-ND certification documents are submitted.

project the land, water, and construction that constitutes the project application. A project applicant does not have to own or control all land or water within a project boundary, but all the area within the project boundary must comply with prerequisites and attempted credits.

walk distance the distance that a pedestrian must travel between origins and destinations without obstruction, in a safe and comfortable environment on a continuous network of sidewalks, all-weather-surface footpaths, crosswalks, woonerfs, or equivalent pedestrian facilities.

	ND
Credit	NPD Credit 11
Points	1 point

Intent

To enable the widest spectrum of people, regardless of age or ability, to more easily participate in community life by increasing the proportion of areas usable by people of diverse abilities.

Requirements

OPTION 1. Projects with Dwelling Units

For each new *project dwelling unit* of the following residential building types, design to the applicable requirements specified:

Single dwelling unit buildings. Design a minimum of 20% of the dwelling units (and not less than one) in accordance with ICC/ANSI A117.1, Type C, Visitable Unit, each of which has an open-space plan for primary functions (an area for cooking, eating, and social gathering), as well as a sleeping area and a full bathroom.

Multiunit building with two or three dwelling units. Design a minimum of 20% of the dwelling units (and not less than one) in accordance with ICC/ANSI A117.1, Type C, Visitable Unit, each of which has a kitchen, dining area, living area, full bathroom, and bedroom on the accessible level. If a project has both attached and detached single dwelling unit buildings, the requirements apply to each type separately. Similarly, if a project has both 2- and 3- dwelling unit buildings, the requirements apply to each type.

Multiunit buildings with four or more dwelling units. This category includes mixed-use buildings with dwelling units. Design a minimum of 20% of the dwelling units (and not less than one) to incorporate the universal design requirements stated below, or comply with Option 2. Choose at least one of the following three strategies for universal design:

a. Throughout the home, include at least five of the following universal design features to facilitate universal function, access, and user ability:

- Easy-to-grip lever door handles.

- Easy-to-grip cabinet and drawer loop handles.

- Easy-to-grip locking mechanisms on doors and windows.

- Easy-to-grip single-lever faucet handles.

- Easy-touch rocker or hands-free switches.

- Motion-detector lighting at entrance, in hallways and stairwells, and in closets, and motion-detector light switches in garages, utility spaces, and basements.

- Large, high-contrast print for controls, signals, and the house or unit numbers.

- A built-in shelf, bench, or table with knee space below, located outside the entry door with weather protection overhead, such as porch or stoop with roof, awning, or other overhead covering.

- A minimum 32-inch clear door opening width for all doorways.

- Tread at the entrance, on stairs, and other areas where slipping is common, with color contrast difference between stair treads and risers.

- Interior floor surfaces (e.g., low-pile carpets, hard-surface flooring) that provide easy passage for a wheelchair or walker, with color contrast between floor surfaces and trim. No carpet is permitted in a kitchen, bathroom, or other wet areas of the dwelling unit.

OR

b. On the main floor of the home (or on another floor, if an elevator or stair lift is provided), provide a kitchen with hard-surface flooring, plumbing with single-lever controls, a 5-foot turning radius, and at least four of the following universal design features to facilitate universal function, access, and user-ability:

- Variable-height (28- to 42-inch) or adjustable work surfaces, such as countertops, sinks, and/or cooktops.

- Clear knee space under sink and cooktops (this requirement can be met by installing removable base cabinets or fold-back or self-storing doors), cooktops and ranges with front or side-mounted controls, and wall-mounted ovens at a height to accommodate a seated adult.

- A toe kick area at the base of lower cabinets with a minimum height of 9 inches, and full-extension drawers and shelves in at least half (by volume) of the cabinets.

- Contrasting color treatment between countertops, front edges, and floor.

- Adjustable-height shelves in wall cabinets.

- Glare-free task lighting to illuminate work areas without too much reflectivity.

OR

c. On the main floor of the building (or on another floor, if an elevator or stair lift is provided), include all of the following:

In at least one accessible bedroom,

- Size the room to accommodate a twin bed with a 5-foot turning radius around the bed.

- Install a clothes closet with a 32-inch clear opening with adjustable-height closet rods and shelves.

In at least one full bathroom on the same floor as the bedroom,

- Provide adequate maneuvering space with a 30-by-48-inch clear floor space at each fixture.

- Center the toilet 18 inches from any side wall, cabinet, or tub, and allow a 3-foot clear space in front.

- Install broad blocking in walls around toilet, tub, and/or shower for future placement and relocation of grab bars

- Provide knee space under the lavatory (this requirement may be met by installing removable base cabinets or fold-back or self-storing doors).

- Install a long mirror whose bottom is no more than 36 inches above the finished floor and whose top is at least 72 inches high.

In addition, all bathrooms must have hard-surface flooring, all plumbing fixtures must have single-lever controls, and tubs or showers must have hand-held shower heads.

OR

OPTION 2. Projects with Noncompliant Public Rights-of-Way or Accessible Travel Routes

For projects with only nonresidential components, or residential components that are not within the scope of Option 1, but have public rights-of-way or other publicly accessible travel routes within the project that are not in compliance with Americans with Disabilities Act (for private sector and local and state government facilities) or the Architectural Barriers Act (for federally funded facilities), design, construct, and/or retrofit 100% of the rights-of-way and/or travel routes in accordance with the ADA-ABA Accessibility Guidelines, as applicable.

1. Benefits and Issues to Consider

Environmental Issues

Dwelling units designed to accommodate a majority of people are more likely to have a long and useful service life. As residents age or new residents move in, fewer materials are wasted retrofitting those units to meet different needs.

Economic and Social Issues

Incorporating universal design principles into dwelling units and public spaces allows the widest possible range of people, regardless of age or ability, to be part of a community and participate in civic life. Most of the modifications necessary for universal design are much less costly if included in the initial construction of the building rather than as part of a renovation.

2. Related Credits

This credit is related to the elevated ground-level entrances requirement of the following credit:

- NPD Credit 1, Walkable Streets

3. Summary of Referenced Standards

U.S. Department of Justice, Americans with Disabilities Act

www.ada.gov

ADA establishes accessibility guidelines for facilities in the private sector, such as places of public accommodation and commercial facilities, and the public sector, such as state and local government offices.

Architectural Barriers Act

www.access-board.gov/about/laws/ABA.htm

ABA establishes accessibility guidelines for facilities designed, built, altered, or leased with federal funds.

International Code Council and American National Standards Institute, ICC/ANSI A117.1

www.iccsafe.org
www.ansi.org/

ICC/ANSI A117.1 provides details, dimensions, and specifications to help building designers develop plans so that a facility offers unobstructed entry and ease of use to all users with disabilities.

4. Implementation

To create a universally accessible community, designers may need to rethink fundamental architectural concepts of adjacencies and transitions. Universal design seeks to create a built environment that can be used by as many people as possible, without adaptations or specialized design. Because elements of universal design, such as variable-height work surfaces, may be beneficial to all users, they can simplify a project and may not incur additional cost. Equal access provisions should be an integral part of the whole-building design process. Accessible features should be incorporated into the planning, programming, design, construction, operation, and maintenance of buildings. Coordinate accessible features such that they optimize the overall site and building design throughout the life-cycle of the project. For projects with dwelling units, determine which residential buildings and dwelling units will contribute to credit requirements. Choose design features from the list of required elements and consider incorporating other universal design features that will contribute to the project's appeal for all users.

For projects outside the scope of Option 1 that have noncompliant public rights-of-way or publicly accessible travel routes, ensure that any new routes are designed and constructed to be compliant with ADA and ABA and that any noncompliant existing routes are retrofitted.

5. Timeline and Team

Incorporating universal design features during the design phase is typically more cost-effective than remodeling a conventionally designed dwelling. For projects with dwelling units, developers and designers should determine during project schematic design which residential buildings and units will contribute to credit requirements. Alert residential designers about universal design and visitability requirements as early as possible to ensure optimal implementation and coordination.

For projects without dwelling units that have noncompliant public rights-of-way or publicly accessible travel routes, developers and designers should determine which are not in compliance and then design, construct, or retrofit rights-of-way and travel routes to meet the credit requirements.

6. Calculations

There are no calculations for this credit.

7. Documentation Guidance

As a first step in preparing to complete the LEED-ND documentation requirements, work through the following measures. Refer to GBCI's website for the complete descriptions of all required documentation.

- For projects with a residential component, maintain a list of all dwelling units according to building type. For each unit, record the specific visitability and universal design strategy employed and its accessible design features.

- For projects with no dwelling units that have noncompliant public rights-of-way or publicly accessible travel routes, maintain maps of all ROWs and travel routes and develop a strategy for designing, constructing, or retrofitting in accordance with the credit requirements in Option 2.

8. Examples

There are no examples for this credit.

9. Exemplary Performance

OPTION 1. Projects with Residential Dwelling Units

Projects may earn an Innovation and Design Process credit for exemplary performance by demonstrating any of the following significant improvements over the baseline thresholds:

Single dwelling unit buildings and multiunit buildings with two or three dwelling units. Design a minimum of 40% of the dwelling units (and not less than one) to comply with ICC/ANSI A117.1, Type C, Visitable Unit.

Multiunit buildings with four or more dwelling units. Design at least 40% of the dwelling units to comply with ICC/ANSI A117.1, Type C, Visitable Unit, and meet at least one universal design requirement, or design at least 20% of the dwelling units to comply with ICC/ANSI A117.1, Type C, Visitable Unit, and meet two universal design requirements.

OPTION 2. Projects with Noncompliant Public Rights-of-Way or Accessible Travel

Option 2 is not eligible for exemplary performance.

10. Regional Variations

There are no regional variations associated with this credit.

11. Resources

Websites

Adaptive Environments, accessibility

www.adaptenv.org/

Adaptive Environments seeks to advance the role of design in achieving universal accessibility by providing access to information, guidance about civil rights laws and codes, and consultation about strategies, precedents, and best practices.

National Center on Accessibility

www.ncaonline.org/

This website offers publications and videos on topics such as retrofitting for accessibility; its technical assistance staff can advise on project design.

New York State University at Buffalo, Center for Inclusive Design and Environmental Access

www.ap.buffalo.edu/idea/

This website provides resources and technical expertise in architecture, product design, facilities management, and social and behavioral sciences to achieve universal accessibility.

North Carolina State University, Center for Universal Design

www.design.ncsu.edu/cud/about_ud/udprinciples.htm

This website outlines the seven principles of universal design.

U.S. Access Board, public rights-of-way designs

www.access-board.gov/prowac/

This website offers guidelines developed by the U.S. Access Board, a federal agency, to help transportation designers and engineers comply with the Americans with Disabilities Act in the design, construction, and alteration of public rights-of-way and paths of travel.

Print Media

"Accessibility Regulations and a Universal Design Philosophy Inspire the Design Process," by B. Knecht, *Architectural Record* (2004).

12. Definitions

dwelling unit living quarters intended for long-term occupancy that provide facilities for cooking, sleeping, and sanitation. This does not include hotel rooms.

project the land, water, and construction that constitutes the project application. A project applicant does not have to own or control all land or water within a project boundary, but all the area within the project boundary must comply with prerequisites and attempted credits.

	ND
Credit	NPD Credit 12
Points	1-2 points

Intent

To encourage responsiveness to community needs by involving the people who live or work in the community in *project* design and planning and in decisions about how it should be improved or how it should change over time.

Requirements

OPTION 1. Community Outreach (1 point)

Meet with adjacent property owners, residents, business owners, and workers; local planning and community development officials; and any current residents or workers at the project site to solicit and document their input on the proposed project prior to commencing a design.

AND

Work directly with community associations and/or the local government to advertise an open community meeting, other than an official public hearing, to generate comments on project design from the beginning.

AND

Host an open community meeting, other than an official public hearing, to solicit and document public input on the proposed project at the beginning of project design.

AND

Modify the project's conceptual design as a direct result of community input, or if modifications are not made, explain why community input did not generate design modifications.

AND

Establish ongoing means for communication between the *developer* and the community throughout the design and construction phases and, in cases where the developer maintains any control during the postconstruction phase.

OR

OPTION 2. Charrette (2 points)

Comply with Option 1 and conduct a design charrette or interactive workshop of at least two days and open to the public that includes, at a minimum, participation by a representative group of nearby property owners, residents, business owners, and workers in the preparation of conceptual project plans and drawings.

OR

OPTION 3. Local Endorsement Pursuant to Evaluation Program (2 points)

Comply with Option 1 and obtain an endorsement from an ongoing local or regional nongovernmental program that systematically reviews and endorses smart growth development projects under a rating and/or jury system.

1. Benefits and Issues to Consider

Environmental Issues

When community stakeholders are engaged early and often in shaping the design of a project, they feel more ownership in the design and the resulting project. A community meeting or charrette is also an excellent opportunity for community members to meet environmental professionals involved in the project and learn about the ecology of preserved areas and the reasons for leaving them undeveloped. Conserved areas, for example, are more likely to be preserved in perpetuity if the community feels a sense of stewardship and responsibility toward them. The community outreach efforts also have the benefit of informing stakeholders about the environmental and health benefits of walkable, compact projects. Similarly, these community events are the perfect time to help the community understand the benefits of any green buildings in the project and how they can keep those buildings functioning at a high level.

Economic and Social Issues

Engaging stakeholders in the planning and design of a project, especially prior to the design phase, can give community members a chance to shape their quality of life. This is important for neighboring property owners, residents, and workers as well as for any stakeholders who might be directly affected by the project.

Incorporating community feedback and values into the project design early can allay investors' fears that opposition later in the process will result in costly lawsuits and construction delays. If the community supports the mission of the project, it may also be easier to attract developers for individual parcels within the project. If community members have identified specific kinds of establishments that are needed in the neighborhood, the businesses that meet those needs are more likely to be successful. This may also reduce the costs associated with market research to determine the most appropriate uses.

2. Related Credits

Community outreach and involvement can affect all aspects of the project, including site layout, streetscape design, planned uses, and green technologies, but no other credits are explicitly related to NPD Credit 12.

3. Summary of Referenced Standards

There are no referenced standards for this credit.

4. Implementation

The public outreach and communications plan should identify all the major stakeholders (including those who may be directly affected by the project), the timing and nature of public meetings or forums, and the way in which citizens and other stakeholders will be engaged in the planning process. Consider creating a project web page, project site office, or regular newsletter to communicate project information.

Advertise any charrette well in advance to all the identified stakeholders. Consider using community social and political networks, such as neighborhood organizations and associations, to publicize the event. Schedule the charrette or workshop on days and at times when a variety of people can attend without taking time off from work. For noncharrette interactive workshops, the minimum two days does not have to be consecutive, but a workshop conducted over two or more consecutive days may be more effective. Ensure that outreach efforts have all the typical elements of a charrette, including a multiday series of public meetings and open houses in which participants shape project design and proceed from alternative concepts to preferred plans to development of a chosen plan.

Alternatively or in conjunction with a charrette, prior to significant design work, hold a series of individual meetings or small focus groups with the major stakeholders to learn about their concerns and hear their ideas. Such individuals and organizations might include residents living close to the project, neighborhood associations, environmental organizations, historic preservation organizations, farmland or open space advocates, local chapters of professional associations (such as the American Planning Association or the American Institute of Architects), and local government departments.

As the project moves forward through successive phases of planning, modify the project as necessary and feasible to address the concerns of residents and stakeholders. If modifications are not made in response to public input, document the reasons. Continue the outreach and communication with meeting participants and the public so that they are informed of the process and major decisions. Hold additional stakeholder meetings and public workshops as needed to ensure that the project meets the community's objectives.

To apply for endorsement from a smart growth recognition program, use the website links under Resources, below. Contact the relevant organization and find out about the evaluation criteria and the timeline for applications. Notify a representative of the organization about the project's interest in the program and seek advice about how to improve the project and comply with the rating system. Once endorsement or recognition has been obtained, work with the organization for assistance with effective public engagement. The endorsement may help overcome local opposition to compact development, mixed-income diverse communities, reduced automobile parking, or other controversial aspects of the project. Note that many endorsement programs primarily target projects that are not yet fully entitled.

5. Timeline and Team

Prepare a public outreach and communications plan early in the project-planning phase. If the project will conduct a design charrette or interactive workshop, schedule it as early in the project timeline as possible, in the conceptual design phase.

The developer should work with the project team's urban planner and communications experts soon after property acquisition to engage stakeholders in the development of the project plan. The developer should work with an individual certified by the National Charrette Institute's Charrette System™ to advertise, design, and implement the charrette or multiday workshop during the conceptual design phase. The developer may work with the urban planner, building architect, civil engineer, and landscape architect to submit an application to a smart growth endorsement program during the conceptual design phase or after permits have been issued, if allowed by the region's recognition program. An endorsement during the conceptual design phase can be useful for gaining entitlements. The developer will continue to work with communications experts to actively engage stakeholders throughout the permitting, engineering, and construction phases (and after construction, if the developer retains any control over the project).

6. Calculations

There are no calculations for this credit.

7. Documentation Guidance

As a first step in preparing to complete the LEED-ND documentation requirements, work through the following measures. Refer to GBCI's website for the complete descriptions of all required documentation.

- Retain a public engagement plan that will be implemented throughout design and construction.

- Retain copies of advertisements for public meetings and charrettes.
- Retain lists of participants and the summaries of public meetings and charrettes.
- Retain early design documents and show any changes made as a result of public involvement.
- Retain explanatory documents if modifications were not made in response to public input.
- Retain website screenshots showing public engagement for the project.
- Retain documents of community support for the project.
- Retain documents indicating smart growth endorsement of the design as a result of a smart growth recognition program.
- Retain documentation of ongoing communication with stakeholders.

8. Examples

There are no examples for this credit.

9. Exemplary Performance

This credit is not eligible for exemplary performance under the Innovation and Design Process.

10. Regional Variations

There are no regional variations associated with this credit.

11. Resources

Websites

National Charrette Institute, public involvement

www.charretteinstitute.org

This website provides guidelines and recommendations for collaborative, open-process public workshops that produce feasible plans.

Smart Growth Alliances Information Network

www.uli.org/CommunityBuilding/Smart%20Growth%20Alliances.aspx

The website of this network, sponsored by the Urban Land Institute, lists all smart growth alliances in the United States, most of which have smart growth recognition programs.

Smart Growth America

www.smartgrowthamerica.org/members.html

This network of nonprofit organizations and government agencies promotes smart growth practices. The website lists the national and local organizations that are members of the Smart Growth America coalition, many of which have endorsement programs.

Print Media

Breaking the Development Logjam, by Douglas R. Porter (Urban Land Institute, 2006).

Building Citizen Involvement: Strategies for Local Government, by Mary Walsh (International City/County Management Association, 1997).

Choosing Our Community's Future: A Citizen's Guide to Getting the Most Out of New Development, by Smart Growth America (Smart Growth America, 2005).

Conducting Community Forums: Engaging Citizens, Mobilizing Communities, by Linda Hoskins and Carol Lukas (Fieldstone Alliance, 2003).

New Technologies for Planning and Public Participation, by American Institute of Certified Planners (AICP, 2004).

NIMBYism: Navigating the Politics of Local Opposition, by Michael Thomsett (Center Line Media, 2004).

12. Definitions

project the land, water, and construction that constitutes the project application. A project applicant does not have to own or control all land or water within a project boundary, but all the area within the project boundary must comply with prerequisites and attempted credits.

developer a public and/or private entity that controls a majority of the project's buildable land and is committed to making a majority of the investments required for the project implementation described in the LEED-ND submission.

LOCAL FOOD PRODUCTION

	ND
Credit	NPD Credit 13
Points	1 point

Intent

To promote community-based food production, improve nutrition through increased access to fresh produce, support preservation of small farms producing a wide variety of crops, reduce the negative environmental effects of large-scale industrialized agriculture, and support local economic development that increases the economic value and production of farmlands and community gardens.

Requirements

FOR ALL PROJECTS

Establish *covenants, conditions, and restrictions* (CC&R) or other forms of deed restrictions that do not prohibit the growing of produce in *project* areas, including greenhouses, any portion of residential front, rear, or side yards; or balconies, patios, or rooftops. Greenhouses but not gardens may be prohibited in front yards that face the *street*.

AND

OPTION 1. Neighborhood Farms and Gardens

Dedicate permanent and viable growing space and/or related facilities (such as greenhouses) within the project according to the square footage areas specified in Table 1 (exclusive of *existing* dwellings). Provide solar access, fencing, watering systems, garden bed enhancements (such as raised beds), secure storage space for tools, and pedestrian access for these spaces. Ensure that the spaces are owned and managed by an entity that includes occupants of the project in its decision making, such as a community group, homeowners' association, or public body.

Table 1. Minimum garden space, by project density

Project density (DU/acre)	Growing space (sf/DU)
> 7 and ≤14	200
> 14 and ≤ 22	100
> 22 and ≤ 28	80
> 28 and ≤ 35	70
> 35	60
DU = dwelling unit; sf = square feet.	

Established community gardens outside the *project boundary* but within a 1/2 mile *walk distance* of the project's geographic center can satisfy this option if the garden otherwise meets all of the option requirements.

OR

OPTION 2. Community-Supported Agriculture

Purchase shares in a *community-supported agriculture (CSA)* program located within 150 miles of the project site for at least 80% of *dwelling units* within the project (exclusive of existing dwelling units) for two years, beginning with each dwelling unit's occupancy until the 80% threshold is reached. Shares must be delivered to a point within 1/2 mile of the project's geographic center on a regular schedule not less than twice per month at least four months of the year.

OR

OPTION 3. Proximity To Farmers' Market

Locate the project's geographic center within a 1/2-mile walk distance of an existing or planned farmers' market that is open or will operate at least once weekly for at least five months annually. Farmers' market vendors may sell only items grown within 150 miles of the project site. A planned farmers' market must have firm commitments from farmers and vendors that the market will meet all the above requirements and be in full operation by the time of 50% occupancy of the project's total square footage.

1. Benefits and Issues to Consider

Environmental Issues

Agricultural land, and in particular the irreplaceable prime soils that much of the country's farmland contains, is being consumed for large-lot, single-use development at a rapid rate. As this farmland is taken out of productive use, more energy must be expended to transport food over long distances or even import it. This in turn results in fossil fuel emissions from transportation. Combined with the chemical inputs from many industrial agricultural practices, sprawl can significantly harm the environment.

Producing food locally, whether in individual gardens, community gardens, or nearby small-scale farms, eliminates many harmful consequences, particularly those related to transportation. When fresh produce and dairy products are transported from nearby growers to supermarkets, farmers' markets, and community supported agriculture drop-offs in metropolitan areas, transportation impacts can be reduced. Local food production demonstrates that green spaces, especially those in urban areas, can be productive as well as attractive. Depending on the plants grown, local garden plots may help recharge depleted soil or provide habitat for animals. In some cases, food production areas can help infiltrate stormwater or receive composted waste products.

Economic and Social Issues

Farmers' markets and community-supported agriculture programs support local food growers; urban residents have a chance to understand where their food comes from and get to know its producers. Educational opportunities for children abound as well. Consider including a community garden plot at or a near a school. Community gardens also offer an excellent opportunity for people to exercise, socialize, and enjoy the outdoors near home.

Food security is an important benefit of local food production, which is more insulated from global food or oil crises that could disrupt food imports. Many farmers' markets offer food at competitive prices and accept food stamps and thus can be accessible to many income levels within a community. In addition to enjoying the health benefits of eating fresh food that has not been treated with chemicals, people who grow food in a home or community garden can save money.

2. Related Credits

Projects that incorporate neighborhood farms and gardens may also wish to design those areas to be water efficient, capture stormwater, use compost from the neighborhood, and reduce or eliminate the use of chemical fertilizers and pesticides. Incorporating such practices may assist in earning the following related credits:

- GIB Credit 4, Water-Efficient Landscaping

- GIB Credit 8, Stormwater Management

- GIB Credit 14, Wastewater Management

- GIB Credit 16, Solid Waste Management Infrastructure

3. Summary of Referenced Standards

There are no referenced standards for this credit.

4. Implementation

Check with local officials to find out whether the zoning code prohibits the growing of food. If it does, work with them to create amendments to the code that apply to, at minimum, the project site. Double-check any standardized or template CC&Rs or deed restrictions to ensure that they do not prohibit areas for growing food. If the project is near existing farms, design the site so that occupants are not disturbed by agricultural vehicles, noises, and smells and the project does not otherwise interfere with farming operations.

Option 1, Neighborhood Farms and Gardens, is available only to projects with residential components. For this option, design the site so that prime agricultural soils or areas highly suitable for farming are used for neighborhood farms and gardens. Design the site such that occupants can easily and safely reach these areas using multiple modes of travel. Incorporate sustainable practices, including reduced or no chemical fertilizer and pesticide use, stormwater capture, graywater reuse, and composting. Consider developing a neighborhood farm stewardship plan for on-site farms or gardens with a description of the following, at a minimum: (1) public or community use and access, including oversight and responsibilities, usage of gardens and produce, and capacity building; (2) a plan for potential capital improvements; (3) provision of supplies; (4) a plan for vehicular access; and (5) community programs, including training and education programs.

Option 2, Community-Supported Agriculture, is also available only to projects with residential components. Explore the locations of regional CSA programs by contacting the local Farm Bureau or visiting the websites of the U.S. Department of Agriculture or nonprofit organizations such as Local Harvest. CSAs that are close to the project are preferable because of the reduced energy for transportation as well as the accessibility for residents. Also consider sustainable practices as a criterion in choosing a CSA. Work with the CSA to determine a delivery system. Delivery locations could be individual residences, local business sites, or community centers. If not all dwelling units will be provided with a CSA subscription, survey new occupants about their interest in subscriptions, and distribute subscriptions accordingly. After two years of providing subscriptions, consider ways to continue supporting local farmers, whether by continuing to subsidize subscriptions, advertising subscriptions, providing dedicated delivery locations, or establishing a farmers' market that includes the CSA farm.

For Option 3, Proximity to Farmers' Market, ensure that the site is designed so that occupants can easily and safely reach the market using multiple modes of travel. For a planned farmers' market, ensure that producers' vehicles can easily reach the site. Planned farmers' markets should ideally have a board of directors made up of producers, consumers, and other community leaders who set policy and manage the operation from year to year.

5. Timeline and Team

In the site selection phase, the developer should consider locations that are close to established farmers' markets yet far enough from existing farms that the development will not hinder their operation. Starting in the earliest conceptual design phase, the project team's urban planners and civil engineers should assist in designing the site so that neighborhood farms and gardens and farmers' markets are easily accessible to project occupants. In the engineering phase, the civil engineer, local farmers, and gardening experts should ensure that the neighborhood farms and gardens will have good soil and drainage and that runoff will not affect nearby properties. During construction, the developer can work with local, state, and federal agricultural agencies to identify CSAs and local producers, establish a board of directors for planned farmers' markets, and create a neighborhood farm stewardship plan. At the end of construction, project attorneys should ensure that CC&Rs and deed restrictions support local food production. At occupancy, developers can advertise the neighborhood farms and gardens and implement the neighborhood farm stewardship plan. Developers can also purchase CSA shares and establish CSA delivery locations at occupancy and work with a board of directors to launch operation of any new farmers' markets.

6. Calculations

The calculations for all three options require a determination of walking distances. See the Getting Started chapter for guidance on shortest path analysis.

OPTION 1. Neighborhood Farms and Gardens

If the project is using a neighborhood farm or garden outside the project boundary to meet the credit requirements, use shortest path analysis to determine whether it is within a 1/2-mile walk distance of the project's geographic center. If the neighborhood farm or garden is inside the project, use the following steps.

Step 1. Take the residential density of the site (from NPD Prerequisite 2) and, referring to Table 1, determine the minimum area (square feet) of growing space per dwelling unit.

Step 2. Calculate the required total area of growing space by multiplying the growing space per dwelling unit by the number of units, according to Equation 1.

Equation 1

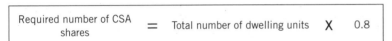

| Total required growing space (sf) | = | Total dwelling units | X | Required growing space (sf) per dwelling unit |

OPTION 2. Community-Supported Agriculture

Calculate the required number of CSA shares by multiplying the number of project dwelling units by 0.8, according to Equation 2:

Equation 2

| Required number of CSA shares | = | Total number of dwelling units | X | 0.8 |

The 0.8 factor reflects the requirement that at least 80% of households participate. Use shortest path analysis to calculate the walking distance from the project's geographic center to the delivery location. The distance must be no more than 1/2-mile.

OPTION 3. Proximity to Farmers' Market

Use shortest path analysis to calculate the walking distance from the project's geographic center to the existing or planned farmers' market. The distance must be no more than 1/2-mile.

7. Documentation Guidance

As a first step in preparing to complete the LEED-ND documentation requirements, work through the following measures. Refer to GBCI's website for the complete descriptions of all required documentation.

- Retain copies of CC&Rs and deed restrictions related to allowable uses.

- Measure the dimensions of any planned farms and gardens, and retain summaries of the planned features and operation of the growing areas.

- Retain information on the ownership and management of neighborhood farms and gardens.

- For existing nearby neighborhood farms and gardens, map their locations in relation to the project.

- For CSAs, retain information on the operations' locations, schedules, and delivery locations.

- For farmers' markets, whether existing or planned, retain information on their locations, schedules, producers, and vendors.

- For farmers' markets, map the location of each producer's farm in relation to the project and retain correspondence with producers that demonstrates their commitment to participate.

8. Examples

There are no examples for this credit.

9. Exemplary Performance

OPTION 1. Neighborhood Farms and Gardens

Projects may earn an Innovation and Design Process credit for exemplary performance by providing more growing space per dwelling unit, as follows:

Table 2. Exemplary performance for minimum garden space, by project density

Project density (DU/acre)	Required growing space (sf/DU)
> 7 and ≤14	400
> 14 and ≤ 22	150
> 22 and ≤ 28	120
> 28 and ≤ 35	105
> 35	90

OPTION 2. Community Supported Agriculture (CSA)

Projects may earn an Innovation and Design Process credit for exemplary performance by purchasing shares in a CSA for 100% of the dwelling units for a minimum of four years.

OPTION 3. Proximity to Farmers' Market

Option 3 is not eligible for exemplary performance.

10. Regional Variations

There are no regional variations associated with this credit.

11. Resources

Websites

American Community Gardens Association

www.communitygarden.org

This nonprofit membership organization provides publications about community gardening.

Local Harvest, farmers' markets

www.localharvest.org

This website can be used to find farmers' markets, family farms, and other local sources of sustainably grown food.

U.S. Department of Agriculture, farmers' markets

www.ams.usda.gov/farmersmarkets/

This website provides a list of farmers' markets in each state, facts about farmers' markets and guidelines on establishing new farmers' markets.

U.S. Department of Agriculture, community-supported agriculture

www.nal.usda.gov/afsic/pubs/csa/csa.shtml

USDA's National Agricultural Library, which runs the Alternative Farming Systems Information Center, maintains information on CSA programs.

American Farmland Trust

www.farmland.org

This website provides information and support about the importance of preserving farmland, farming practices that lead to a healthy environment, and the link between local consumption and production of food.

FamilyFarmed.org

www.familyfarmed.org

This organization supports the growth of a regional food system in the Midwest by establishing markets for many organic and sustainable family farms.

Print Media

City Bountiful: A Century of Community Gardening in America, by Laura Lawson (University of California Press, 2005).

The Farmers' Market Book: Growing Food, Cultivating Community, by Jennifer Meta Robinson and J. A. Hartenfeld (Quarry Books, 2007).

The New Farmers' Market: Farm-Fresh Ideas for Producers, Managers & Communities, by Vance Corum, Marcie Rosenzweig, and Eric Gibson (New World Publishing, 2005).

12. Definitions

community-supported agriculture (CSA) a farm operation for which a community of individuals pledges support so that the farmland becomes, either legally or informally, the community's farm. The growers and consumers provide mutual support, sharing the risks and benefits of food production. Consumers receive portions of the farm's harvest throughout the growing season.

covenants, conditions, and restrictions limitations that may be placed on a property and its use and are made a condition of holding title or lease.

dwelling unit living quarters intended for long-term occupancy that provide facilities for cooking, sleeping, and sanitation. This does not include hotel rooms.

existing present on the date of submission of LEED-ND certification documents; similarly, an element or condition that exists is present on the date that LEED-ND certification documents are submitted.

project the land, water, and construction that constitutes the project application. A project applicant does not have to own or control all land or water within a project boundary, but all the area within the project boundary must comply with prerequisites and attempted credits.

project boundary the platted property line of the project defining land and water within it. Projects located on publicly owned campuses that do not have internal property lines must delineate a sphere-of-influence line to be used instead. *Project site* is equivalent to the land and water inside the project boundary. The project must not contain noncontiguous parcels, but parcels can be separated by public rights-of-way. Projects may also have enclaves of nonproject properties that are not subject to the rating system, but such enclaves cannot exceed 2% of the total project area and cannot be described as certified.

street a dedicated right-of-way that can accommodate one or more modes of travel, excluding alleys and paseos. A street is suitable for primary entrances and provides access to the front and/ or sides of buildings and lots. A street may be privately owned as long as it is deeded in perpetuity for general public use. A street must be an addressable thoroughfare (for mail purposes) under the standards of the applicable regulating authority.

walk distance the distance that a pedestrian must travel between origins and destinations without obstruction, in a safe and comfortable environment on a continuous network of sidewalks, all-weather-surface footpaths, crosswalks, woonerfs, or equivalent pedestrian facilities.

TREE-LINED AND SHADED STREETS

	ND
Credit	NPD Credit 14
Points	1-2 points

Intent

To encourage walking, bicycling, and transit use and discourage excessive motoring speeds. To reduce urban heat island effects, improve air quality, increase evapotranspiration, and reduce cooling loads in buildings.

Requirements

OPTION 1. Tree-Lined Streets (1 point)

Design and build the *project* to provide street trees on both sides of at least 60% of new and *existing streets* within the project and on the project side of bordering streets, between the vehicle travel way and walkway, at intervals averaging no more than 40 feet (excluding driveways and utility vaults).

AND/OR

OPTION 2. Shaded Streets (1 point)

Trees or other structures provide shade over at least 40% of the length of sidewalks on streets within or contiguous to the project. Trees must provide shade within ten years of landscape installation. Use the estimated crown diameter (the width of the shade if the sun is directly above the tree) to calculate the shaded area.

AND

FOR ALL PROJECTS INVOLVING STREET TREE PLANTINGS

Obtain a registered landscape architect's determination that planting details are appropriate to growing healthy trees, taking into account tree species, root medium, and width and soil volume of planter strips or wells, and that the selected tree species are not considered *invasive* in the project context according to USDA or the state agricultural extension service.

1. Benefits and Issues to Consider

Environmental Issues

Attractive street trees and shading structures can enhance the atmosphere of the streetscape and entice people to walk. Shaded sidewalks reduce the heat island effect, and when buildings are located near the street, shade from trees may help lower the temperature of the buildings. Trees are also an important natural air and water filtration system. Consider using street trees as part of a stormwater management plan and irrigating them, if necessary, with rainwater or recycled graywater. Mature trees can block artificial light from leaving the site, preserving the night sky.

Economic and Social Issues

In urban areas, street trees may offer reprieve from otherwise uninterrupted hardscape. The shade and beauty of street trees can increase property values, especially when an entire street is shaded. Trees can be expensive to install, so consider using native species that will not be time-intensive or costly to maintain. Architectural shading devices can also provide aesthetic value to a street and improve the pedestrian experience.

2. Related Credits

Street trees provide many environmental benefits: They enhance streetscapes for pedestrians, improve building energy efficiency, reduce stormwater runoff, remove air pollutants, mitigate heat islands, and reduce light pollution. Projects can reduce the need for potable water use for street trees by reusing wastewater or graywater and by planting drought-tolerant species. For these reasons, earning this credit may assist in earning the following related credits:

- NPD Credit 1, Walkable Streets
- GIB Credit 2, Building Energy Efficiency
- GIB Credit 4, Water-Efficient Landscaping
- GIB Credit 7, Minimized Site Disturbance in Design and Construction
- GIB Credit 8, Stormwater Management
- GIB Credit 9, Heat Island Reduction

3. Summary of Referenced Standards

There are no referenced standards for this credit.

4. Implementation

For Option 1, consider the site's ecosystem and work with a landscape architect to select tree species that are most appropriate to the area and the individual planting sites. Deciduous trees allow buildings to benefit from solar heat gain during the winter months. Using native and adapted tree species can reduce the need for irrigation, chemical fertilizers, and chemical pesticides. Avoid invasive species and those that may create a nuisance because of their fruits or flowers. Work with the landscape architect to determine the feasibility of retaining existing street trees or transplanting trees from planned construction zones. For boulevards with center islands, consider planting trees in the islands.

If possible, in addition to meeting credit requirements with regard to root medium and soil volume, work with a landscape architect to ensure that street trees will infiltrate and evapotranspire stormwater. Consider using pervious pavement near street trees to enhance the stormwater management benefits and the health of the trees. If irrigation is needed for street trees, consider using graywater or treated wastewater for irrigation.

For Option 2, the measures that can create shade along sidewalks include street trees, awnings, trellises, structures, and other architectural shading devices. If the project is attempting to achieve GIB Credit 9, Heat Island Reduction, Option 1, Nonroof Measures, use designs and calculations from that credit as a starting point for meeting this credit (but note that this credit applies only to sidewalks, not all nonroof site hardscapes). For street trees, a landscape architect can determine the typical crown diameter ten years after installation. Shade along the length of sidewalks should be measured by tree crown diameter, which is the width of shade when the sun is directly above the tree. For streets bordering the project, the sidewalk on the project's side of the street should be included in calculations.

For both Options, if trees will be placed in locations likely to be reflected in building glazing, take specific measures to avoid bird collisions. Such measures include using exterior shading devices, introducing etched or frit patterns in the glass, and creating "visual markers"—differentiated planes, materials, textures, colors, opacity, or other visually contrasting features that help fragment window reflections and reduce overall transparency and reflectivity.

5. Timeline and Team

Beginning in the conceptual design phase, work with the project team's landscape architect and urban planner to designate tree-lined streets and shaded sidewalks. For preliminary plans for permitting, work with the landscape architect to select tree species and locations for trees and shade structures or devices. In the engineering phase, work with the landscape architect and civil engineer to determine tree root medium, size of tree wells, irrigation, and stormwater management. During installation of vegetation or during construction of shade-providing structures, work with the landscape architect and civil engineer to ensure that installation and construction are completed according to specifications. When selecting street trees and developing planting plans, it may be helpful to consult with a certified arborist in addition to the landscape architect.

6. Calculations

OPTION 1. Tree-Lined Streets

Step 1. Sum the linear feet of streets that will have street trees, planted at intervals averaging 40 feet or less, along both sides (or on the project side of streets bordering the project). Existing street trees that will be retained may be used in calculations. Determine the percentage of tree-lined streets by dividing the length of tree-lined segments of streets by the total length of all streets within and bordering the project, and multiplying by 100 (Equation 1). The result must be 60% or higher.

Equation 1

$$\% \text{ tree-lined streets} = \frac{\sum \text{tree-lined portions of streets}}{\text{Total length of streets}} \times 100$$

Step 2. For the tree-lined portions of streets used for Step 1, measure the distance between each street tree along each block (subtracting driveways and utility vaults), in linear feet (lf). Do not measure the distance between trees that are across the street or around the corner from one another. Determine the average distance between trees by dividing the sum of all of the measured distances by the total number of measured distances (Equation 2). The average distance must not exceed 40 feet.

Equation 2

$$\text{Average distance between trees} = \frac{\text{Tree-lined portions of streets (lf)}}{\text{Number of intervals between trees}}$$

OPTION 2. Shaded Streets

Determine the percentage of sidewalks that will be shaded by dividing the total length of all shaded sidewalks by the total length of all sidewalks, and multiplying by 100 (Equation 3). Sidewalks whose widths are only partially shaded may be counted for purposes of sidewalk length.

Equation 3

$$\text{\% shaded sidewalks} = \frac{\sum \text{shaded segments}}{\text{Total length of sidewalks}} \times 100$$

7. Documentation Guidance

As a first step in preparing to complete the LEED-ND documentation requirements, work through the following measures. Refer to GBCI's website for the complete descriptions of all required documentation.

- Prepare a list of street tree species used and obtain documentation from a landscape architect or certified arborist that they are not invasive.

- For each size and species of street tree, retain documentation about the planting specifications.

- Retain information about the trees' estimated crown diameters ten years after planting.

8. Examples

Example 1. Tree-Lined Streets

A 9-acre project has 0.31 mile of tree-lined streets and a total of 0.45 mile of streets. Blocks A, C, D, and F within the project will be tree-lined. The team determines the distances between the trees (Table 1).

Table 1. Example determination for street tree requirements

Block	Tree interval	Distance (linear feet)
A	Tree A1 to Tree A2	33
	Tree A2 to Tree A3	38
	Tree A3 to Tree A4	42
	Tree A4 to Tree A5	39
	Tree A 5 to Tree A6	45
	Tree A6 to Tree A7	33
	Tree A7 to Tree A8	49
C	Tree C1 to Tree C2	48
	Tree C2 to Tree C3	34
	Tree C3 to Tree C4	36
	Tree C4 to Tree C5	39
	Tree C5 to Tree C6	45
	Tree C6 to Tree C7	33
	Tree C7 to Tree C8	32
	Tree C8 to Tree C9	40
D	Tree D1 to Tree D2	40
	Tree D2 to Tree D3	38
	Tree D3 to Tree D4	33
	Tree D4 to Tree D5	37
	Tree D5 to Tree D6	38
	Tree D6 to Tree D7	34
	Tree D7 to Tree D8	36
	Tree D8 to Tree D9	35
	Tree D9 to Tree D10	39
	Tree D10 to Tree D11	41
F	Tree F1 to Tree F2	35
	Tree F2 to Tree F3	33
	Tree F3 to Tree F4	37
	Tree F4 to Tree F5	39
	Tree F5 to Tree F6	34
	Tree F6 to Tree F7	42
	Tree F7 to Tree F8	45
	Tree F8 to Tree F9	36
	Tree F9 to Tree F10	35
	Tree F10 to Tree F11	38
Total		1,331
Average		38

In this example, the percentage of streets that are tree-lined is (.31 miles / .45) miles x 100 = 69% (Equation 1). The average distance between street trees is 1,331 feet / 35 intervals = 38 feet (Equation 2). The project meets the requirement for 60% tree-lined streets with trees spaced no farther apart than an average of 40 feet.

Example 2. Shaded Streets

A 5-acre project has 2,850 linear feet of sidewalks. Trees and trellises along several blocks will provide shade to 1,599 linear feet of the sidewalks. The percentage of sidewalks that are shaded is 1,599 / 2,850 x 100 = 56% (Equation 3). The project meets the requirement for a minimum of 40% shading of sidewalks.

9. Exemplary Performance

OPTION 1. Tree-Lined Streets

Projects may earn an Innovation and Design Process credit for exemplary performance by providing street trees on both sides of at least 90% of new and existing streets within the project and on the project side of bordering streets; the trees must be between the vehicle travel way and the walkway at intervals averaging no greater than 40 feet (excluding driveways and utility vaults).

OPTION 2. Shaded Streets

Projects may earn an Innovation and Design Process credit by providing trees or other structures that shade at least 60% of the length of sidewalks on streets within or contiguous to the project. The required coverage of any tree shade must be provided within ten years of landscape installation, based on estimated crown diameter.

10. Regional Variations

There are no regional variations associated with this credit.

11. Resources

Websites

American Forests

www.americanforests.org/graytogreen/air/

The American Forests website has resources on the value of urban forests and a tool to help calculate the amount of air pollutants that a city's trees can remove each year.

City of Davis, California, parking lot shading

www.city.davis.ca.us/pb/pdfs/planning/forms/Parking_Lot_Shading_Guidelines.pdf
www.city.davis.ca.us/pcs/trees/master.cfm

This website provides an example ordinance to make streets more walkable by providing at least 50% shading.

U.S. Department of Agriculture, plants database

www.plants.usda.gov

This website contains a database of plants with information on whether they are native or introduced to certain states. It also lists state and federal noxious weeds.

Birds and Buildings Forum

www.birdsandbuildings.org

This website provides a compilation of bird-safe building design guidelines.

Print Media

Trees in Urban Design, 2nd edition, by Henry F. Arnold (Van Nostrand Reinhold, 1992).

Street Design for Healthy Neighborhoods, by Dan Burden, Michael Wallwork, Ken Sides, Ramon Trias, and Harrison Bright Rue (Local Government Commission, 2002).

12. Definitions

existing present on the date of submission of LEED-ND certification documents; similarly, an element or condition that exists is present on the date that LEED-ND certification documents are submitted.

invasive plant either an indigenous or nonindigenous species or strain that is characteristically adaptable, aggressive, has a high reproductive capacity, and tends to overrun the ecosystems it inhabits.

project the land, water, and construction that constitutes the project application. A project applicant does not have to own or control all land or water within a project boundary, but all the area within the project boundary must comply with prerequisites and attempted credits.

street a dedicated right-of-way that can accommodate one or more modes of travel, excluding alleys and paseos. A street is suitable for primary entrances and provides access to the front and/or sides of buildings and lots. A street may be privately owned as long as it is deeded in perpetuity for general public use. A street must be an addressable thoroughfare (for mail purposes) under the standards of the applicable regulating authority.

NEIGHBORHOOD SCHOOLS

	ND
Credit	NPD Credit 15
Points	1 point

Intent

To promote community interaction and engagement by integrating *schools* into the neighborhood. To support students' health by encouraging walking and bicycling to school.

Requirements

Include in the *project* a residential component that constitutes at least 30% of the project's total building square footage, and locate or design the project such that at least 50% of the *dwelling units* are within a 1/2-mile *walk distance* of an *existing* or new elementary or middle school building entrance or within a 1-mile walk distance of an existing or new high school building entrance. For any new school, the school district or equivalent organization must commit in a legally binding warrant that the school will be open by the time of occupancy of 50% of the project dwelling units.

Streets within and/or bordering the *project boundary* that lead from dwelling units to the school site must have a complete network of sidewalks on both sides and either bicycle lanes or traffic control and/or calming measures. If the school is planned as part of the project, it must be designed such that pedestrians and cyclists can easily reach building entrances without crossing bus zones, parking entrances, and student drop-off areas.

AND

New school campuses must not exceed the following:

- High schools, 15 acres.

- Middle schools, 10 acres.

- Elementary schools, 5 acres.

Schools combining grade levels from more than one category may use the grade level with the higher allowable acreage.

Facilities on the school site for which there is a formal joint-use agreement with another entity, such as athletic facilities, playgrounds, and multipurpose spaces in buildings, may be deducted from the total site area of the school.

1. Benefits and Issues to Consider

Environmental Issues

Integrating new schools into the neighborhood or supporting existing community schools and ensuring that routes to these schools are safe and comfortable will reduce car trips for parents and increase physical activity for children. If a new school is planned as part of the project, consider how both walking and bicycling can be made convenient and attractive to children. Creating schools that are sized appropriately for the scale of the neighborhood is an important way to conserve land, reduce the need for parking facilities, and ensure that each school is a unique part of a neighborhood.

Schools offer numerous opportunities for the youngest residents of a community to learn about sustainability. In addition to educating students about any green building features of their school, consider introducing children to as many features of the community as possible, such as recycling facilities, conserved areas, food production areas, and public transportation systems.

Economic and Social Issues

Schools are incredibly valuable community resources that naturally bring together members of the community and create a shared sense of purpose. Consider capitalizing on this by integrating joint-use facilities, such as sports fields, a swimming pool, or a community center. Site the school in a connected location in the core of the community, rather than on its edge, to ensure that it is easy to access and that community members can keep an eye on children as they walk or bicycle to school.

2. Related Credits

Projects designed or located within a short walking distance of schools are more likely to have interconnected street networks, which result in shorter walking distances. Measures used to meet this credit's requirements for sidewalks and traffic-calming measures can be used to fulfill the Walkable Streets credit. A neighborhood school may have recreation facilities that are open to the general public. For these reasons, achieving this credit's requirements may assist in earning the following related credits:

- NPD Credit 1, Walkable Streets

- NPD Credit 6, Street Network

- NPD Credit 10, Recreation Facilities

3. Summary of Referenced Standards

There are no referenced standards for this credit.

4. Implementation

To determine whether there are any existing schools in the vicinity of the site, contact the local school district. To determine whether new schools are planned in the area, contact the local school district and review the district's facilities master plan and capital improvement budget. A legally binding warrant that a school will be operating by a certain date is usually found in the approved capital improvement plan, a written commitment by the school district, or another document showing that funding is guaranteed and construction will occur. Note that the limit on new school size applies to any new school used for this credit, whether or not it is on the project site.

For any new school that will be constructed on the site, ensure that pedestrians and bicyclists will be able to easily reach the school from adjacent streets and trails. Consider installing paved sidewalks along public rights-of-way that bound the school site on all sides, for easy access. Limit the size of the school site to avoid increasing the distance between the school and the neighborhoods it serves. Large sites tend to increase trip length and make motor vehicle trips necessary for students and staff. Encourage community use of school facilities during days and hours when classes are not in session.

Consider building the school using sustainable building practices that meet LEED or other green building certification standards.

For any schools—planned or existing, on the site or nearby—ensure that people can easily and safely reach the school using a variety of transportation modes. Traffic-control and traffic-calming measures might include on-street parking, street trees, narrow streets, clearly marked crosswalks, controlled intersections, and caution signs.

Any elementary, middle, or high school, public or private, may qualify for this credit, but no other educational institutions are eligible. That is, community colleges, universities, continuing education institutions, technical training institutes, and preschools are ineligible. However, if an elementary, middle, or high school also houses educational facilities for other groups (such as preschoolers or adults), then it qualifies for this credit. Refer to the definition for *school*.

5. Timeline and Team

In the site selection phase, the developer can consult the jurisdiction's school facilities master plan and locate the project near existing and planned schools. In the conceptual design phase, the developer should work with the local school district and local community to determine whether a new school should be part of the project. Starting in the conceptual design phase, the developer should also work with the urban planner, landscape architect, and civil engineer to design the street network and streetscape so that children and staff can safely and easily reach school entrances using multiple transportation modes.

6. Calculations

Step 1. Use the percentage residential component of the project (residential square footage divided by total building square footage).

Step 2. Identify existing and planned schools within and near the project.

Step 3. Use shortest path analysis to create a table of walking distances from each project dwelling units to the closest school. See the Getting Started chapter for guidance on shortest path analysis.

Alternative Step 3. Use shortest path analysis to determine the walking distance from the farthest dwelling unit to each school. If a site or vicinity map clearly shows that other dwelling units are closer to the school than the measured dwelling unit, the team may count the closer entrances without measuring their walk distances.

Step 4. Using the shortest path results, count the dwelling units within a 1/2-mile walk of the entrance to an elementary or middle school, or within a 1-mile walk of the entrance to a high school.

Step 5. Calculate the percentage of dwelling units within the required walking distance of schools by dividing the number of qualifying dwelling units by the total number of dwelling units, then multiplying by 100 (Equation 1). The result must be at least 50%.

Equation 1

$$\% \text{ dwelling units within walking distance} = \frac{\sum \text{Dwelling units within walking distance}}{\text{Total dwelling units}} \times 100$$

7. Documentation Guidance

As a first step in preparing to complete the LEED-ND documentation requirements, work through the following measures. Refer to GBCI's website for the complete descriptions of all required documentation.

- Obtain information on the location and type of existing schools near the project.
- Obtain information on the boundaries and size of planned schools within or near the project.
- Retain shared-use agreements between schools and other organizations.

8. Examples

A mixed-use project has a total area of 153,000 square feet, 62,000 of which is residential. A middle school near the project is within the following walking distances:

Table 1. Example walking distances to elementary or middle school

Building	Dwelling units	Walk distance to school (feet)	Dwelling units within 2,640 feet
Multi-family Building A	15	2,345	15
Multi-family Building B	10	2,538	10
Townhouse A	1	2,647	0
Townhouse B	1	2,698	0
Townhouse C	1	2,750	0
Townhouse D	1	2,794	0
Duplex A	2	2,694	0
Duplex B	2	2,754	0
Total	33		25

To meet the requirements, the residential component must be at least 30% of the total square footage. In this case, the percentage that is residential exceeds 30%: (62,000 / 153,000) x 100 = 41%.

The percentage of dwelling units within a 1/2-mile walk distance of the middle school is (25 / 33) x 100 = 76% (Equation 1). Since the percentage exceeds 50%, this project meets both credit requirements.

9. Exemplary Performance

This credit is not eligible for exemplary performance under Innovation and Design Process.

10. Regional Variations

There are no regional variations associated with this credit.

11. Resources

Websites

Institute of Transportation Engineers, traffic calming
www.ite.org/traffic/
This webpage includes descriptions of traffic-calming strategies, a searchable library of reports (such as *Trip Generation* and *Parking Generation*), articles about traffic calming, and other resources related to traffic engineering.

National Center for Safe Routes to School

www.saferoutesinfo.org

This organization's website describes best practices for improving the ability of children to walk and bicycle to school.

Pedestrian and Bicycle Information Center

www.bicyclinginfo.org/engineering/calming.cfm

This webpage provides information about bicycle and pedestrian design and infrastructure, as well as traffic-calming strategies.

National Clearinghouse for Educational Facilities, Smart Growth & Schools

www.edfacilities.org/rl/smart_growth.cfm

The National Clearinghouse for Education Faciliites was created by the Department of Education in 1997 and is managed by the National Institute for Building Sciences. This clearinghouse provides information on planning, building, and maintaining safe, healthy, and high performance schools.

Schools for Successful Communities: An Element of Smart Growth

www.epa.gov/piedpage/pdf/SmartGrowth_schools_Pub.pdf

This report, jointly created by the Council of Educational Facility Planners International and the Environmental Protection Agency, includes many resources and case studies for successful school development.

Smart Growth America, Children & Schools

www.smartgrowthamerica.org/children.html

This nonprofit organization helps states, communities, and other interested stakeholders in adopting policies and legislation that supports compact development. Their website includes multiple resources on the role of schools and implementation assistance for successful community design.

Victoria Transportation Policy Institute

www.vtpi.org

This independent research organization provides consulting and publicly available research about solutions to emerging transportation issues, including walkability.

Print Media

Context Sensitive Solutions in Designing Major Urban Thoroughfares for Walkable Communities, by Institute of Transportation Engineers (ITE, 2006).

Street Design for Healthy Neighborhoods, by Dan Burden, Michael Wallwork, Ken Sides, Ramon Trias, and Harrison Bright Rue (Local Government Commission, 2002).

Streets & Patterns, by Stephen Marshall (Spon Press, 2005).

Urban Design: Street and Square, by Cliff Moughtin (Architectural Press, 2003).

Why Johnny Can't Walk to School: Historic Neighborhoods in the Age of Sprawl, by Constance Beaumont and Elizabeth Pianca (National Trust for Historic Preservation, 2002).

12. Definitions

dwelling unit living quarters intended for long-term occupancy that provide facilities for cooking, sleeping, and sanitation. This does not include hotel rooms.

existing present on the date of submission of LEED-ND certification documents; similarly, an element or condition that exists is present on the date that LEED-ND certification documents are submitted.

project the land, water, and construction that constitutes the project application. A project applicant does not have to own or control all land or water within a project boundary, but all the area within the project boundary must comply with prerequisites and attempted credits.

project boundary the platted property line of the project defining land and water within it. Projects located on publicly owned campuses that do not have internal property lines must delineate a sphere-of-influence line to be used instead. *Project site* is equivalent to the land and water inside the project boundary. The project must not contain noncontiguous parcels, but parcels can be separated by public rights-of-way. Projects may also have enclaves of nonproject properties that are not subject to the rating system, but such enclaves cannot exceed 2% of the total project area and cannot be described as certified.

school a kindergarten, elementary, or secondary institution for the academic instruction of children.

street a dedicated right-of-way that can accommodate one or more modes of travel, excluding alleys and paseos. A street is suitable for primary entrances and provides access to the front and/or sides of buildings and lots. A street may be privately owned as long as it is deeded in perpetuity for general public use. A street must be an addressable thoroughfare (for mail purposes) under the standards of the applicable regulating authority.

walk distance the distance that a pedestrian must travel between origins and destinations without obstruction, in a safe and comfortable environment on a continuous network of sidewalks, all-weather-surface footpaths, crosswalks, woonerfs, or equivalent pedestrian facilities.

Green Infrastructure and Buildings focuses on measures that can reduce the environmental consequences of the construction and operation of buildings and infrastructure. In the United States, buildings account for 39% of energy consumption, including 71% of electricity consumption, and 14% of potable water use.[1] Globally, building construction uses 40% of raw materials.[2] Sustainable building technologies reduce waste and use energy, water, and materials more efficiently than conventional building practices.

Including certified green buildings in projects is one way to reduce negative environmental effects. These buildings achieve substantially better performance across a range of environmental issues, and in many cases the cost per square foot can be comparable to that of conventional buildings.

Energy efficiency is an essential strategy for reducing building-related pollution and greenhouse gas emissions, which are possibly the most negative environmental consequence of building operation. Production of electricity from fossil fuels is responsible for air pollution, water pollution, and more than one-third of U.S. greenhouse gas emissions; hydroelectric generation plants can degrade river habitats; and nuclear power presents waste disposal problems and safety concerns. Building systems—including electrical, lighting, HVAC, and others—can be designed to significantly reduce energy consumption compared with conventional designs and practices.

District heating and cooling systems can improve energy efficiency because they use large plants that are typically more efficient than building-based equipment. District systems can also take advantage of waste heat from on-site energy generation, improving the efficiency of those systems. On-site power generation is another energy management strategy. These systems reduce the transmission losses inherent in utility-supplied electricity; they may also increase power reliability and decrease residents' energy costs by supplementing or replacing utility-supplied electricity. Use of renewable energy on-site further reduces environmental impacts. Solar orientation can also reduce energy consumption.

The environmental consequences of building construction can be lessened by reducing construction and demolition waste through the reuse of existing buildings. Because buildings consume 40% of the stone, gravel, and sand and 25% of the virgin wood used in the world,[3] reuse reduces the environmental effects associated with the extraction, manufacture, and transportation of these materials. Reducing the volume of construction and demolition waste through building reuse can lower disposal costs and slow the filling of landfills, which consume undeveloped land and can cause air and water pollution. Reuse of existing components can also reduce the cost of construction.

Using materials with recycled content conserves raw materials and supports recycling of construction wastes so that they can be diverted from landfills. Many commonly used products are now available with recycled content, including metals, concrete, masonry, acoustic tile, carpet, ceramic tile, and insulation. Most recycled-content products exhibit performance similar to products containing only virgin materials and can be easily incorporated into building projects at little or no additional cost.

1   U.S. DOE Buildings Energy Data Book and U.S. Geological Survey.
2   Lenssen and Roodman, "Worldwatch Paper 124: A Building Revolution: How Ecology and Health Concerns Are Transforming Construction." Worldwatch Institute, 1995.
3   Lisa Mastny, "Purchasing Power: Harnessing Institutional Procurement for People and the Planet." Paper 166. Worldwatch Institute, 2003.

GIB OVERVIEW

Conventional building practices typically alter watershed hydrology and impair local water resources and ecosystems. Changes to hydrology may deplete aquifers, reduce stream base flow, and cause thermal stress, flooding, and stream channel erosion. New developments can be designed to minimize changes to natural hydrology and stream health by reducing the velocity, volume, temperature, and pollutant content of stormwater runoff.

Urban heat islands are another consequence of standard development patterns and practices. The use of dark, nonreflective materials for parking, roofs, walkways, and other surfaces raises ambient temperatures when radiation from the sun is absorbed and transferred through convection and conduction back to surrounding areas. As a result, ambient temperatures in urban areas can be artificially elevated by more than 10°F compared with surrounding undeveloped areas. This results in increased cooling loads in the summer, requiring larger HVAC equipment and additional electricity consumption. Heat islands exacerbate air pollution through the increased generation of electricity used for cooling and contribute to the formation of smog. Heat islands are also detrimental to wildlife habitat. Plants and animals are sensitive to high temperatures and may not thrive when temperatures increase.

Water use can also be reduced through improved design and technologies that conserve water and reduce pressure on water supply. Indoors, potable water consumption can be reduced by using low-flow plumbing fixtures and waterless urinals. Outdoor water use, primarily for landscape maintenance, accounts for 36% of U.S. water consumption and can be reduced through careful plant selection and landscape design.[4] Wastewater can also be reused for landscape maintenance. Water conservation protects the natural water cycle and saves water resources for future generations by reducing amounts withdrawn from rivers, streams, underground aquifers, and other water bodies. Another benefit of potable water conservation is reduced energy and chemical use at municipal water treatment facilities. In addition to conserving precious potable water, wastewater reuse reduces the amount of wastewater released into environmentally stressed streams and rivers. Lower consumption of potable water and reuse of wastewater can also lessen demands on overburdened municipal wastewater treatment systems.

Site design provides another opportunity to reduce the environmental consequences of development. Site plans should preserve the existing tree canopy and native vegetation to the extent possible while accommodating compact development. Preserving existing vegetation can reduce stormwater runoff, mitigate the urban heat island effect, reduce the energy needed for heating and cooling, and reduce landscaping installation and maintenance costs. Trees also reduce air pollution, provide wildlife habitat, and make outdoor areas more pleasant for walking and recreation.

The construction process itself is often damaging to site ecology, indigenous plants, and animal populations. This problem can be minimized by confining construction activities to certain areas on the site and restricting the development footprint. Protection of open space and sensitive areas through the use of strict boundaries reduces damage to the site ecology, resulting in preservation of trees, native vegetation, and wildlife habitat. Construction can also cause soil erosion by wind and water, and soil that leaves the site can cause water and air pollution. Also, loss of topsoil may lead to increased stormwater runoff, which pollutes nearby water bodies. Topsoil loss may also mean that more irrigation, fertilizer and pesticides are needed. These problems can be prevented by development and implementation of an erosion and sedimentation control plan.

---

4   U.S. Environmental Protection Agency, Office of Water, Water-Efficient Landscaping. 2002. www.epa.gove/owm/water-efficiency/final_final.pdf (accessed January 2005).

Resources for Learning More

Websites

U.S. Department of Energy

www.buildingsdatabook.eere.energy.gov/?id=view_book

DOE's on-line *Buildings Energy Data Book* provides information on energy consumption in the United States in 2008.

U.S. Geological Survey

www.water.usgs.gov/watuse

This website provides information on water consumption in the United States in 1990, 1995, and 2000.

Print Media

"A Building Revolution: How Ecology and Health Concerns Are Transforming Construction," by Lenssen and Roodman (Worldwatch Institute, 1995).

Costing Green: A Comprehensive Cost Database and Budgeting Methodology, by Lisa Matthiessen and Peter Morris (Davis Langdon, 2004).

CREDIT	TITLE	POINTS
GIB Prerequisite 1	Certified Green Building	Required
GIB Prerequisite 2	Minimum Building Energy Efficiency	Required
GIB Prerequisite 3	Minimum Building Water Efficiency	Required
GIB Prerequisite 4	Construction Activity Pollution Prevention	Required
GIB Credit 1	Certified Green Buildings	5 points
GIB Credit 2	Building Energy Efficiency	2 points
GIB Credit 3	Building Water Efficiency	1 point
GIB Credit 4	Water-Efficient Landscaping	1 point
GIB Credit 5	Existing Building Reuse	1 point
GIB Credit 6	Historic Resource Preservation and Adaptive Use	1 point
GIB Credit 7	Minimized Site Disturbance in Design and Construction	1 point
GIB Credit 8	Stormwater Management	4 points
GIB Credit 9	Heat Island Reduction	1 point
GIB Credit 10	Solar Orientation	1 point
GIB Credit 11	On-Site Renewable Energy Sources	3 points
GIB Credit 12	District Heating and Cooling	2 points
GIB Credit 13	Infrastructure Energy Efficiency	1 point
GIB Credit 14	Wastewater Management	2 points
GIB Credit 15	Recycled Content in Infrastructure	1 point
GIB Credit 16	Solid Waste Management Infrastructure	1 point
GIB Credit 17	Light Pollution Reduction	1 point

CERTIFIED GREEN BUILDING

	ND
Prerequisite	GIB Prerequisite 1
Points	Required

Intent

To encourage the design, construction, and retrofit of buildings that utilize green building practices.

Requirements

Design, construct, or retrofit one whole building within the *project* to be certified through LEED for New Construction, LEED for Existing Buildings: Operations & Maintenance, LEED for Homes, LEED for Schools, LEED for Retail: New Construction, or LEED for Core and Shell (with at least 75% of the floor area certified under LEED for Commercial Interiors or LEED for Retail: Commercial Interiors), or through a green building rating system requiring review by independent, impartial, third-party certifying bodies as defined by ISO/IEC 17021.

1. Benefits and Issues to Consider

Environmental Issues

The built environment has tremendous consequences for our natural resources and the health of our communities. In 2006, the U.S. Department of Energy reported that U.S. buildings accounted for 72.4% of electricity consumption.[5] According to the Energy Information Administration, in 2008, buildings in the United States were responsible for 38% of all carbon dioxide emissions.[6] In 2000, the U.S. Geological Survey reported that the nation's buildings used 13.6% of all potable water, or 15 trillion gallons per year.[7]

Certification of at least one building through a recognized, third-party verification rating system is an important way to acknowledge the benefits of including green buildings in a sustainable neighborhood. Green buildings include features that address many aspects of sustainable design, and when integrated, they produce results greater than the sum of their parts. Green buildings typically address issues as varied as biodiversity, conservation of natural resources, and healthful indoor environments for occupants.

Economic Issues

The costs of building certification can vary widely, based on the experience of the project design team, the ambitiousness of the design, and the number of buildings being certified. Studies are beginning to show that green buildings do not necessarily cost more to construct than conventional buildings and may command price premiums. Green buildings also deliver many economic benefits to owners and tenants, such as reduced operating costs and improved productivity of building occupants. Cost analyses can project and weigh the effect of these reductions on the possibly higher lease values of such buildings.

2. Related Credits

Strategies that must be implemented for this prerequisite may assist in achieving other GIB credits related to buildings, and the following credit in particular:

- GIB Credit 1, Certified Green Building

3. Summary of Referenced Standards

U.S. Green Building Council, LEED rating systems

www.usgbc.org/leed

The LEED rating systems establish criteria for building design, construction, and operation using strategies aimed at improving performance in energy savings, water efficiency, emissions reduction, indoor environmental quality, and stewardship of resources and sensitivity to their impacts.

International Organization for Standardization, ISO/IEC 17021

www.iso.org

This ISO standard specifies principles and requirements for the competence, consistency, and impartiality of third-party conformity assessment bodies performing audit and certification activities. Entities that conduct audit and certification activities are called third-party conformity assessment bodies.

---

5 U.S. Department of Energy, Office of Energy Efficiency and Renewable Energy, 2008 Buildings Energy Data Book. www.btscoredatabook.net/TableView.aspx?table=6.1.1 (accessed November 2008).

6 Energy Information Administration. Assumptions to the Annual Energy Outlook 2008. www.eia.doe.gov/oiaf/aeo/assumption/ (accessed November 2008).

7 Susan S. Hutson, Nancy L. Barber, Joan F. Kenny, Kristin S. Linsey, Deborah S. Lumia, and Molly A. Maupin, Estimated Use of Water in the United States in 2000. U.S. Geological Survey, 2004. www.pubs.usgs.gov/circ/2004/circ1268/ (accessed November 2008).

4. Implementation

Review other LEED rating systems and their requirements for certification to determine which rating system is most appropriate for a particular building type in the project. If the project comprises more than one type of a similar building, consider getting all buildings of that type certified, since the effort involved with certification will decrease significantly with experience.

If using a LEED rating system, include a LEED Accredited Professional as part of the project team, for help in understanding the certification process for buildings. This will also help earn IDP Credit 2, LEED Accredited Professional. For the project's integrated design team, seek architects, engineers, contractors, builders, and other professionals who have experience with green building techniques or are willing to learn about them. Attend a green building workshop or a workshop on the LEED building rating systems.

Any building designed, constructed, or retrofitted as part of the project may satisfy this prerequisite if the appropriate type of certification is earned. Certifications that were earned preproject do not achieve the prerequisite.

5. Timeline and Team

The phase at which the project begins integrating green measures, the experience of the project team, the building type and location, and the targeted LEED level can all influence the costs of green building. The best ways to make green building cost-effective are to begin at the earliest project phases, use an integrated design process, and select an experienced project team. When sustainability goals are clearly articulated from the outset and incorporated into the design of the whole building, rather than approached as a series of additional features, the higher the potential cost savings and the more sustainable the building.

The approach to certifying a green building might change depending on whether the team is applying for conditional approval, precertification, or certification. Horizontal developers may choose to partner with vertical developers who intend to design and construct buildings that will earn LEED or other compliant certification.

6. Calculations

There are no calculations for this prerequisite.

7. Documentation Guidance

As a first step in preparing to complete the LEED-ND documentation requirements, work through the following measure. Refer to GBCI's website for the complete descriptions of all required documentation.

- Obtain a copy of the LEED certification award letter or official document from another green building certification program.

8. Examples

There are no examples for this prerequisite.

9. Exemplary Performance

This prerequisite is not eligible for exemplary performance under Innovation and Design Process.

10. Regional Variations

LEED Green Building rating systems include regional priority credits that address the most important environmental concerns for every region of the United States. Refer to specific rating systems for further guidance.

11. Resources

Websites

Green Building Certification Institute

www.gbci.org

This website provides detailed information about LEED project registration and certification, as well as LEED professional credentialing.

U.S. Green Building Council, LEED program

www.usgbc.org/leed

This website provides detailed information about the LEED rating systems, including information about project registration and certification, professional accreditation, and additional resources.

Print Media

Fundamentals of Integrated Design for Sustainable Building, by Marian Keeler and Bill Burke (John Wiley & Sons, 2009).

Green Building through Integrated Design, by Jerry Yudelson (McGraw-Hill, 2009).

LEED for Homes Reference Guide (USGBC, 2008).

LEED Reference Guide for Green Building Design and Construction (USGBC, 2009).

LEED Reference Guide for Green Interior Design and Construction (USGBC, 2009).

LEED Reference Guide for Green Building Operations and Maintenance (USGBC, 2009).

12. Definitions

project the land, water, and construction that constitutes the project application. A project applicant does not have to own or control all land or water within a project boundary, but all the area within the project boundary must comply with prerequisites and attempted credits.

MINIMUM BUILDING ENERGY EFFICIENCY

	ND
Prerequisite	GIB Prerequisite 2
Points	Required

Intent

To encourage the design and construction of energy-efficient buildings that reduce air, water, and land pollution and adverse environmental effects from energy production and consumption.

Requirements

The following requirement applies to 90% of the building floor area (rounded up to the next whole building) of all nonresidential buildings, mixed-use buildings, and *multiunit residential* buildings four stories or more constructed as part of the *project* or undergoing major renovations as part of the project.

New buildings must demonstrate an average 10% improvement over ANSI/ASHRAE/IESNA Standard 90.1-2007 (with errata but without addenda). Buildings undergoing major renovations must demonstrate an average 5% improvement over ANSI/ASHRAE/IESNA Standard 90.1-2007.

Projects must document building energy efficiency using one or a combination of the following:

a. Produce a LEED-compliant energy model following the methodology outlined in the LEED rating system appropriate to each building's scope, including demonstration by a whole building project computer simulation using the building performance rating method in Appendix G of ANSI/ASHRAE/IESNA Standard 90.1-2007. Appendix G requires that the energy analysis done for the building performance rating method include all energy costs associated with the building project. Projects in California may use Title 24-2005, Part 6, in place of ANSI/ASHRAE/IESNA Standard 90.1-2007.

b. Comply with the prescriptive measures of the ASHRAE Advanced Energy Design Guide listed below, appropriate to each building's scope. Comply with all applicable criteria as established in the guide for the climate zone in which the project is located.

   - ASHRAE Advanced Energy Design Guide for Small Office Buildings 2004 (office occupancy buildings less than 20,000 square feet).

   - ASHRAE Advanced Energy Design Guide for Small Retail Buildings 2006 (retail occupancy buildings less than 20,000 square feet).

   - ASHRAE Advanced Energy Design Guide for Small Warehouses and Self-Storage Buildings 2008 (warehouse or self-storage occupancy less than 50,000 square feet).

   - ASHRAE Advanced Energy Design Guide for K-12 School Buildings (K-12 school occupancy less than 200,000 square feet).

c. For buildings less than 100,000 square feet, comply with the prescriptive measures identified in the Advanced Buildings™ Core Performance™ Guide developed by the New Buildings Institute, as follows:

GIB PREREQUISITE 2

- Comply with Section 1, Design Process Strategies, and Section 2, Core Performance Requirements, of the Core Performance Guide.

- Health care, warehouse and laboratory projects are ineligible for this path.

If method (a) is used for all of the floor area evaluated in this prerequisite, the total percentage improvement is calculated as a sum of energy costs for each building compared with a baseline. If any combination of methods (a), (b), and (c) is used, the total percentage improvement is calculated as a weighted average based on building floor area. In determining the weighted average, buildings pursuing (a) will be credited at the percentage value determined by the energy model. Buildings pursuing (b) or (c) will be credited at 12% better than ANSI/ASHRAE/IESNA Standard 90.1–2007 for new buildings and 8% better for *existing* building renovations.

AND

For new *single-family residential* buildings and new multiunit residential buildings three stories or fewer, 90% of the buildings must meet ENERGY STAR or equivalent criteria. Projects may demonstrate compliance with ENERGY STAR criteria through the prescriptive requirements of a Builder Option Package, the *Home Energy Rating System (HERS)* index, or a combination of the two.

Project teams wishing to use ASHRAE-approved addenda for the purposes of this credit may do so at their discretion. Addenda must be applied consistently across all LEED credits.

1. Benefits and Issues to Consider

Environmental Issues

Energy efficiency reduces the environmental burdens associated with producing and using energy. Fossil fuels, such as coal and oil, are the most common source of energy used in buildings. However, these fuels are also finite resources. The process of extracting and consuming energy from fossil fuels causes many environmental problems, including air and water pollution, land degradation, solid waste generation, and greenhouse gas emissions. Mounting evidence connects fossil fuel–based energy use with climate change as well as serious risks to environmental and human health and safety. Data from the U.S. Energy Information Administration show that buildings are responsible for almost half (48%) of all energy consumed and greenhouse gases emitted annually.[8] The U.S. Environmental Protection Agency estimates that if the energy efficiency of commercial and industrial buildings improved by 10%, the resulting reductions in greenhouse gas emissions would be equivalent to taking about 30 million vehicles off the road.[9]

Sources of energy other than fossil fuels also carry environmental costs. Hydropower activities, for example, can alter aquatic ecosystems and harm endangered species. Nuclear power plants pose an environmental threat when they are decommissioned without appropriate storage sites for spent fuel. Given both the environmental effects inherent in most energy-production processes and our limited energy supplies, efficiency measures are an important strategy for managing the consequences of energy consumption.

Economic Issues

Optimizing energy performance can reduce overall operating costs. Changing operational strategies to avoid energy use—for example, turning off lights and HVAC systems when the building is unoccupied—can often be done at zero or very low initial cost and rapid payback. Even seemingly small conservation measures can be significant; for instance, replacing a single incandescent lamp with a fluorescent lamp, which uses up to 75% less energy and lasts significantly longer, can save more than $30 in energy costs over the lifetime of the lamp.[10]

2. Related Credits

Improving building energy efficiency may assist in achieving the following related credit:

- GIB Credit 2, Building Energy Efficiency

Additionally, these related credits may help minimize building energy needs:

- GIB Credit 5, Existing Building Reuse

- GIB Credit 9, Heat Island Reduction

- GIB Credit 10, Solar Orientation

- GIB Credit 11, On-Site Renewable Energy Sources

- GIB Credit 12, District Heating and Cooling

8   Architecture 2030. "The Building Sector: A Hidden Culprit." www.architecture2030.org/ current_situation/building_sector.html (accessed November 2008).

9   U.S. Environmental Protection Agency, "Facts About Energy Use in Commercial and Industrial Facilities." www.energystar.gov/index.cfm?c=learn_more.fast_facts (accessed November 2008).

10 U.S. Environmental Protection Agency, "ENERGY STAR® Home Improvement Tips." www.energystar.gov/index.cfm?c=cfls.pr_cfls (accessed November 2008).

3. Summary of Referenced Standards

ANSI/ASHRAE/IESNA Standard 90.1–2007, Energy Standard for Buildings Except Low-Rise Residential

www.ashrae.org

This standard was formulated by American Society of Heating, Refrigerating and Air-Conditioning Engineers (ASHRAE) with the Illuminating Engineering Society of North America (IESNA) under an American National Standards Institute (ANSI) consensus process. It establishes minimum requirements for the energy-efficient design of buildings with these exceptions: single-family houses, multiunit structures of three habitable stories or fewer above grade, manufactured houses (mobile and modular homes), buildings that do not use electricity or fossil fuel, and equipment and building systems that use energy primarily for industrial, manufacturing, or commercial processes). Building envelope requirements are provided for semiheated spaces, such as warehouses. The standard addresses the following categories:

- Section 5. Building envelope (including semiheated spaces, such as warehouses).

- Section 6. Heating, ventilation, and air-conditioning (including parking garage ventilation, freeze protection, exhaust air recovery, and condenser heat recovery for service water heating).

- Section 7. Service water heating (including swimming pools).

- Section 8. Power (including all building power distribution systems).

- Section 9. Lighting (including exit signs, building exterior, grounds, and parking garages).

- Section 10. Other equipment (including all permanently wired electrical motors).

Within each section are mandatory provisions and additional prescriptive requirements. Some sections also contain performance alternatives. The energy cost budget method allows certain prescriptive requirements to be exceeded, provided energy cost savings are made in other areas. However, in all cases, the mandatory provisions must still be met.

New Building Institute, Advanced Buildings Core Performance™ Guide

www.advancedbuildings.net

The Advanced Building Core Performance program offers a predictable alternative to energy performance modeling and a simple set of prescriptive criteria for significantly increasing building energy performance, beyond the requirements of ASHRAE 90.1–2004, in all climate zones. It updates and replaces the Advanced Building Benchmark program.

ASHRAE, Advanced Energy Design Guide for Small Office Buildings 2004

www.ashrae.org

The Advanced Energy Design Guide series provides a sensible approach to achieving advanced levels of energy savings without having to resort to detailed calculations or analysis. This guide is for office buildings up to 20,000 square feet; such buildings make up the bulk of office space in the United States. The strategies provide benefits and savings for the building owner while maintaining the quality and functionality of the space.

ASHRAE, Advanced Energy Design Guide for Small Retail Buildings 2006

www.ashrae.org

The Advanced Energy Design Guide series provides a sensible approach to achieving advanced levels of energy savings without having to resort to detailed calculations or analysis. This guide focuses on retail buildings up to 20,000 square feet that use unitary heading and air-conditioning equipment; such buildings represent a significant amount of commercial retail space in the United States.

ASHRAE, Advanced Energy Design Guide for Small Warehouses and Self Storage Buildings 2008

www.ashrae.org

The Advanced Energy Design Guide series provides a sensible approach to achieving advanced levels of energy savings without having to resort to detailed calculations or analysis. This guide focuses on warehouses up to 50,000 square feet and self-storage buildings that use unitary heating and air-conditioning equipment; such facilities make up a significant amount of commercial warehouse space in the United States.

ASHRAE, Advanced Energy Design Guide for K–12 School Buildings

www.ashrae.org

The Advanced Energy Design Guide series provides a sensible approach to achieving advanced levels of energy savings without having to resort to detailed calculations or analysis. This guide focuses on elementary, middle, and high school buildings, which have a wide variety of heating and air-conditioning requirements. Options for daylighting, an important component in schools, are included.

ENERGY STAR®, Target Finder Rating Tool

www.energystar.gov/index.cfm?c=new_bldg_design.bus_target_finder

ENERGY STAR is a government-industry partnership managed by the U.S. Environmental Protection Agency and the U.S. Department of Energy. Target Finder is an on-line tool that can establish energy performance goals for a project. It uses data such as zip code and building type to calculate the estimated total energy use for the building and then assigns an energy performance rating on a scale of 1 to 100. The zip code indicates the climate conditions that the building would experience in a normal year (based on a 30-year climate average) so that energy use intensity for the target (based on the energy fuel mix typical in the region) can be estimated. The tool displays the percentage electricity and natural gas assumption used to calculate design targets. The energy use intensity generated by Target Finder reflects the distribution of energy performance in commercial buildings derived from data in the U.S. Department of Energy's Commercial Buildings Energy Consumption Survey. The ratings generated by Target Finder provide a useful benchmark for estimating and comparing a building's energy use with that of other buildings and for determining a project's goals for energy efficiency. Assessing energy consumption early in the process enables teams to employ a holistic approach in making design decisions that improve the building's performance. Energy performance targets are more easily achieved if all the building's systems enhance one another; attempting to increase energy efficiency after construction is less successful because only small changes are possible without major disruption and additional cost.

Residential Energy Service Network, HERS Index

www.natresnet.org/

RESNET established the Home Energy Rating System index as a scoring system for relative energy use of homes. A HERS index of 100 represents the energy use of a reference "standard" home (based on the 2006 International Energy Conservation Code), and a HERS index of 0 represents a net zero energy home. Each 1-point decrease in the index corresponds to a 1% reduction in energy consumption compared with the reference home. A HERS index rating involves an analysis of a home's construction plans and on-site inspections.

4. Implementation

The prerequisite is earned if at least 90% of project buildings achieve a minimum energy efficiency. Project buildings are categorized into two groups—nonresidential, mixed-use, and multiunit residential buildings four stories or more; and single-family residential and multiunit residential three stories or less—and the 90% requirement is applied to each. The 10% allowance accommodates projects that have a small number of buildings with special energy characteristics, such as laboratories.

For the first group, compliance can be achieved in four ways: a performance modeling method, two prescriptive methods, or a combination of all methods. Whichever method is used, new construction must demonstrate a 10% energy improvement over the baseline, and major renovations, a 5% improvement over the baseline. In both instances, the baseline is measured from ANSI/ASHRAE/IESNA Standard 90.1–2007.

If the performance modeling path is selected, the percentage improvement is based on the sum of energy costs for each building compared with the baseline. If any combination of the performance and prescriptive paths is used, the percentage improvement is calculated as a weighted average of the floor areas to which the methods have been applied. In calculating the weighted average, performance-rated buildings are credited with the energy savings percentage value determined by the energy model. Buildings using the prescriptive methods are credited at 12% better than Standard 90.1–2007 for new construction and 8% better for renovations.

Energy modeling may be a desirable option for large buildings and may result in the greatest gains in energy efficiency. Buildings that are pursuing LEED Building Design & Construction certifications may already be using an energy model. Smaller buildings and projects with greater financial constraints may consider the ASHRAE Advanced Energy Design Guide (AEDG), although not all buildings are eligible for the AEDG prescriptive paths. The Advanced Buildings™ Core Performance™ Guide applies to a wider range of buildings while still offering a prescriptive compliance path. Consider the type and size of each building and the team's financial and technical resources before selecting a compliance path.

For the second group, single-family and multiunit residential three stories or less, new construction must meet ENERGY STAR or equivalent criteria. Compliance with ENERGY STAR criteria is demonstrated through a builder option package prescriptive requirement, the Home Energy Rating System (HERS) index, or a combination of the two.

ASHRAE 90.1–2007 Overview

The following paragraphs describe the applicable sections of ASHRAE 90.1–2007.

Section 5. Building Envelope Requirements. (ASHRAE 90.1–2007) These requirements apply to enclosed spaces whose heating system has an output capacity of 3.4 Btu/hour/square foot or more, and to spaces whose cooling system has a sensible output capacity of 5 Btu/hour/square foot or more. ASHRAE 90.1–2007 Section 5.4 describes mandatory provisions for insulation installation (5.4.1); window, skylight, and door ratings (5.4.2); and air leakage (5.4.3). Section 5.5 contains the prescriptive provisions for fenestration and opaque assemblies.

Each county in the United States is assigned to 1 of 8 climate zones (ASHRAE 90.1–2007, Table B-1).

Figure 1. Climate Zones

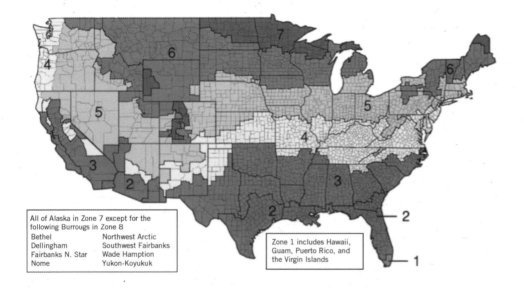

All of Alaska in Zone 7 except for the
following Burrougs in Zone 8
Bethel	Northwest Arctic
Dellingham	Southwest Fairbanks
Fairbanks N. Star	Wade Hamption
Nome	Yukon-Koyukuk

Zone 1 includes Hawaii,
Guam, Puerto Rico, and
the Virgin Islands

Climate zone assignments for Canada and other countries can be determined from ASHRAE 90.1–2007, Tables B-2 and B-3.

Prescriptive building envelope requirements are determined based on the building's climate zone classification (ASHRAE Standard 90.1–2007, Tables 5.5-1 to 5.5-8). For projects following the prescriptive compliance method, all building envelope components must meet the minimum insulation and maximum U-factor and solar heat gain coefficients (SHGC) requirements listed for the project's climate zone. Window area must be less than 40% of the gross wall area, and the skylight area must be less than 5% of the gross roof area.

Section 6. Heating, Ventilation and Air-Conditioning Requirements. (ASHRAE Standard 90.1–2007) The requirements of Section 6 apply to all building HVAC systems. Mandatory provisions for HVAC performance are documented in ASHRAE 90.1–2007, Section 6.4, and include minimum system efficiency requirements (6.4.1), load calculation requirements (6.4.2), controls requirements (6.4.3), HVAC system construction and insulation requirements (6.4.4), and completion requirements (6.4.5). ASHRAE 90.1–2007, Section 6.4.3.4, lists minimum control schemes for thermostats (off-hours, including setback and optimum start/stop), stair and elevator vents, outdoor air supply and exhaust vents, heat pump auxiliary heat, humidification and dehumidification, freeze protection, snow- and ice-melting systems, and ventilation for high-occupancy areas.

ASHRAE Standard 90.1–2007, Section 6.5, provides a prescriptive compliance option. Prescriptive provisions are included for air and water economizers (6.5.1); simultaneous heating and cooling limitations (6.5.2); air system design and control, including fan power limitation and variable speed drive control (6.5.3); hydronic system design and control, including variable flow pumping (6.5.4); heat rejection equipment (6.5.5); energy recovery from exhaust air and service water heating systems (6.5.6); kitchen and fume exhaust hoods (6.5.7); radiant heating systems (6.5.8); and hot gas bypass limitations (6.5.9).

Project teams must meet the minimum efficiency requirements for system components listed in ASHRAE 90.1–2007, Tables 6.8.1A-G, even if using the energy cost budget or performance-based compliance methods. For projects served by existing HVAC systems, such as a central plant on a campus or district heating and cooling, the exception to Section 6.1.1.2 applies. The existing systems and existing equipment are not required to comply with the standard. Occupant-controlled swirl floor diffusers meet the intent of the ASHRAE 90.1–2007, Section 6.4.3.1, requirement for individually controlled zone controls, similar to operable windows in a naturally ventilated and cooled space.

Section 7. Service Water Heating Requirements. (**ASHRAE 90.1–2007**) These requirements include mandatory provisions (7.4) and a choice of prescriptive (7.5) or performance-based compliance (Appendix G). Mandatory provisions include requirements for load calculations (7.4.1), efficiency (7.4.2), piping insulation (7.4.3), controls (7.4.4), pool heaters and pool covers (7.4.5), and heat traps for storage tanks (7.4.6).

Section 8. Power Requirements. (**Section 8.4.1**) These requirements address mandatory provisions related to voltage drop for feeder conductors at design load. Voltage drop is the reduction in voltage in an electrical circuit between the source and load. One strategy for compensating for the effect of voltage drop is to lower overall resistance by increasing the diameter of a conductor between source and load.

Section 9. Lighting Requirements. (**ASHRAE 90.1–2007**) These requirements apply to all lighting installed on the building site, including interior and exterior lighting. Mandatory provisions include minimum requirements for controls (9.4.1), tandem wiring (9.4.2), luminaire source efficacy for exit signs (9.4.3), exterior lighting power definitions (9.4.5), and luminaire source efficacy for exterior lighting fixture (9.4.4). Per 9.4.1.2, occupancy controls are required in classrooms, conference rooms, and employee lunch and break rooms. Interior lighting compliance must be documented using either the building area method (9.5) or the space-by-space method (9.6). (See the Implementation and Calculations sections in this reference guide for additional guidance on lighting power calculations.)

Section 10. Other Equipment Requirements. (10.4) **This section** includes mandatory performance provisions for electric motors that are within the scope of the Energy Policy Act of 1992. This section sets minimum nominal efficiency for electric motors based on design class designation, synchronous speed (RPM), and motor horsepower.

Section 11. Energy Cost Budget Method. (**ASHRAE 90.1–2007**) The energy cost budget method is not an acceptable alternative option for compliance with this prerequisite.

Appendix G. The Performance Rating Method. (**ASHRAE 90.1–2007**) Appendix G describes the required building performance simulation method. The performance rating method does not exempt projects from also meeting the mandatory ASHRAE 90.1–2007 requirements listed for this prerequisite.

Additional Strategies for Nonresidential, Mixed-Use, and Multiunit Residential Buildings Four Stories or More

In a campus setting with a central plant, improving plant efficiency affects all buildings on the district heating and cooling system. By installing a combined heat and power system designed to meet thermal and electrical base loads, a facility can often increase its operational efficiency and decrease energy costs.

On USGBC's website, see the guidance on combined heat and power systems that supply electricity and/or recovered thermal energy.

Projects may be able to take credit for natural ventilation in the energy modeling. However, projects demonstrating natural ventilation savings will be evaluated on a case-by-case basis. To demonstrate the process and the results, be prepared to provide the following:

- Detailed project description.

- Clear identification of the areas with natural ventilation.

- Detailed description or references that document the modeling algorithms and/or methodology for the natural ventilation portion of the energy model.

- All thermostat, fan, infiltration, and other appropriate schedules for naturally ventilated areas.

- Verification that the range of unmet load hours is similar for both the design and the baseline building, to ensure that savings are not claimed for hours outside the control parameters.

The team must clearly demonstrate that the operational schedule used to model the natural ventilation system aligns with occupants' anticipated behavior. For example, the model cannot assume that natural ventilation will occur when no one is in the building to operate the system.

Guidance for Single-Family Homes and Multiunit Residential Three Stories or Less

The mandatory minimum level of energy performance requires that a qualifying home be designed to meet the energy performance requirements of the ENERGY STAR for Homes program. Under this prerequisite, compliance must be demonstrated using a HERS-approved energy analysis software program. The ENERGY STAR Builder Option Package is another way to achieve the prerequisite; it requires no software or energy modeling. Although a new home must meet the energy performance requirements of ENERGY STAR, it need not be ENERGY STAR labeled.

Approved HERS software is listed on the RESNET website, at www.resnet.us, but is available only to HERS-trained energy raters or HERS providers. Thus, projects that plan to use the performance pathway must be modeled by individuals who have access to the HERS-approved software and have been trained in its use. A LEED for Homes Certification Provider can find a qualified HERS-trained energy modeler, and in some cases the modeler may also be an energy rater.

As part of the modeling process, every energy-related aspect of a home is evaluated for its efficiency (or inefficiency). The HERS index reflects insulation levels, air sealing, window size and specifications, distribution system, space heating and cooling equipment size, water heating, lighting, appliances, and renewable energy.

Work with an energy rater to determine the most appropriate measures for each project; the most economical and effective strategies will vary based on the home design and location.

An ENERGY STAR home may not get credit for renewable energy systems as a component of the minimum HERS index of 85 for homes located in International Energy Conservation (IECC) climate zones 1 through 5 (or a HERS index of 80 for homes located in IECC climate zones 6 through 8). After the ENERGY STAR efficiency requirements have been met, the project can take credit for renewables.

5. Timeline and Team

The project team should consider building energy efficiency an integral component of the neighborhood at the outset of project planning. The design team should include experienced energy efficiency specialists in architecture and mechanical and electrical engineering.

6. Calculations

Weighted Average for Buildings with Different Performance in Energy Modeling

If all project buildings follow compliance path (a), a weighted average for overall performance improvement must be calculated using the total design energy cost compared with the baseline energy cost (Equation 1).

Equation 1

$$\text{Overall building energy performance} = \frac{\text{Building 1 design cost} + \text{Building 2 design cost} + \text{Building 3 design cost}}{\text{Building 1 baseline cost} + \text{Building 2 baseline cost} + \text{Building 3 baseline cost}}$$

Weighted Average for Buildings with Different Compliance Paths

If project buildings use any combination of compliance paths (a), (b), and (c), a weighted average for overall performance improvement must be calculated based on floor area. First determine the equivalent performance improvement for each building according to the credit requirements: the result of the energy model for path (a); 12% for new construction using paths (b) or (c); or 8% for major renovations using paths (b) or (c). Then use the results from these three approaches to determine the weighted average for buildings with different compliance paths.

7. Documentation Guidance

As a first step in preparing to complete the LEED-ND documentation requirements, work through the following measures. Refer to GBCI's website for the complete descriptions of all required documentation.

- For ASHRAE compliance, list any addenda used, and retain copies of ASHRAE compliance forms.

- Determine the climate zone for the project location.

- Calculate energy use by type.

- Maintain a list of energy end uses for the project building (for both the baseline case and the design case).

- If the project is using the prescriptive compliance path, assemble documentation demonstrating that the project meets all applicable requirements.

8. Examples

A project has six buildings (Table 1). The two large office buildings are not eligible for either prescriptive compliance path and require LEED-compliant energy models. The multiunit residential building would be eligible for the Advanced Buildings™ Core Performance™ Guide compliance path, but the project team decides that the improved energy efficiency offered by energy modeling justifies using an energy model. However, the energy modeling path poses project-specific challenges for the small laboratory. Since the lab has unique energy characteristics and accounts for less than 10% of the total floor area in the category (it is 4,000 square feet, and the total floor area of the nonresidential, mixed-use, and multiunit residential buildings is

590,000 square feet), it may be excluded. The project team uses ENERGY STAR for the two single-family homes. Regardless of whether the buildings are new construction or existing structures undergoing major renovation (50% or more of the building's gross square footage), it is the total building square footage that is used for the calculations.

Table 1. Example determination of energy savings for six-building project

Project building	Area (sf)	Compliance path	Percentage of total area	Energy savings (%)
Office A	300,000	Modeling (a)	51	20
Office B	200,000	Prescriptive (b)	34	12
Multifamily residential (6 stories)	90,000	Prescriptive (a)	15	12
Single-Family A	2,000	ENERGY STAR	—	—
Single-Family B	2,000	ENERGY STAR	—	—
Laboratory	4,000	NA	—	—

The following equations illustrate the calculation of weighted average energy savings for the buildings using the energy modeling and prescriptive paths.

	Energy savings		Percentage of total area (sf)		Weighted energy savings (%)
Office A	20%	X	51%	=	10.2
Office B	12%	X	34%	=	4.1
Multifamily residential	12%	X	15%	=	1.8
Total					16.1

9. Exemplary Performance

This prerequisite is not eligible for exemplary performance under Innovation and Design Process.

10. Regional Variations

ASHRAE 90.1–2007 accounts for regional variance with eight climate zones and three climate subzones; the standard specifies the minimum envelope and glazing property requirements for each.

11. Resources

Websites

U.S. Environmental Protection Agency, Combined Heat and Power Partnership

www.epa.gov/chp

Information on cogeneration, also called combined heat and power, is available from EPA through the CHP Partnership, a voluntary program seeking to reduce the environmental effects of power generation by promoting CHP. The partnership works closely with energy users, the CHP industry, state and local governments, and other clean energy stakeholders to facilitate the development of new projects and promote their environmental and economic benefits.

Whole Building Design Guide

www.wbdg.org

This portal links to current information pertaining to building design guidance, project management, and operations and maintenance, with resource pages devoted to particular green building topics. The Whole Building Design Guide is offered by the National Institute of Building Sciences in collaboration with federal agencies, private sector companies, nonprofit organizations, and educational institutions.

Print Media

ANSI/ASHRAE/IESNA Standard 90.1–2007 User's Manual (ASHRAE, 2008). The ANSI/ASHRAE/ IESNA Standard 90.1–2007 User's Manual was developed as a companion document to the ANSI/ASHRAE/IESNA Standard 90.1–2007, Energy Standard for Buildings Except Low-Rise Residential Buildings. The manual explains the new standard and includes sample calculations, useful reference material, and information on the intent and application of the standard. It contains illustrations and examples and tables of reference data. It also includes a complete set of compliance forms and worksheets that can be used to document compliance with the standard. The manual is helpful to architects and engineers applying the standard to the design of buildings, plan examiners and field inspectors who must enforce the standard in areas where it is adopted as code, and contractors who must construct buildings in compliance with the standard. A compact disk is included that contains electronic versions of the compliance forms found in the manual.

12. Definitions

existing present on the date of submission of LEED-ND certification documents; similarly, an element or condition that exists is present on the date that LEED-ND certification documents are submitted.

Home Energy Rating System (HERS) index a scoring system established by the Residential Energy Services Network (RESNET) in which a home built to the specifications of the HERS Reference Home (based on the 2006 International Energy Conservation Code) scores 100, and a net zero energy home scores 0. The lower a home's HERS Index, the more energy efficient it is.

multiunit residential consisting of four or more residential units sharing a common entry.

project the land, water, and construction that constitutes the project application. A project applicant does not have to own or control all land or water within a project boundary, but all the area within the project boundary must comply with prerequisites and attempted credits.

single-family residential any residential unit other than multiunit residential, including single, duplex, triplex, row house, townhouse and semiattached residential building types.

MINIMUM BUILDING WATER EFFICIENCY

	ND
Prerequisite	GIB Prerequisite 3
Points	Required

Intent

To reduce effects on natural water resources and reduce burdens on community water supply and wastewater systems.

Requirements

For nonresidential buildings, mixed-use buildings, and multifamily residential buildings four stories or more:

Indoor water usage in new buildings and buildings undergoing major renovations as part of the *project* must be an average 20% less than in baseline buildings. The baseline usage is based on the requirements of the Energy Policy Act of 1992 and subsequent rulings by the Department of Energy, the requirements of the Energy Policy Act of 2005, and the fixture performance standards in the 2006 editions of the Uniform Plumbing Code or International Plumbing Code as to fixture performance. Calculations are based on estimated occupant usage and include only the following fixtures and fixture fittings (as applicable to the project scope): water closets (toilets), urinals, lavatory faucets, showers, kitchen sink faucets, and prerinse spray valves.

The water efficiency threshold is calculated as a weighted average of water usage for the buildings constructed as part of the project based on their conditioned square footage. Projects may also follow the LEED for Multiple Buildings and On-Campus Building Application Guide alternative calculation methodology to show compliance with this prerequisite.

Table 1. National commercial efficiency baselines

Commercial fixtures, fittings, or appliances	Baseline water usage
Commercial toilet	1.6 gpf[1] Except blow-out fixtures, 3.5 gpf
Commercial urinal	1.0 gpf
Commercial lavatory (restroom) faucet	2.2 gpm at 60 psi, private applications only (hotel-motel guest rooms, hospital patient rooms) 0.5 gpm at 60 psi[2] all others except private applications 0.25 gallons per cycle for metering faucets
Commercial prerinse spray valve (for food service applications)	Flow rate ≤ 1.6 gpm (no pressure specified; no performance requirement)

[1] EPAct 1992 standard for toilets applies to both commercial and residential models.
[2] In addition to EPAct requirements, the American Society of Mechanical Engineers standard for public lavatory faucets is 0.5 gpm at 60 psi (ASME A112.18.1-2005). This maximum has been incorporated into the national Uniform Plumbing Code and the International Plumbing Code.

Table 2. National residential efficiency baselines

Residential Fixtures, Fittings, and Appliances	Baseline water usage
Residential toilet	1.6 gpf[3]
Residential lavatory (bathroom) faucet	2.2 gpm at 60 psi
Residential kitchen faucet	
Residential showerhead	2.5 gpm at 80 psi per shower stall[4]

gpf = gallons per flush; psi = pounds per square inch.
Source: Adapted from information developed and summarized by the U.S. EPA Office of Water.
[3] EPAct 1992 standard for toilets applies to both commercial and residential models.
[4] Residential shower compartment (stall) in dwelling units: The total allowable flow rate from all flowing showerheads at any given time, including rain systems, waterfalls, bodysprays, bodyspas, and jets, shall be limited to the allowable showerhead flow rate as specified above (2.5-gpm) per shower compartment, where the floor area of the shower compartment is less than 2,500 sq.in. For each increment of 2,500 sq.in. of floor area thereafter or part thereof, an additional showerhead with total allowable flow rate from all flowing devices equal to or less than the allowable flow rate as specified above shall be allowed. Exception: Showers that emit recirculated non-potable water originating from within the shower compartment while operating are allowed to exceed the maximum as long as the total potable water flow does not exceed the flow rate as specified above.

The following fixtures, fittings, and appliances are outside the scope of the water use reduction calculation:

    a. Commercial steam cookers.

    b. Commercial dishwashers.

    c. Automatic commercial ice makers.

    d. Commercial (family-sized) clothes washers.

    e. Residential clothes washers.

    f. Standard and compact residential dishwashers.

AND

For new *single-family residential* buildings and new *multiunit residential* buildings three stories or fewer, 90% of buildings must use a combination of fixtures that would earn 3 points under LEED for Homes 2008 Credit 3, Indoor Water Use.

1. Benefits and Issues to Consider

Environmental Issues

Reducing water use in buildings for urinals, toilets, showerheads, and faucets decreases the total amount withdrawn from rivers, streams, underground aquifers, and other water bodies. It protects the natural water cycle, saves water resources for future generations, and in aggregate, allows municipalities to reduce or defer the capital investment needed for water supply and wastewater treatment infrastructure.

Conserving municipally supplied water also reduces chemical inputs at the water treatment plant, as well as reduces energy use and the associated greenhouse gas emissions from treatment and distribution. The energy use and associated emissions from supplying municipal water vary greatly across the United States and depend on the utility's water sources, the distances water is transported, and the type of water treatment applied. End-use water efficiency can greatly reduce negative environmental impacts. Comparing the environmental effects of off-site treatment and supply with those of on-site treatment is a worthwhile exercise. Because water heating in commercial buildings accounts for nearly 15% of building energy use, conservation measures will also reduce end-use energy and energy-related pollution.

Economic Issues

Reductions in water consumption decrease building operating costs and bring about wider economic benefits. Reduced water consumption allows municipalities to lessen or defer the capital investment needed for water supply and wastewater treatment infrastructure, thereby leading to more stable municipal taxes and water rates.

Many cost-effective systems and fixtures currently on the market support compliance with the requirement, but the cost of water efficiency measures varies widely. For example, installing tamperproof faucet aerators on existing fixtures is a small expense compared with a rainwater-harvesting or graywater-recycling system. High-efficiency toilets and dry fixtures, such as nonwater toilet systems, often have higher initial costs than standard models.

Newer technologies may also have higher costs and limited availability because of production constraints, and they may entail different maintenance and repair expenses, such as special cartridge components and cleaning and sealing fluids. Teams should perform a full cost-benefit and life-cycle study before installing such products.

2. Related Credits

Achieving this prerequisite will help meet the requirements for GIB Credit 3, Building Water Efficiency, and may also support the following credits:

- GIB Credit 4, Water-Efficient Landscaping

- GIB Credit 8, Stormwater Management

- GIB Credit 14, Wastewater Management

Additionally, one of the prerequisite compliance paths is the achievement of LEED for Homes 2008 Credit 3, Indoor Water Use, which would assist any buildings concurrently registered for LEED for Homes.

3. Summary of Referenced Standards

Energy Policy Act of 1992 (as amended)

This legislation, known as EPAct, addresses energy and water use in commercial, institutional, and residential facilities.

Energy Policy Act of 2005

This version of the EPAct statute became U.S. law in August 2005; it updates previous standards for energy and water use in commercial, institutional, and residential facilities.

International Association of Plumbing and Mechanical Officials Publication IAPMO/ American National Standards Institute UPC 1–2006, Uniform Plumbing Code 2006, Section 402.0, Water-Conserving Fixtures and Fittings

www.iapmo.org

UPC defines water-conserving fixtures and fittings for water closets, urinals, and metered faucets. This ANSI-accredited code safeguards life, health, property, and public welfare by regulating and controlling the design, construction, installation, materials, location, operation, and maintenance or use of plumbing systems.

International Code Council, International Plumbing Code 2006, Section 604, Design of Building Water Distribution System

www.iccsafe.org

IPC defines maximum flow rates and consumption for plumbing fixtures and fittings, including public and private lavatories, showerheads, sink faucets, urinals, and water closets.

4. Implementation

At a neighborhood scale, water efficiency should be considered at the outset as an integral part of project design principles. For LEED-ND, this means specifying water-efficient fixtures and strategies throughout the project's buildings.

Effective ways to reduce water use include installing flow restrictors or reduced-flow aerators on lavatory, sink, and shower fixtures; installing and maintaining metering controls on faucets; installing high-efficiency flush fixtures, such as high-efficiency water closets and urinals; and collecting rainwater. In certain cases, however, faucets with low-flow rates are not appropriate. Using a low-flow rate for tasks involving a predetermined volume of water, like filling pots in a kitchen sink, does not save water and will likely cause user dissatisfaction and inefficiencies. Consider alternative strategies to reduce water use, such as installing special-use pot fillers and faucets or foot pedal–operated faucets.

WaterSense, a partnership program sponsored by EPA, helps consumers identify the most water-efficient products and programs. WaterSense-labeled products exceed the requirements of the Uniform Plumbing Code and the International Plumbing Code for some fixtures and fittings. WaterSense products and other high-efficiency plumbing fixtures, fittings, and appliances can be installed in the same way as conventional EPAct plumbing fixtures and fittings, as well as ENERGY STAR appliances.

To determine the most effective strategies for a particular condition, analyze the water efficiency options available to the project based on location, code compliance (plumbing and safety), and overall project function. Determine where in the building the most water is used, evaluate potential water-efficiency technologies, and examine the impacts of alternative fixtures and technologies. Compare the design case water use with the calculated EPAct baseline to determine the optimal water savings for plumbing fixtures and fittings. Once the design case water use has been determined, compare the volumes of water required for each end use with the volumes of alternative sources of water available on-site. Perform a detailed climate analysis to determine the availability of on-site resources and choose strategies that are appropriate and cost-effective.

Table 3. UPC and IPC standards for plumbing fixture water use

Fixture	UPC and IPC standards	EPA WaterSense standards
Water closets (gallons per flush, gpf)	1.60	1.28
Urinals (gpf)	1.00	0.5[a]
Showerheads (gallons per minute, gpm[b])	2.50	2.0[c]
Public lavatory faucets and aerators (gpm[d])	0.5	
Private lavatory faucets and aerators (gpm[d])	2.2	1.5
Public metering lavatory faucets (gallons per metering cycle)	0.25	
Kitchen and sink faucets (gpm)	2.20	
Metering faucets (gallons per metering cycle)	0.25	

a On May 22, 2008, EPA issued a notification of intent to develop a specification for high-efficiency urinals. WaterSense anticipates establishing a maximum allowable flush volume of 0.5 gpf.
b When measured at a flowing water pressure of 80 pounds per square inch (psi).
c On May 22, 2008, EPA issued a notification of intent to develop a specification for showerheads. WaterSense anticipates establishing a single maximum flow rate of 2.0 gpm.
d When measured at a flowing water pressure of 60 psi.

5. Timeline and Team

During predesign, setting water goals and strategies involves the owner, architect, and engineers. Identify local water utilities and governing authorities and research codes and applicable water laws. Learn the process for obtaining permits and approval and set water goals and strategy.

During design development, the engineering team should develop and design water reuse and treatment systems, perform preliminary LEED calculations, and confirm or reassess water goals. In construction documents, the architect, working with the owner, should specify efficient fixtures and appliances and complete LEED calculations and documentation. During construction, the design team and owner should confirm proper selection, installation, and operation of water fixtures, fittings, and systems.

6. Calculations

There are two calculations associated with this credit; depending on the project, either or both may be required.

Calculation 1. Nonresidential Buildings (Except Schools), Mixed-Use Buildings, and Multiunit Residential Buildings Four Stories or More

The calculated water use reduction for the project is the difference between the design case and a baseline case. The percentage is determined by dividing the design case use by the baseline use. The methodology differs from traditional plumbing design, in which calculations are based on fixture counts; under this prerequisite, the water use calculation is based on fixture and fitting water consumption rates and estimated use by the occupants. Occupants' estimated use is determined by calculating full-time equivalent (FTE) and transient occupants and applying appropriate fixture use rates to each. It may be advantageous to divide each facility per building into fixture usage groups, calculate water use for each, and sum the values to determine whole building performance.

Fixture Usage Groups

Fixture usage groups are subsets of facilities used by different types of occupants. For each group, complete the on-line form calculator. Indicate which fixtures are involved and which occupants they serve. If all occupants within a building have access to all fixtures, or if all fixtures are standard throughout the building, enter only a single fixture usage group. That is the simpler approach, but it may be more appropriate to define two or more groups to account for different fixtures in one area of the building or special usage patterns by a population within the building.

Calculating Occupancy in Nonresidential Buildings (Except Schools), Mixed-UseBuildings, and Multiunit Residential Buildings Four Stories or More

Count building occupants by occupancy type. In buildings with multiple shifts, use the number of FTEs from all shifts. Include the following:

- Full-time staff.
- Part-time staff.
- Transients (visitors, retail customers).
- Residents.

For projects that include residential spaces, the number of residents should be estimated based on the number and size of units in the project. Generally, assume two residents per one-bedroom unit, three residents per two-bedroom unit, etc. If occupancy is not known (e.g., mixed-use and core and shell projects for which the tenants of the building are unknown during design), use Table 4, Default Occupancy Counts, for guidance. If actual occupancy is known, project teams must use actual counts for calculating occupancy. Note that these occupancy assumptions differ from the LEED-ND definition of *planned occupancy* and instead take the values used for water efficiency calculations in the LEED 2009 Building Design & Construction rating systems.

Table 4. Default occupancy counts

	Gross square feet per occupant	
	Employees	**Transients**
General office	250	0
Retail, general	550	130
Retail, service (e.g., financial, auto)	600	130
Restaurant	435	95
Grocery store	550	115
Medical office	225	330
R&D, laboratory	400	0
Warehouse, distribution	2,500	0
Warehouse, storage	20,000	0
Hotel	1,500	700
Educational, daycare	630	105
Educational, K–12	1,300	140
Educational, postsecondary	2,100	150

Sources:
ANSI/ASHRAE/IESNA Standard 90.1–2004 (Atlanta, 2004).
2001 Uniform Plumbing Code (Los Angeles).
California Public Utilities Commission, 2004–2005 Database for Energy Efficiency Resources (DEER) Update Study (2008).
California State University, Capital Planning, Design and Construction Section VI, Standards for Campus Development Programs (Long Beach, CA, 2002).
City of Boulder Planning Department, Projecting Future Employment—How Much Space per Person (Boulder, CO, 2002).
Metro, 1999 Employment Density Study (Portland, OR 1999).
American Hotel and Lodging Association, Lodging Industry Profile (Washington, DC, 2008).
LEED for Core & Shell Core Committee, personal communication (2003–2006).
LEED for Retail Core Committee, personal communication (2007).
OWP/P, Medical Office Building Project Averages (Chicago, 2008).
OWP/P, University Master Plan Projects (Chicago, 2008).
U.S. General Services Administration, Childcare Center Design Guide (Washington, DC, 2003).

Calculate the FTE number of occupants based on a standard eight-hour daily occupancy period (40 hours per week). An eight-hour occupant has an FTE value of 1.0, and part-time occupants have an FTE value based on their hours per day divided by 8. FTE calculations for each shift of the project must be used consistently for all LEED-ND credits.

Estimate the transient building occupants, such as students, visitors, and customers. Transient occupants can be reported as either daily totals or full-time equivalents. When using daily totals for transients, match the fixture uses for each occupancy type with the values shown in Tables 5 and 6 (e.g., for the daily total of students, assume 0.5 lavatory faucet uses per daily student visitor). If transients are reported as a daily full-time equivalent value, fixture uses for FTEs must be assumed regardless of the transient population's identity (e.g., for students reported as FTEs, assume three lavatory faucet uses per student FTE). Use a transient occupancy number that is a representative daily average over the course of a year. If the number of transient visitors per day for retail facilities is unknown, use the default occupancy counts in Table 4.

Tables 5 and 6 provide default fixture use values for different occupancy types. These values should be used in the calculations for this credit unless special circumstances warrant modifications. Most buildings with students, visitors, and retail customers will also have FTE occupants. Half of all students and visitors are assumed to use a flush fixture and a lavatory faucet in the building and are not expected to use a shower or kitchen sink. A fifth of retail customers are assumed to use a flush and a flow fixture in the building and no shower or kitchen sink. The default for residential occupants is five uses per day of water closet and lavatory faucet, one shower, and four kitchen sink uses. For consistency across LEED-ND projects, the calculations require the use of a balanced, one-to-one male-female ratio unless project conditions warrant an alternative. Provide a narrative description to explain any special circumstances.

Table 5. Commercial default fixture uses

Fixture	Duration	Uses / day		
		FTE	Transient	Retail customer
Water closet (female)	n/a	3	0.5	0.2
Water closet (male)[a]	n/a	1	0.1	0.1
Urinal (female)	n/a	0	0	0
Urinal (male)	n/a	2	0.4	0.1
Lavatory faucet	15	3	0.5	0.2
Shower	300	0.1	0	0
Kitchen sink	15	1	0	0

[a] If urinals are not installed for the fixture usage group, then use the water closet (female) usage rates for the male water closet usage.

Table 6. Residential default fixture uses

Fixture	Duration	Uses / day
Water closet (female)	n/a	5
Water closet (male)	n/a	5
Urinal (female)	n/a	n/a
Urinal (male)	n/a	n/a
Lavatory faucet	60	5
Shower	480	1
Kitchen sink	60	4

Calculating Occupancy in Schools

Count the total building occupants for each occupancy type. In buildings with multiple shifts, use the number of full-time equivalents (FTEs) from all shifts. Include the following:

- Full-time staff.

- Part-time staff.

- Students.

- Transients (volunteers, visitors).

Calculate the FTE number of occupants based on a standard eight-hour occupancy period. An eight-hour occupant has an FTE value of 1.0, and part-time occupants have an FTE value based on their hours per day divided by 8. FTE calculations for each shift of the project must be used consistently for all LEED-ND credits. Estimate the transient building occupants, such as volunteers, visitors, and customers. Transient occupants can be reported as either daily totals or full-time equivalents. When using daily totals for transients, match the fixture uses for each occupancy type with the values shown in Table 7 (e.g., for the daily total of volunteers counted as transients, assume 0.5 lavatory faucet uses per transient volunteer). If transients are reported as a daily full-time equivalent value, fixture uses for FTEs must be assumed regardless of the transient population's identity (e.g., for volunteers reported as FTEs, assume three lavatory faucet uses per volunteer FTE). Use a transient occupancy number that is a representative daily average over the course of a year.

In deciding whether to count individuals as transients or FTE occupants, consider their plumbing fixture use patterns. For example, a volunteer who serves four hours each day in an elementary school will likely have the same plumbing usage patterns as full-time staff. This volunteer could therefore be considered to have a staff FTE value of 0.5. On the other hand, an individual who attends a high school basketball game may be expected to use the water closets and lavatory faucets in the school building infrequently and therefore should be counted as a visitor. Report transients as average daily totals.

Table 7. Default fixture uses in schools, by occupancy type

Fixture Type	FTE	Student	Transient
Water closet			
Female	3	3	0.5
Male	1	1	0.1
Urinal			
Female	0	0	0
Male	2	2	0.4
Lavatory faucet (duration 15 sec; 12 sec with autocontrol)	3	3	0.5
Shower	0.1	0	0
Kitchen sink, nonresidential (duration 15 sec)	1	0	0

Calculating Annual Occupancy for Schools with Multiple Sessions

A session is a discrete period of school building operation. A session can be defined by a season or by other variations in building occupancy and usage, such as weekend programming by a community organization. If the school building is used for more than one session annually, calculate the session percentage for each session, based on the number of days in the session divided by the total number of days during which the school building operates annually, using Equation 1.

Equation 1

$$\% \text{ session} = \frac{\text{Days in session}}{\text{Annual days of operation}}$$

Then calculate the annual occupants of each sex by multiplying the number of occupants in each session by the session percentage (from Equation 1) and adding the results of all sessions together, using Equation 2.

Equation 2

$$\text{Annual occupants by sex} = \left[\begin{array}{c} \text{Session A FTEs} \\ \text{by sex} \\ \text{X} \\ \text{\% Session} \end{array} \right] + \left[\begin{array}{c} \text{Session B FTEs} \\ \text{by sex} \\ \text{X} \\ \text{\% Session} \end{array} \right]$$

Design Case Water Consumption

The design case annual water use is determined by totaling the annual volume of each fixture type. The design case must use the manufacturer's listed flow rates and flush volumes for installed plumbing fixtures and fittings, expressed in gallons per minute (gpm), gallons per flush (gpf), or gallons per cycle (gpc). Obtain these data from the manufacturer's product literature.

Table 8. Sample water consumption for plumbing fixtures and fittings

Flush fixture	Flow rate
Conventional water closet	1.6 gpf
High-efficiency toilet (HET), single-flush, gravity	1.28 gpf
HET, single-flush, pressure-assist	1.0 gpf
HET, dual-flush (full-flush)	1.6 gpf
HET, dual-flush (low-flush)	1.1 gpf
HET, foam-flush	0.05 gpf
Nonwater toilet	0.0 gpf
Conventional urinal	1.0 gpf
High-efficiency urinal (HEU)	0.5 gpf
Nonwater urinal	0.0 gpf
Flow fixture	
Conventional private lavatory	2.2 gpm
Conventional public lavatory	0.5 gpm or ≤ 0.25 gpc
Conventional kitchen sink	2.2 gpm
Low-flow kitchen sink	1.8 gpm
Conventional shower	2.5 gpm
Low-flow shower	1.8 gpm
gpf = gallons per flush; gpm = gallons per minute; gpc = gallons per cycle.	

Plumbing fixtures in residences, apartments, and dormitories, private (nonpublic) bathrooms in transient lodging facilities (hotels and motels), and private bathrooms in hospitals and nursing facilities are considered private or private-use facilities. All other facilities not defined as private or private-use are considered public or public-use facilities.

Baseline Case Water Consumption

The baseline case annual water use is determined by setting the fixture and fitting water consumption to the baseline rates listed in the requirements (as opposed to actual installed values in the design case).

Eligible Fixtures

This prerequisite is limited to savings generated by the water-using fixtures listed in Table 1.

Calculation 2. New Multiunit Residential Building Three Stories or Fewer and New Single-Family Residential Buildings

To comply with the requirements, 90% of buildings in this category must install any combination of fixtures that would earn 3 points according to Table 8 (from LEED for Homes 2008 Credit 3, Indoor Water Use).

Table 9. Low-rise and single-family fixtures and fittings

Fixture or fitting	High efficiency (1 point each)	Very high efficiency (2 points each)
Lavatory faucet	≤ 2.0 gpm	≤ 1.5 gpm OR meet U.S. EPA WaterSense specification
Shower	≤ 2.0 gpm per stall	≤ 1.75 gpm per stall
Toilet	≤ 1.3 gpf OR dual-flush and meet ASME A112.19.14 OR meet U.S. EPA WaterSense specification	≤ 1.1 gpf

To determine compliance, count the buildings that are new multiunit residential buildings three stories or fewer and new single-family residential buildings. Next, determine how many of these buildings would earn 3 points according to Table 8. A building counts toward the 90% requirement for the category only if all its fixtures and/or fittings meet the specifications in Table 8. Then calculate the percentage of buildings that are in compliance.

7. Documentation Guidance

As a first step in preparing to complete the LEED-ND documentation requirements, work through the following measures. Refer to GBCI's website for the complete descriptions of all required documentation.

- Determine the type and number of occupants.

- Retain manufacturers' data showing the water consumption rates, manufacturer, and model of each fixture and fitting.

- Define any usage groups, if applicable, and list the plumbing fixtures for each.

- Compile information about system schematics and capacity of any rainwater or graywater systems.

- List fixtures and fittings for all low-rise and single-family residential buildings, with flush and flow rates.

8. Examples

Example 1.

The results of various water-saving strategies for a 1.2-million-square-foot office building are shown in Figure 1. Savings are based on a water rate of $1.33 per 1,000 gallons.

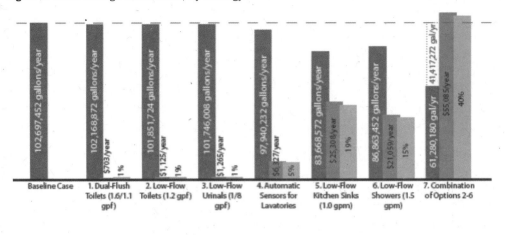

Figure 1. Water savings assessment, by strategy

Annual Water Consumption
Annual Water Utility Savings
Percent Savings over Baseline Case
Annual Water Saved

Example 2.

A project consists of a nonresidential building, six multiunit residential buildings three stories or fewer, and 24 single-family residential buildings. The required calculation applies to both new construction and major renovations (50% or more of the building's gross square footage).

For the nonresidential building, a hotel, the team first determines the fixture usage groups. The ground floor includes a restaurant open to the public, the hotel lobby, and administrative offices. The upper floors contain guest rooms. Restaurant, back-of-house, and guestroom restroom facilities each have different fixture and fitting models. The project team establishes three fixture usage groups to account for the distinct populations in the building and the specific restroom facilities they use: (1) restaurant (customers and restaurant staff), (2) administrative back-of-house (hotel administrators and staff), and (3) guest rooms (hotel guests).

For the low-rise multiunit residential buildings and single-family homes (a total of 30 buildings), at least 90% of buildings must comply with the credit requirement. In this case, at least 27 of the buildings must implement measures from Table 8 that would earn at least 3 points under LEED for Homes 2008 Credit 3, Indoor Water Use.

9. Exemplary Performance
This prerequisite is not eligible for exemplary performance under Innovation and Design Process.

10. Regional Variations
Local building and health codes differ in their treatment of alternative plumbing fixtures, such as nonwater urinals, dual-flush water closets, and nonwater toilets. Confirm the legality of nontraditional approaches with code officials before selecting plumbing fixtures.

Where rainwater harvesting proves expensive and complex, graywater may be a more appropriate replacement for potable water for use in flush fixtures. Also consider regional variations in the quality of graywater and rainwater when selecting fixtures. Determine whether minimum standards for supply water quality have been established for specific fixtures by their manufacturers.

11. Resources

Websites

Alliance for Water Efficiency

www.a4we.org/resource-library/default.aspx

This U.S.-Canadian organization has one of the largest collections of free water-efficiency information in North America, covering a wide variety of products, technologies, and issues for both residential and nonresidential applications.

American Rainwater Catchment Systems Association

www.arcsa.org

ARCSA was founded to promote rainwater catchment systems in the United States. Its website provides regional resources, suppliers, membership information, and publications, **such as the** *Texas Guide to Rainwater Harvesting*.

American Water Works Association, Water Wiser

www.awwa.org/waterwiser

This web clearinghouse provides articles, reference materials, and papers on all forms of water efficiency.

California Urban Water Conservation Council

www.cuwcc.org/resource-center/product-information.aspx

This website has a large library of technical information on water efficiency for design professionals, specifiers, builders, and consumers.

Environmental Building News, water efficiency

www.buildinggreen.com/auth/article.cfm/2008/2/3/Water-Doing-More-With-Less

The website of this publication features an article on building water efficiency, titled "Water: Doing More with Less."

National Oceanic and Atmospheric Administration, National Climatic Data Center

www.ncdc.noaa.gov/oa/ncdc.html

The NCDC website is useful for researching local climate information such as data for rainwater harvesting calculations, and it also includes links to state climate offices.

North Carolina Division of Pollution Prevention and Environmental Assistance, water efficiency

www.p2pays.org/ref/01/00692.pdf

Water Efficiency Manual for Commercial, Industrial, and Institutional Facilities presents the best practices recommended by several North Carolina state agencies.

Rocky Mountain Institute, water efficiency

www.rmi.org/sitepages/pid128.php

This portion of RMI's website is devoted to water conservation and efficiency. The site contains information on watershed management and commercial, industrial, and institutional water use and articles on policy and implementation.

U.S. Department of the Interior, water measurement

www.usbr.gov/pmts/hydraulics_lab/pubs/wmm

Water Measurement Manual: A Water Resources Technical Publication is a guide on effective water measurement practices.

U.S. Environmental Protection Agency, water conservation

www.epa.gov/OWOW/nps/chap3.html

How to Conserve Water and Use It Effectively provides guidance for commercial, industrial, and residential water users on saving water and reducing sewage volumes.

U.S. Environmental Protection Agency, Water Use Efficiency Program

www.epa.gov/owm/water-efficiency

This website provides an overview of EPA's Water Use Efficiency Program and information about using water more efficiently.

U.S. Environmental Protection Agency, WaterSense

www.epa.gov/watersense

The WaterSense program helps U.S. consumers save water and protect the environment by labeling high-quality, water-efficient products that do not require a change in lifestyle. Businesses and organizations can partner with WaterSense.

Water Closet Performance Testing

www.allianceforwaterefficiency.org/Maximum_Performance_%28MaP%29_Testing.aspx

This site provides two reports on independent test results for toilet flush performance and reliability.

Print Media

"Choosing a Toilet" (*Fine Homebuilding*)
Available at www.taunton.com/finehomebuilding/pages/h00042.asp.

"High-Efficiency Urinals (HEUs), U.S. and Canada" (Alliance for Water Efficiency, 2009)
Available at www.a4we.org/uploadedFiles/Resource_Center/Library/products/urinals/HEU-2009-03-06.pdf.

Maximum Performance (MaP) Testing of Popular Toilet Models, 14th edition (2009)
Available at www.cuwcc.org/WorkArea/showcontent.aspx?id=12052.

On-Site Wastewater Treatment Systems Manual (U.S. Environmental Protection Agency, 2002)
Available at www.epa.gov/nrmrl/pubs/625r00008/html/625R00008.htm.

Water, Sanitary and Waste Services for Buildings, fourth edition, by A. Wise and J. Swaffield (Longman Scientific & Technical, 1995).

12. Definitions

multiunit residential consisting of four or more residential units sharing a common entry.

project the land, water, and construction that constitutes the project application. A project applicant does not have to own or control all land or water within a project boundary, but all the area within the project boundary must comply with prerequisites and attempted credits.

single-family residential any residential unit other than multiunit residential, including single, duplex, triplex, row house, townhouse and semiattached residential building types.

	ND
Prerequisite	GIB Prerequisite 4
Points	Required

Intent

To reduce pollution from construction activities by controlling soil erosion, waterway sedimentation, and airborne dust generation.

Requirements

Create and implement an erosion and sedimentation control plan for all new construction activities associated with the *project*. The plan must incorporate practices such as phasing, seeding, grading, mulching, filter socks, stabilized site entrances, preservation of *existing* vegetation, and other best management practices (BMPs) to control erosion and sedimentation in runoff from the entire project site during construction. The plan must list the BMPs employed and describe how they accomplish the following objectives:

    a. Prevent loss of soil during construction by stormwater runoff and/or wind erosion, including but not limited to stockpiling of topsoil for reuse.

    b. Prevent sedimentation of any affected stormwater conveyance systems or receiving streams.

    c. Prevent polluting the air with dust and particulate matter.

The erosion and sedimentation control plan must describe how the project team will do the following:

    a. Preserve vegetation and mark clearing limits.

    b. Establish and delineate construction access.

    c. Control flow rates.

    d. Install sediment controls.

    e. Stabilize soils.

    f. Protect slopes.

    g. Protect drain inlets.

    h. Stabilize channels and outlets.

    i. Control pollutants.

    j. Control dewatering.

    k. Maintain the BMPs.

    l. Manage the erosion and sedimentation control plan.

The BMPs must be selected from the Washington State Department of Ecology's *Stormwater Management Manual for Western Washington, Volume II, Construction Stormwater Pollution Prevention* (2005 edition), or a locally approved equivalent, whichever is more stringent, and must comply with all federal, state, and local erosion and sedimentation control regulations.

1. Benefits and Issues to Consider

Environmental Issues

The loss of topsoil is the most significant on-site consequence of erosion. Topsoil is biologically active and contains organic matter and plant nutrients. It supports plant life, regulates water flow, and maintains the biodiversity of soil microbes and beneficial insects that control disease and pest outbreaks. Loss of nutrients, soil compaction, and decreased biodiversity can severely limit the vitality of landscaping. This can lead to additional site management and environmental concerns, such as increased use of fertilizers, irrigation, and pesticides, as well as increased stormwater runoff that pollutes nearby lakes and streams.

The off-site consequences of erosion from developed sites include a variety of water quality issues. Runoff from developed sites carries pollutants, sediments, and excess nutrients that disrupt aquatic habitats in the receiving waters. Nitrogen and phosphorus from runoff hasten eutrophication by causing unwanted plant growth in aquatic systems, including algal blooms that alter water quality and habitat conditions. Such growth can also decrease recreation potential and diminish the species diversity of indigenous plants, fish, and terrestrial animals.

Excess sedimentation also contributes to the degradation of water bodies and aquatic habitats. The buildup of sediments in stream channels can lessen flow capacity as well as increase flooding and turbidity levels. Turbidity reduces sunlight penetration into water and reduces photosynthesis in aquatic vegetation, causing lower oxygen levels that cannot support diverse communities of aquatic life.

Airborne dust from construction activity can have both environmental and human health consequences. Fine dust particles enter airways and lungs with ease and have been linked to numerous health problems, including asthma, decreased lung function, and breathing difficulties. In addition, dust particles can travel long distances before settling in water bodies, increasing the acidity of lakes and streams and changing nutrient balances.

Economic Issues

Erosion and sedimentation control measures are required by local building codes in most areas to minimize difficult and expensive mitigation measures in receiving waters. The cost will include some minimal expense associated with installing and inspecting the control measures, particularly before and after storm events, and will vary depending on the type, location, topography, and soil conditions of the project.

2. Related Credits

Minimizing site disturbance during construction and carrying out site restoration efforts to prevent erosion and sedimentation will also contribute to achievement of the following credits:

- SLL Credit 6, Steep Slope Protection
- SLL Credit 7, Site Design for Habitat or Wetland and Water Body Conservation
- SLL Credit 8, Restoration of Habitat or Wetlands and Water Bodies
- GIB Credit 7, Minimized Site Disturbance in Design and Construction
- GIB Credit 8, Stormwater Management

3. Summary of Referenced Standards

Washington State Department of Ecology, Stormwater Management Manual for Western Washington: Volume 2, Construction Stormwater Pollution Prevention
The 2005 edition of this Washington State manual provides a comprehensive set of best management practices to prevent and reduce erosion and sedimentation pollution.

4. Implementation

Create an erosion and sedimentation control (ESC) plan during the design phase of the project. Erosion on existing sites typically results from foot traffic that kills vegetation, steep slopes where stormwater sheet flow exceeds vegetation's holding power, runoff that exceeds vegetation's holding power, or vehicle traffic on unpaved areas. Identifying and eliminating these and other causes will minimize soil loss and preserve the quality of receiving waters. Consider employing strategies such as temporary and permanent seeding, mulching, earth dikes, silt fencing, sediment traps, and sediment basins. Compare best management practices (BMPs) from locally approved manuals or regulations with BMPs from the Washington State manual and choose the more stringent measures for erosion and sedimentation control. If the recommended BMPs are comparable in stringency, select those that are most appropriate to the project site.

Typically, the civil engineer identifies erosion-prone areas and soil stabilization measures. The contractor then adopts a plan to implement the measures presented by the civil engineer and responds to rain events and other activities accordingly. It is recommended that the ESC be incorporated into the construction drawings and specifications, with clear instructions regarding responsibilities, scheduling, and inspections.

If a stormwater pollution prevention plan is required by local regulations, an ESC plan may already exist. In that case, confirm that the plan meets the prerequisite requirements and is implemented. If a plan is not required for purposes other than LEED, use the referenced standard listed above as a guideline on how to compose the plan. Table 1 shows common strategies for controlling erosion and sedimentation on construction sites.

Table 1. Strategies for Controlling Erosion and Sedimentation

Control Technology	Description
Stabilization	
Temporary Seeding	Plant fast-growing grasses to temporarily stabilize soils
Permanent Seeding	Plant grass, trees, and shrubs to permanently stabilize soil
Mulching	Place hay, grass, woodchips, straw, or gravel on the soil surface to cover and hold soils
Structural Control	
Earth Dike	Construct a mound of stabilized soil to divert surface runoff volumes from distributed areas or into sediment basins or sediment traps
Silt Fence	Construct posts with a filter fabric media to remove sediment from stormwater volumes flowing through the fence
Sediment Trap	Excavate a pond area or construct earthen embankments to allow for settling of sediment from stormwater volumes
Sediment Basin	Construct a pond with a controlled water release structure to allow for settling of sediment from stormwater volumes

5. Timeline and Team

During the design phase, the civil engineer or landscape architect should compare local codes with the requirements of this prerequisite and create an erosion and sedimentation control plan. This professional should have specific training in ESC measures. The general contractor should work with the project team's civil engineer or landscape architect to implement the plan during all phases of the construction. The general contractor should photograph and maintain erosion and sedimentation control measures on-site during the various stages of construction. Once the site is stabilized, the general contractor should remove any temporary erosion and sedimentation control measures.

6. Calculations

There are no calculations for this prerequisite.

7. Documentation Guidance

As a first step in preparing to complete the LEED-ND documentation requirements, work through the following measures. Refer to GBCI's website for the complete descriptions of all required documentation.

- Develop an erosion and sedimentation control drawing and/or a written ESC plan with specifications that detail the best management practices and the responsible parties for implementation.

- Over the course of the site work activities, document implementation of the ESC plan through date-stamped photos, inspection logs or reports, descriptions of corrective action in response to problems, etc.

8. Examples

There are no examples for this prerequisite.

9. Exemplary Performance

This prerequisite is not eligible for exemplary performance under Innovation and Design Process.

10. Regional Variations

The comprehensiveness and stringency of local ESC codes vary. Compare local BMPs with those in the Washington State manual; compliance with the prerequisite requires choosing the more stringent measures.

11. Resources

Websites

Certified Professionals in Erosion and Sediment Control Inc.
www.cpesc.net
Search the CPESC directory or the directory of certified professionals in stormwater quality on this website to find local professionals.

Environment Canada, sedimentation
www.ec.gc.ca/water/en/nature/sedim/e_sedim.htm
This website includes information on the environmental effects of sedimentation.

Erosion Control Technology Council
www.ectc.org
This nonprofit organization develops performance standards, testing procedures, and guidance on the application and installation of rolled erosion control products, hydraulic erosion control products, and sediment retention fiber rolls.

Great Lakes Information Network, soil erosion and sedimentation
www.great-lakes.net/envt/pollution/erosion.html
This resource provides links to general resources, education and training opportunities, materials, manuals, maps and other resources related to soil erosion, sedimentation and watershed management in the Great Lakes region.

International Erosion Control Association
www.ieca.org
This nonprofit membership organization's mission is to connect, educate, and develop the worldwide erosion and sediment control community.

U.S. Environmental Protection Agency, Construction General Permit Program
www.cfpub.epa.gov/npdes/stormwater/cgp.cfm
This website provides information on the U.S. EPA's stormwater permit program.

Washington State Department of Ecology, stormwater management
www.ecy.wa.gov/programs/wq/stormwater/manual.html
This site provides copies of the *Stormwater Management Manual for Western Washington*, the volume referenced in the prerequisite.

Print Media
Stormwater Management for Construction Activities, Document 832R92005 (U.S. Environmental Protection Agency).

12. Definitions

existing present on the date of submission of LEED-ND certification documents; similarly, an element or condition that **exists** is present on the date that LEED-ND certification documents are submitted.

project the land, water, and construction that constitutes the project application. A project applicant does not have to own or control all land or water within a project boundary, but all the area within the project boundary must comply with prerequisites and attempted credits.

CERTIFIED GREEN BUILDINGS

	ND
Credit	GIB Credit 1
Points	1-5 points

Intent

To encourage the design, construction, and retrofit of buildings that utilize green building practices.

Requirements

OPTION 1. Projects with 10 or Fewer Habitable Buildings

Design, construct, or retrofit one building as part of the project, beyond the prerequisite, to be certified under one of the following LEED green building rating systems: LEED for New Construction, LEED for Existing Buildings, LEED for Homes, LEED for Schools, LEED for Retail: New Construction, or LEED for Core & Shell (with at least 75% of the floor area certified under LEED for Commercial Interiors or LEED for Retail: Commercial Interiors) or through a green building rating system requiring review by independent, impartial, third-party certifying bodies as defined by ISO/IEC 17021. Additional points (up to 5) may be earned for each additional certified building that is part of the project.

OR

OPTION 2. Projects of All Sizes

Design, construct, or retrofit a percentage of the total project building square footage, beyond the prerequisite requirement, to be certified under one of the LEED green building rating systems listed above or through a green building rating system requiring review by independent, impartial, third-party certifying bodies as defined by ISO/IEC 17021.

Table 1. Points for green building certification

Percentage of square footage certified	Points
≥ 10% and < 20%	1
≥ 20% and < 30%	2
≥ 30% and < 40%	3
≥ 40% and < 50%	4
≥ 50%	5

AND

FOR ALL PROJECTS

Detached *accessory dwelling units* must be counted as separate buildings. Accessory dwellings attached to a main building are not counted separately.

1. Benefits and Issues to Consider

For a summary of the benefits of including green buildings in the project, please see GIB Prerequisite 1, Certified Green Building.

Additional benefits may be realized if multiple green buildings are incorporated into the project. Certain recycled or locally sourced materials may be cheaper if ordered in bulk for a number of buildings. Consider whether efficiencies of scale can be achieved for infrastructure systems (e.g., district heating and cooling). A project team may face a learning curve on its first green building, but designing subsequent buildings on the same project site will likely be much easier.

2. Related Credits

Achieving independent, third-party green certification is related to this prerequisite:

- GIB Prerequisite 1, Certified Green Building

3. Summary of Referenced Standards

U.S. Green Building Council, LEED rating systems
www.usgbc.org/leed
The LEED rating systems establish criteria for building design, construction, and operation using strategies aimed at improving performance in energy savings, water efficiency, emissions reduction, indoor environmental quality, and stewardship of resources and sensitivity to their impacts.

International Organization for Standardization, ISO/IEC 17021
www.iso.org
This ISO standard specifies principles and requirements for the competence, consistency, and impartiality of third-party conformity assessment bodies performing audit and certification activities. Entities that conduct audit and certification activities are called third-party conformity assessment bodies.

4. Implementation

Refer to the Implementation section under GIB Prerequisite 1, Certified Green Building.

5. Timeline and Team

Refer to the Timeline and Team section under GIB Prerequisite 1, Certified Green Building.

6. Calculations

There are no calculations for this credit.

7. Documentation Guidance

As a first step in preparing to complete the LEED-ND documentation requirements, work through the following measure. Refer to GBCI's website for the complete descriptions of all required documentation.

- Assemble information about the building's green certification.

8. Examples

There are no examples for this credit.

9. Exemplary Performance

Option 1 is not eligible for exemplary performance under Innovation and Design Process. Projects that use Option 2 may earn 1 additional point by achieving certification for 90% of project square footage.

10. Regional Variations

There are no regional variations associated with this credit.

11. Resources

Websites

U.S. Green Building Council, LEED program

www.usgbc.org/leed

This website provides detailed information about the LEED rating systems, including information about project registration and certification, professional accreditation, and additional resources.

Print Media

Fundamentals of Integrated Design for Sustainable Building, by Marian Keeler and Bill Burke (John Wiley & Sons, 2009).

LEED for Homes Reference Guide (USGBC, 2008).

LEED Reference Guide for Green Building Design and Construction (USGBC, 2009).

LEED Reference Guide for Green Interior Design and Construction (USGBC, 2009).

LEED Reference Guide for Green Building Operations and Maintenance (USGBC, 2009).

12. Definitions

accessory dwelling unit a subordinate dwelling unit that is attached to a principal building or contained in a separate structure on the same property as the principal unit.

project the land, water, and construction that constitutes the project application. A project applicant does not have to own or control all land or water within a project boundary, but all the area within the project boundary must comply with prerequisites and attempted credits.

BUILDING ENERGY EFFICIENCY

	ND
Credit	GIB Credit 2
Points	2 points

Intent

To encourage the design and construction of energy-efficient buildings that reduce air, water, and land pollution and adverse environmental effects from energy production and consumption.

Requirements

The following requirement applies to 90% of the building floor area (rounded up to the next whole building) of all nonresidential buildings, mixed-use buildings, and *multiunit residential* buildings four stories or more constructed as part of the *project* or undergoing major renovations as part of the project.

New buildings must demonstrate an average 18% (1 point) or 26% (2 points) improvement over ANSI/ASHRAE/IESNA Standard 90.1–2007 (with errata but without addenda). Buildings undergoing major renovations as part of the project must demonstrate an average 14% (1 point) or 22% (2 points) improvement over ANSI/ASHRAE/IESNA Standard 90.1–2007.

Projects must document building energy efficiency using one or a combination of the following:

a. Produce a LEED-compliant energy model following the methodology outlined in the LEED rating system appropriate to each building's scope, including demonstration by a whole building project computer simulation using the building performance rating method in Appendix G of ANSI/ASHRAE/IESNA Standard 90.1–2007. Appendix G requires that the energy analysis done for the building performance rating method include all energy costs associated with the building project. Projects in California may use Title 24–2005, Part 6, in place of ANSI/ASHRAE/IESNA Standard 90.1–2007.

b. Comply with the prescriptive measures of the ASHRAE Advanced Energy Design Guide listed below, appropriate to each building's scope. Comply with all applicable criteria as established in the guide for the climate zone in which the project is located.

   - ASHRAE Advanced Energy Design Guide for Small Office Buildings 2004 (office occupancy buildings less than 20,000 square feet).

   - ASHRAE Advanced Energy Design Guide for Small Retail Buildings 2006 (retail occupancy buildings less than 20,000 square feet).

   - ASHRAE Advanced Energy Design Guide for Small Warehouses and Self-Storage Buildings 2008 (warehouse or self-storage occupancy less than 50,000 square feet).

   - ASHRAE Advanced Energy Design Guide for K–12 School Buildings (K–12 school occupancy less than 200,000 square feet).

c. For buildings less than 100,000 square feet, comply with the prescriptive measures identified in the Advanced Buildings™ Core Performance™ Guide developed by the New Buildings Institute, as follows:

   - Comply with Section 1, Design Process Strategies, and Section 2, Core Performance Requirements, of the Core Performance Guide.

■ Health care, warehouse and laboratory projects are ineligible for this path.

If method (a) is used for all of the floor area evaluated in this prerequisite, the total percentage improvement is calculated as a sum of energy costs for each building compared with a baseline. If any combination of methods (a), (b), and (c) is used, the total percentage improvement is calculated as a weighted average based on building floor area. In determining the weighted average, buildings pursuing (a) will be credited at the percentage value determined by the energy model. Buildings pursuing (b) or (c) will be credited at 12% better than ANSI/ASHRAE/IESNA Standard 90.1–2007 for new buildings and 8% better for *existing* building renovations.

AND

For new *single-family residential* buildings and new multiunit residential buildings three stories or fewer, 90% of the buildings must achieve a *Home Energy Rating System (HERS)* index score of at least 75.

Project teams wishing to use ASHRAE-approved addenda for the purposes of this credit may do so at their discretion. Addenda must be applied consistently across all LEED credits.

1. Benefits and Issues to Consider

For a summary of the benefits of reduced building energy consumption, please see GIB Prerequisite 2, Minimum Building Energy Efficiency.

	GIB
ND	Credit 2

2. Related Credits

Improving building energy efficiency is related to the following prerequisite:

- GIB Prerequisite 2, Minimum Building Energy Efficiency.

Achieving several other related credits may also help minimize building energy needs:

- GIB Credit 5, Existing Building Reuse

- GIB Credit 9, Heat Island Reduction

- GIB Credit 10, Solar Orientation

- GIB Credit 11, On-Site Renewable Energy Sources

- GIB Credit 12, District Heating and Cooling

3. Summary of Referenced Standards

ANSI/ASHRAE/IESNA Standard 90.1–2007, Energy Standard for Buildings Except Low-Rise Residential

www.ashrae.org

This standard was formulated by American Society of Heating, Refrigerating and Air-Conditioning Engineers (ASHRAE) with the Illuminating Engineering Society of North America (IESNA) under an American National Standards Institute (ANSI) consensus process. It establishes minimum requirements for the energy-efficient design of buildings with these exceptions: single-family houses, multiunit structures of three habitable stories or fewer above grade, manufactured houses (mobile and modular homes), buildings that do not use electricity or fossil fuel, and equipment and building systems that use energy primarily for industrial, manufacturing, or commercial processes). Building envelope requirements are provided for semiheated spaces, such as warehouses. The standard addresses the following categories:

- Section 5. Building envelope (including semiheated spaces, such as warehouses).

- Section 6. Heating, ventilation, and air-conditioning (including parking garage ventilation, freeze protection, exhaust air recovery, and condenser heat recovery for service water heating).

- Section 7. Service water heating (including swimming pools).

- Section 8. Power (including all building power distribution systems).

- Section 9. Lighting (including exit signs, building exterior, grounds, and parking garages).

- Section 10. Other equipment (including all permanently wired electrical motors).

Within each section are mandatory provisions and additional prescriptive requirements. Some sections also contain performance alternatives. The energy cost budget method allows certain prescriptive requirements to be exceeded, provided energy cost savings are made in other areas. However, in all cases, the mandatory provisions must still be met.

New Building Institute, Advanced Buildings Core Performance™ Guide

www.advancedbuildings.net

The Advanced Building Core Performance program offers a predictable alternative to energy performance modeling and a simple set of prescriptive criteria for significantly increasing building energy performance, beyond the requirements of ASHRAE 90.1–2004, in all climate zones. It updates and replaces the Advanced Building Benchmarked program.

ASHRAE, *Advanced Energy Design Guide for Small Office Buildings 2004*
www.ashrae.org
The Advanced Energy Design Guide series provides a sensible approach to achieving advanced levels of energy savings without having to resort to detailed calculations or analysis. This guide is for office buildings up to 20,000 square feet; such buildings make up the bulk of office space in the United States. The strategies provide benefits and savings for the building owner while maintaining the quality and functionality of the space.

ASHRAE, *Advanced Energy Design Guide for Small Retail Buildings 2006*
www.ashrae.org
The Advanced Energy Design Guide series provides a sensible approach to achieving advanced levels of energy savings without having to resort to detailed calculations or analysis. This guide focuses on retail buildings up to 20,000 square feet that use unitary heading and air-conditioning equipment; such buildings represent a significant amount of commercial retail space in the United States.

ASHRAE, *Advanced Energy Design Guide for Small Warehouses and Self Storage Buildings 2008*
www.ashrae.org
The Advanced Energy Design Guide series provides a sensible approach to achieving advanced levels of energy savings without having to resort to detailed calculations or analysis. This guide focuses on warehouses up to 50,000 square feet and self-storage buildings that use unitary heating and air-conditioning equipment; such facilities make up a significant amount of commercial warehouse space in the United States.

ASHRAE, *Advanced Energy Design Guide for K-12 School Buildings*
www.ashrae.org
The Advanced Energy Design Guide series provides a sensible approach to achieving advanced levels of energy savings without having to resort to detailed calculations or analysis. This guide focuses on elementary, middle, and high school buildings, which have a wide variety of heating and air-conditioning requirements. Options for daylighting, an important component in schools, are included.

ENERGY STAR®, Target Finder Rating Tool
www.energystar.gov/index.cfm?c=new_bldg_design.bus_target_finder
ENERGY STAR is a government-industry partnership managed by the U.S. Environmental Protection Agency and the U.S. Department of Energy. Target Finder is an on-line tool that can establish energy performance goals for a project. It uses data such as zip code and building type to calculate the estimated total energy use for the building and then assigns an energy performance rating on a scale of 1 to 100. The zip code indicates the climate conditions that the building would experience in a normal year (based on a 30-year climate average) so that energy use intensity for the target (based on the energy fuel mix typical in the region) can be estimated. The tool displays the percentage electricity and natural gas assumption used to calculate design targets. The energy use intensity generated by Target Finder reflects the distribution of energy performance in commercial buildings derived from data in the U.S. Department of Energy's Commercial Buildings Energy Consumption Survey. The ratings generated by Target Finder provide a useful benchmark for estimating and comparing a building's energy use with that of other buildings and for determining a project's goals for energy efficiency. Assessing energy consumption early in the process enables teams to employ a holistic approach in making design decisions that improve the building's performance. Energy performance targets are more easily achieved if all the building's systems enhance one another; attempting to increase energy efficiency after construction is less successful because only small changes are possible without major disruption and additional cost.

4. Implementation

Implementation is the same as for GIB Prerequisite 2, Minimum Building Energy Efficiency, except that projects must document at least 18% (1 point) or 26% (2 points) improvement over the baseline for at least 90% of new nonresidential, mixed-use, or multifamily buildings four stories or more; or at least 14% (1 point) or 22% (2 points) improvement for major renovations of the same building types. At least 90% of new single-family and multiunit residential buildings three stories or less must score at least 75 on the HERS index.

See the Implementation section under GIB Prerequisite 2 for additional guidance.

5. Timeline and Team

The project team should consider building energy efficiency an integral component of the neighborhood at the outset of project planning. The design team should include experienced energy efficiency specialists in design and mechanical and electrical engineering.

6. Calculations

See the Calculations section under GIB Prerequisite 2. For new construction, the results must show savings of at least 18% or 26%, and for major renovations, at least 14% or 22%, depending on the number of points being attempted.

7. Documentation Guidance

As a first step in preparing to complete theLEED-ND documentation requirements, work through the following measures. Refer to GBCI's website for the complete descriptions of all required documentation.

- For ASHRAE compliance, list any addenda used, and retain copies of ASHRAE compliance forms.

- Determine the climate zone for the project location.

- Calculate energy use by type.

- Maintain a list of energy end uses for the project building (for both the baseline case and the design case).

- If the project is using the prescriptive compliance path, assemble documentation demonstrating that the project meets all applicable requirements.

8. Examples

See the Examples section under GIB Prerequisite 2, and note this credit's higher threshold requirements for percentage savings.

9. Exemplary Performance

Projects with nonresidential buildings, mixed-use buildings, and multiunit residential buildings four stories or more may earn an Innovation and Design Process credit for exemplary performance by demonstrating a 34% improvement over ANSI/ASHRAE/IESNA Standard 90.1–2007 for new buildings and a 30% improvement for buildings undergoing major renovations for at least 90% of the building floor area.

Projects with new one- to three-family townhouse residential buildings and new multiunit residential buildings three stories or fewer may earn an exemplary performance credit by achieving a HERS index score of at least 65 for at least 90% of buildings.

If a project includes the types of buildings addressed in both scenarios, both thresholds must be achieved to earn the additional point.

10. Regional Variations

ASHRAE 90.1–2007 accounts for regional variance with eight climate zones and three climate subzones; the standard specifies the minimum envelope and glazing property requirements for each.

11. Resources

Websites

American Council for an Energy-Efficient Economy

www.aceee.org

ACEEE is a nonprofit organization dedicated to advancing energy efficiency by conducting technical and policy assessments; advising policymakers and program managers; collaborating with businesses, public interest groups, and other organizations; and providing education and outreach through conferences, workshops, and publications.

ENERGY STAR®, energy upgrades

www.energystar.gov/index.cfm?c=business.bus_upgrade_manual

The *Buildings Upgrade Manual* is a strategic guide for planning and implementing energy-saving building upgrades. It provides general methods for reviewing and adjusting system control settings, plus procedures for testing and correcting calibration and operation of system components, such as sensors, actuators, and controlled devices.

New Buildings Institute, Inc.

www.newbuildings.org

The New Buildings Institute is a nonprofit, public-benefits corporation dedicated to making buildings better for people and the environment. Its mission is to promote energy efficiency in buildings through technology research, guidelines, and codes.

U.S. Department of Energy, Building Energy Codes Program

www.energycodes.gov

This program provides comprehensive resources for states and code users, with news, compliance software, code comparisons, and a database of state energy contacts, code status, code history, DOE grant recipients, and construction data. The program is also updating the COMCheck-EZ™ compliance tool to include ANSI/ASHRAE/IESNA Standard 90.1–2007. This compliance tool includes the prescriptive path and trade-off compliance methods. The software generates appropriate compliance forms as well.

U.S. Department of Energy, Office of Energy Efficiency and Renewable Energy

www.eere.energy.gov/

This extensive website for energy efficiency links to DOE-funded sites that address buildings and energy. Of particular interest is the tools directory, which includes the Commercial Buildings Energy Consumption Tool for estimating end-use consumption in commercial buildings. This tool allows the user to define a set of buildings by principal activity, size, age, region, climate zone, and fuels (main heat, secondary heat, cooling, and water heating) and view the resulting energy consumption and expenditure estimates in tabular form.

U.S. Environmental Protection Agency, Combined Heat and Power Partnership

www.epa.gov/chp

Information on cogeneration, also called combined heat and power, is available from EPA through the CHP Partnership, a voluntary program seeking to reduce the environmental effects of power generation by promoting CHP. The partnership works closely with energy users, the CHP industry, state and local governments, and other clean energy stakeholders to facilitate the development of new projects and promote their environmental and economic benefits.

Print Media

ANSI/ASHRAE/IESNA Standard 90.1–2007 User's Manual (ASHRAE, 2008).
The ANSI/ASHRAE/IESNA Standard 90.1–2007 User's Manual was developed as a companion document to the ANSI/ASHRAE/IESNA Standard 90.1–2007, Energy Standard for Buildings Except Low-Rise Residential Buildings. The manual explains the new standard and includes sample calculations, useful reference material, and information on the intent and application of the standard. It is abundantly illustrated and contains numerous examples and tables of reference data. It also includes a complete set of compliance forms and worksheets that can be used to document compliance with the standard. The manual is helpful to architects and engineers applying the standard to the design of buildings, plan examiners and field inspectors who must enforce the standard in areas where it is adopted as code, and contractors who must construct buildings in compliance with the standard. A compact disk is included that contains electronic versions of the compliance forms found in the manual.

12. Definitions

existing present on the date of submission of LEED-ND certification documents; similarly, an element or condition that **exists** is present on the date that LEED-ND certification documents are submitted.

Home Energy Rating System (HERS) index a scoring system established by the Residential Energy Services Network (RESNET) in which a home built to the specifications of the HERS Reference Home (based on the 2006 International Energy Conservation Code) scores 100, and a net zero energy home scores 0. The lower a home's HERS Index, the more energy efficient it is.

multiunit residential consisting of four or more residential units sharing a common entry.

project the land, water, and construction that constitutes the project application. A project applicant does not have to own or control all land or water within a project boundary, but all the area within the project boundary must comply with prerequisites and attempted credits.

single-family residential any residential unit other than multiunit residential, including single, duplex, triplex, row house, townhouse and semiattached residential building types.

BUILDING WATER EFFICIENCY

	ND
Credit	GIB Credit 3
Points	1 point

Intent

To reduce effects on natural water resources and reduce burdens on community water supply and wastewater systems.

Requirements

For nonresidential buildings, mixed-use buildings, and multifamily residential buildings four stories or more:

Indoor water usage in new buildings and buildings undergoing major renovations as part of the *project* must be an average 40% less than in baseline buildings. The baseline usage is based on the requirements of the Energy Policy Act of 1992 and subsequent rulings by the Department of Energy, the requirements of the Energy Policy Act of 2005, and the fixture performance standards in the 2006 editions of the Uniform Plumbing Code or International Plumbing Code as to fixture performance. Calculations are based on estimated occupant usage and include only the following fixtures and fixture fittings (as applicable to the project scope): water closets (toilets), urinals, lavatory faucets, showers, kitchen sink faucets, and prerinse spray valves.

The water efficiency threshold is calculated as a weighted average of water usage for the buildings constructed as part of the project based on their conditioned square footage. Projects may also follow the LEED for Multiple Buildings and On-Campus Building Application Guide alternative calculation methodology to show compliance with this prerequisite.

Table 1. National commercial efficiency baselines

Commercial fixtures, fittings, or appliances	Baseline water usage
Commercial toilet	1.6 gpf[1] Except blow-out fixtures, 3.5 gpf
Commercial urinal	1.0 gpf
Commercial lavatory (restroom) faucet	2.2 gpm at 60 psi, private applications only (hotel-motel guest rooms, hospital patient rooms) 0.5 gpm at 60 psi[2] all others except private applications 0.25 gallons per cycle for metering faucets
Commercial prerinse spray valve (for food service applications)	Flow rate ≤ 1.6 gpm (no pressure specified; no performance requirement)

[1] EPAct 1992 standard for toilets applies to both commercial and residential models.
[2] In addition to EPAct requirements, the American Society of Mechanical Engineers standard for public lavatory faucets is 0.5 gpm at 60 psi (ASME A112.18.1-2005). This maximum has been incorporated into the national Uniform Plumbing Code and the International Plumbing Code.

Table 2. National residential efficiency baselines

Residential Fixtures, Fittings, and Appliances	Baseline water usage
Residential toilet	1.6 gpf[3]
Residential lavatory (bathroom) faucet	2.2 gpm at 60 psi
Residential kitchen faucet	
Residential showerhead	2.5 gpm at 80 psi per shower stall[4]

gpf = gallons per flush; psi = pounds per square inch.
Source: Adapted from information developed and summarized by the U.S. EPA Office of Water.
[3] EPAct 1992 standard for toilets applies to both commercial and residential models.
[4] Residential shower compartment (stall) in dwelling units: The total allowable flow rate from all flowing showerheads at any given time, including rain systems, waterfalls, bodysprays, bodyspas, and jets, shall be limited to the allowable showerhead flow rate as specified above (2.5-gpm) per shower compartment, where the floor area of the shower compartment is less than 2,500 sq.in. For each increment of 2,500 sq.in. of floor area thereafter or part thereof, an additional showerhead with total allowable flow rate from all flowing devices equal to or less than the allowable flow rate as specified above shall be allowed. Exception: Showers that emit recirculated non-potable water originating from within the shower compartment while operating are allowed to exceed the maximum as long as the total potable water flow does not exceed the flow rate as specified above.

The following fixtures, fittings, and appliances are outside the scope of the water use reduction calculation:

a. Commercial steam cookers.

b. Commercial dishwashers.

c. Automatic commercial ice makers.

d. Commercial (family-sized) clothes washers.

e. Residential clothes washers.

f. Standard and compact residential dishwashers.

AND

For new *single-family residential* buildings and new *multiunit residential* buildings three stories or fewer, 90% of buildings must use a combination of fixtures that would earn 5 points under LEED for Homes 2008 Credit 3, Indoor Water Use.

1. Benefits and Issues to Consider

For a summary of the benefits of reduced building water consumption, please see GIB Prerequisite 3, Minimum Building Water Efficiency.

2. Related Credits

Improving building water efficiency may assist in achieving the following related credits:

- GIB Prerequisite 3, Minimum Building Water Efficiency
- GIB Credit 4, Water-Efficient Landscaping
- GIB Credit 8, Stormwater Management
- GIB Credit 14, Wastewater Management

3. Summary of Referenced Standards

Energy Policy Act of 1992 (as amended)

This legislation, known as EPAct, addresses energy and water use in commercial, institutional, and residential facilities.

Energy Policy Act of 2005

This version of the EPAct statute became U.S. law in August 2005; it updates previous standards for energy and water use in commercial, institutional, and residential facilities.

International Association of Plumbing and Mechanical Officials Publication IAPMO/ American National Standards Institute UPC 1–2006, Uniform Plumbing Code 2006, Section 402.0, Water-Conserving Fixtures and Fittings

www.iapmo.org

UPC defines water-conserving fixtures and fittings for water closets, urinals, and metered faucets. This ANSI-accredited code safeguards life, health, property, and public welfare by regulating and controlling the design, construction, installation, materials, location, operation, and maintenance or use of plumbing systems.

International Code Council, International Plumbing Code 2006, Section 604, Design of Building Water Distribution System

www.iccsafe.org

IPC defines maximum flow rates and consumption for plumbing fixtures and fittings, including public and private lavatories, showerheads, sink faucets, urinals, and water closets.

4. Implementation

Implementation is the same as for GIB Prerequisite 3, Minimum Building Water Efficiency, except that indoor water usage must be an average 40% less than in baseline buildings.

See the Implementation section under GIB Prerequisite 3 for additional guidance.

5. Timeline and Team

During predesign, setting water goals and strategies involves the owner, architect, and engineers. Identify local water utilities and governing authorities and research codes and applicable water laws. Learn the process for obtaining permits and approval and set water goals and strategy.

During design development, the engineering team should develop and design water reuse and treatment systems, perform preliminary LEED calculations, and confirm or reassess water goals. In construction documents, the architect, working with the owner, should specify efficient fixtures and appliances and complete LEED calculations and documentation. During construction, the design team and owner should confirm proper selection, installation, and operation of water fixtures, fittings, and systems.

6. Calculations

See the Calculations section under GIB Prerequisite 3.

7. Documentation Guidance

As a first step in preparing to complete the LEED-ND documentation requirements, work through the following measures. Refer to GBCI's website for the complete descriptions of all required documentation.

- Determine the type and number of project occupants.
- Define any usage groups, if applicable, and list the plumbing fixtures for each.
- Retain manufacturers' data showing the water consumption rates, manufacturer, and model of each fixture and fitting.
- Compile information about system schematics and capacity of any rainwater or graywater systems.

8. Examples

See the Examples section under GIB Prerequisite 3.

9. Exemplary Performance

Projects with nonresidential buildings, mixed-use buildings, and multifamily residential buildings four stories or more may earn an Innovation and Design Process credit for exemplary performance by reducing indoor water use in new buildings and buildings undergoing major renovations as part of the project to, on average, 50% of the water use in baseline buildings.

Projects with new multiunit residential buildings three stories or fewer and new single-family residential buildings may earn an exemplary performance credit by using a combination of water fixtures that would earn 6 points under LEED for Homes 2008 Credit 3, Indoor Water Use, in 90% of buildings.

If a project includes the types of buildings addressed in both scenarios, both thresholds must be achieved to earn the additional point.

10. Regional Variations

Local building and health codes differ in their treatment of alternative plumbing fixtures, such as waterless urinals, dual-flush water closets, and nonwater toilets. Confirm the legality of nontraditional approaches with code officials before selecting plumbing fixtures.

Where rainwater harvesting proves expensive and complex, graywater may be a more appropriate replacement for potable water for use in flush fixtures. Also consider regional variations in the quality of graywater and rainwater when selecting fixtures. Determine whether minimum standards for supply water quality have been established for specific fixtures by their manufacturers.

11. Resources

Websites

Alliance for Water Efficiency
www.a4we.org/resource-library/default.aspx
This U.S.-Canadian organization has one of the largest collections of free water-efficiency information in North America, covering a wide variety of products, technologies, and issues for both residential and nonresidential applications.

American Rainwater Catchment Systems Association

www.arcsa.org

ARCSA was founded to promote rainwater catchment systems in the United States. Its website provides regional resources, suppliers, membership information, and publications, **such as the** *Texas Guide to Rainwater Harvesting*.

American Water Works Association, Water Wiser

www.awwa.org/waterwiser

This web clearinghouse provides articles, reference materials, and papers on all forms of water efficiency.

California Urban Water Conservation Council

www.cuwcc.org/resource-center/product-information.aspx

This website has a large library of technical information on water efficiency for design professionals, specifiers, builders, and consumers.

Environmental Building News, water efficiency

www.buildinggreen.com/auth/article.cfm/2008/2/3/Water-Doing-More-With-Less

The website of this publication features an article on building water efficiency, titled *"Water: Doing More with Less."*

National Oceanic and Atmospheric Administration, National Climatic Data Center

www.ncdc.noaa.gov/oa/ncdc.html

The NCDC website is useful for researching local climate information such as data for rainwater harvesting calculations, and it also includes links to state climate offices.

North Carolina Division of Pollution Prevention and Environmental Assistance, water efficiency

www.p2pays.org/ref/01/00692.pdf

Water Efficiency Manual for Commercial, Industrial, and Institutional Facilities presents the best practices recommended by several North Carolina state agencies.

Rocky Mountain Institute, water efficiency

www.rmi.org/sitepages/pid128.php

This portion of RMI's website is devoted to water conservation and efficiency. The site contains information on watershed management and commercial, industrial, and institutional water use and articles on policy and implementation.

U.S. Department of the Interior, water measurement

www.usbr.gov/pmts/hydraulics_lab/pubs/wmm

Water Measurement Manual: A Water Resources Technical Publication is a guide on effective water measurement practices.

U.S. Environmental Protection Agency, water conservation

www.epa.gov/OWOW/nps/chap3.html

How to Conserve Water and Use It Effectively provides guidance for commercial, industrial, and residential water users on saving water and reducing sewage volumes.

U.S. Environmental Protection Agency, Water Use Efficiency Program

www.epa.gov/owm/water-efficiency

This website provides an overview of EPA's Water Use Efficiency Program and information about using water more efficiently.

U.S. Environmental Protection Agency, WaterSense

www.epa.gov/watersense

The WaterSense program helps U.S. consumers save water and protect the environment by labeling high-quality, water-efficient products that do not require a change in lifestyle. Businesses and organizations can partner with WaterSense.

Water Closet Performance Testing
www.allianceforwaterefficiency.org/Maximum_Performance_%28MaP%29_Testing.aspx
This site provides two reports on independent test results for toilet flush performance and reliability.

Print Media
"Choosing a Toilet" (*Fine Homebuilding*)
Available at www.taunton.com/finehomebuilding/pages/h00042.asp.

Constructed Wetlands for Wastewater Treatment and Wildlife Habitat: 17 Case Studies, Publication 832/B-93-005 (U.S. Environmental Protection Agency, 1993).

"High-Efficiency Urinals (HEUs), U.S. and Canada" (Alliance for Water Efficiency, 2009) Aavailable at www.a4we.org/uploadedFiles/Resource_Center/Library/products/urinals/HEU-2009-03-06.pdf.

Maximum Performance (MaP) Testing of Popular Toilet Models, 14th edition (2009)
Available at www.cuwcc.org/WorkArea/showcontent.aspx?id=12052.

On-Site Wastewater Treatment Systems Manual (U.S. Environmental Protection Agency, 2002),
Available at www.epa.gov/nrmrl/pubs/625r00008/html/625R00008.htm.

Water, Sanitary and Waste Services for Buildings, fourth edition, by A. Wise and J. Swaffield (Longman Scientific & Technical, 1995).

12. Definitions

multiunit residential consisting of four or more residential units sharing a common entry.

project the land, water, and construction that constitutes the project application. A project applicant does not have to own or control all land or water within a project boundary, but all the area within the project boundary must comply with prerequisites and attempted credits.

single-family residential any residential unit other than multiunit residential, including single, duplex, triplex, row house, townhouse and semiattached residential building types.

WATER-EFFICIENT LANDSCAPING

	ND
Credit	GIB Credit 4
Points	1 point

Intent

To limit or eliminate the use of *potable water* and other natural surface or subsurface water resources on *project* sites, for landscape irrigation.

Requirements

Reduce water consumption for outdoor landscape irrigation by 50% from a calculated midsummer baseline case. Reductions may be attributed to any combination of the following strategies:, among others:

a. Plant species, plant density, and microclimate factor.

b. Irrigation efficiency.

c. Use of captured rainwater.

d. Use of recycled wastewater.

e. Use of water treated and conveyed by a public agency specifically for nonpotable uses.

f. Use of other nonpotable water sources, such as stormwater, air-conditioning condensate, and foundation drain water.

Projects with no new or *existing* landscape irrigation requirements automatically meet the credit requirements.

Groundwater seepage that is pumped away from the immediate vicinity of buildings slabs and foundations can be used for landscape irrigation and meet the intent of this credit. However, it must be demonstrated that doing so does not affect site stormwater management systems.

1. Benefits and Issues to Consider

Environmental Issues

Landscape irrigation practices in the United States consume large quantities of potable water. Outdoor uses, primarily landscaping, account for 30% of the 26 billion gallons of water consumed daily in the United States.[11] Improved landscaping practices can dramatically reduce and even eliminate irrigation needs. Maintaining or reestablishing native or adapted plants on building sites fosters a self-sustaining landscape that requires minimal supplemental water and attracts native wildlife, creating a building site integrated with its natural surroundings. In addition, native or adapted plants tend to require less fertilizer and pesticides, minimizing water quality degradation and other negative environmental impacts.

Water-efficient landscaping helps conserve local and regional potable water resources.

Consideration of water issues during the planning stage of the project can encourage development where resources can support it and prevent development that would exceed the resource capacity.

Economic Issues

Landscaping designed for the local climate and the site's microclimate is the most effective strategy to avoid escalating water costs for irrigation. The cost can be reduced or eliminated through thoughtful planning and careful plant selection and layout. Native or adapted plants further reduce operating costs because they require less fertilizer and maintenance than turf grass.

Using alternative water sources for irrigation also reduces the amount of wastewater delivered to water treatment facilities, which can provide cost savings while reducing both demand on the municipal infrastructure and the negative environmental impacts associated with large-scale treatment facilities. Irrigation system efficiency varies widely, and high-efficiency systems can also reduce potable water consumption.

2. Related Credits

Techniques used to meet the requirements of this credit, including wastewater reuse and stormwater capture and reuse, may assist in achieving the following credits:

- GIB Credit 3, Building Water Efficiency
- GIB Credit 8, Stormwater Management
- GIB Credit 14, Wastewater Management

If the outdoor planted areas are recreation facilities, neighborhood farms and gardens, street trees, or green roofs, also refer to the following credits:

- NPD Credit 10, Access to Recreation Facilities
- NPD Credit 14, Tree-Lined and Shaded Streets
- GIB Credit 9, Heat Island Reduction

3. Summary of Referenced Standards

There are no referenced standards for this credit.

4. Implementation

Projects without any landscaped or naturally vegetated areas are not eligible for the credit. Projects with minimal landscaped areas are eligible for the credit if the planted areas, including roof and courtyard garden space or outdoor planters, cover at least 3% of the development footprint.

---

11 Georgia Department of Natural Resources, Pollution Prevention Assistance Division, "The Sustainable Office Toolkit." www.p2ad.org/toolkit/modules_4_1.html (accessed May 2008).

For previously developed sites, contour the land to allow planted areas to absorb stormwater. For sites that are not previously developed, preserve the natural hydrology of the site as much as possible.

Develop a site map showing existing or planned structures, topography, orientation, sun and wind exposure, use of space, and existing vegetation. Plan water-use zones: high (requiring regular watering), moderate (needing occasional watering), and low (dependent on natural rainfall). Analyze the soil in each zone and amend it if necessary. Perform shadow profiles of landscape areas for each season based on middle-of-the-day conditions and illustrate the plant selections within the profiles.

Design landscaping with climate-tolerant native or adapted plants that can survive on natural rainfall. Choose plants that will easily adapt to the site. Planting native or adapted plants is an excellent approach to water efficiency because these species are, by definition, adapted to the climate and rainfall patterns of the area. It is possible to eliminate or significantly cut the need for permanent irrigation with strategies like xeriscaping, which employs native and adapted plants. Also see the native plant provisions of SLL Credit 8, Restoration of Habitat or Wetlands and Water Bodies, and SLL Credit 9, Long-Term Conservation Management of Habitat or Wetlands and Water Bodies. Minimize the area covered with conventional turf grass. Plant turf grass only for functional benefits, as in recreational areas.

Regularly check irrigation systems for efficient and effective operation; verify watering schedules and duration on a monthly basis. Use low-volume, drip irrigation systems where applicable; use smart irrigation controllers throughout. Provide computer-controlled monitoring and schedule modifications from central locations.

Do not irrigate plants when evapotranspiration rates, moisture conditions, and precipitation make it unnecessary. To prevent mold in and around buildings, make sure irrigation systems do not saturate walls or introduce water into building air intakes.

Mulching and composting conserve water and help foster optimal soil conditions. Mulch trees, shrubs, and flower beds to conserve moisture and prevent evaporative water loss from the soil surface, thus reducing the need for irrigation.

Hose bibs are not considered permanent irrigation and can be used for temporary irrigation during droughts. Temporary irrigation during the first year of building occupancy can help establish healthy plants that will need less water in the future.

When designing the landscape and selecting plant materials to reduce water consumption, keep these other ideas in mind: consider shade, aesthetics, and vistas for all areas used by pedestrians; plant trees to shade buildings and hardscapes and reduce the heat island effect; do not plant invasive species; select plants that need little or no fertilization; if fertilizers are required, specify organic and nonpetrochemical types; and use integrated pest management practices, such as avoiding monocultures and diversifying species to discourage disease and insect infestations.

Technologies

Efficient irrigation technology, stormwater reuse and capture, and advanced on-site wastewater treatment are all excellent ways of achieving this credit; they allow for a broad plant species palette while still conserving potable water supplies. High-efficiency irrigation strategies include the use of microirrigation systems, moisture sensors, rain shut-offs, and weather-based evapotranspiration controllers. Drip irrigation systems apply water slowly and directly to the roots of plants, using less water than sprinklers.

Efficient irrigation rotary heads can provide a greater radius of coverage and dispense water at a lower precipitation rate than conventional systems. Properly pressurized spray heads and nozzles maximize efficiency by delivering the correct size of water droplets and are not affected by wind and sun. For example, when pressure is too high, water droplets are too small and the spray pattern is distorted by wind, thereby decreasing efficiency. Pressure regulation is critical to the efficiency to drip and spray systems.

Smart irrigation controls should be included wherever possible; consult the Irrigation Association for further guidance (www.irrigation.org). Whereas conventional controllers turn irrigation on at the same time every day for a set duration, these sensors conserve water by adjusting irrigation times based on daily weather. Rain sensors enhance water savings further by suspending the daily irrigation cycle based on precipitation levels.

Stormwater collection systems (e.g., cisterns, underground tanks) can significantly reduce or completely eliminate the amount of potable water used for irrigation. Stormwater and rainwater can be collected and then filtered for use in irrigation. Metal, clay, or concrete-based roofing materials are ideal for rainwater harvest; asphalt or lead-containing materials will contaminate the water. Stormwater with high mineral content or acidity may damage systems or plants, but pollutants can be filtered out by soil or mechanical systems before being applied to plants. Check local rainfall quantity and quality, since collection systems may be inappropriate in areas with rainfall of low quantity or poor quality.

Using groundwater that must be pumped away from the building's basement or foundation to irrigate the landscape is an innovative way to achieve this credit. However, installing a well specifically to collect groundwater for irrigation does not meet the intent of the credit to reduce potable water use for irrigation.

5. Timeline and Team

Early in the design process, the landscape designer should determine the most appropriate use of native vegetation and the most efficient irrigation technology for the project site. Include the developer, architect, civil engineer, and mechanical engineer in evaluating the feasibility of using nonpotable water for irrigation. Prior to construction completion, the landscape designer should draft season-specific maintenance plans for planted areas. After the initial landscape design team meeting, the landscape architect or civil engineer should perform the baseline and design irrigation calculations to assess compliance with this credit.

6. Calculations

To calculate the percentage reduction in potable water use for this credit, establish a baseline water use rate for the project and then calculate the efficient water-use rate according to the steps listed below.

Standard Assumptions and Variables

All calculations are based on irrigation during July.

- The landscape coefficient (K_L) indicates the volume of water lost via evapotranspiration and varies with the plant species, microclimate, and planting density. The formula for determining the landscape coefficient is given in Equation 1.

- The species factor (k_s) accounts for variation in water needs by different plant species, divided into three categories (high, average, and low water need). To determine the appropriate category for a plant species, use plant manuals and professional experience. This factor is somewhat subjective; however, landscape professionals know the general water needs of plant species. Landscapes can be maintained in acceptable condition at about 50% of the reference evapotranspiration (ET_o) value, and thus the average value of k_s is 0.5. If a species does not require irrigation once it is established, then the effective $k_s = 0$ and the resulting $K_L = 0$.

- The density factor (k_d) accounts for the number of plants and the total leaf area of a landscape. Sparsely planted areas will have less evapotranspiration than densely planted areas. An average k_d is applied to areas where shading from trees is 60% to 100%. This is equivalent to shrubs and groundcovers that shade 90% to 100% of the landscape area. Low k_d values are found where shading from trees is less than 60%, or where shrub and groundcover shading is less than 90%. For instance, a 25% ground shading from trees results in a k_d value of 0.5. In mixed plantings, where the tree canopy shades understory shrubs and groundcovers, evapotranspiration increases. This represents the highest level of landscape density; the k_d value is 1.0 to 1.3.

- The microclimate factor (k_{mc}) accounts for environmental conditions specific to the landscape, including temperature, wind, and humidity. For instance, parking lots increase wind and temperature effects on adjacent landscapes. The average k_{mc} is 1.0; this refers to conditions where evapotranspiration is unaffected by buildings, pavements, reflective surfaces, and slopes. High-k_{mc} conditions occur where evaporative potential is increased by heat-absorbing and reflective surfaces or exposure to high winds; examples include parking lots, west sides of buildings, west- and south-facing slopes, medians, and areas experiencing wind tunnel effects. Low-k_{mc} landscapes include shaded areas and areas protected from wind, such as north sides of buildings, courtyards, areas under wide building overhangs, and north-facing slopes.

Step 1. Create the design case.

Determine the landscape area for the project. This number must represent the as-designed landscape area and must use the same project boundary used throughout the submission. Sort the total landscape area into the major vegetation types (trees, shrubs, groundcover, mixed, and turf grass), listing the area for each.

Determine the following characteristics for each landscape area: species factor (k_s), density factor (k_d), and microclimate factor (k_{mc}). Recommended values for each are provided in Table 1. Select the low, average, or high value for each parameter as appropriate for the site. Project teams must be prepared to justify any variance from the recommended values..

Table 1. Landscape factors

Vegetation	Species factor (k_s)			Density factor (k_d)			Microclimate factor (k_{mc})		
	Low	Average	High	Low	Average	High	Low	Average	High
Trees	0.2	0.5	0.9	0.5	1.0	1.3	0.5	1.0	1.4
Shrubs	0.2	0.5	0.7	0.5	1.0	1.1	0.5	1.0	1.3
Groundcovers	0.2	0.5	0.7	0.5	1.0	1.1	0.5	1.0	1.2
Mixed trees, shrubs, groundcovers	0.2	0.5	0.9	0.6	1.1	1.3	0.5	1.0	1.4
Turf grass	0.6	0.7	0.8	0.6	1.0	1.0	0.8	1.0	1.2

Calculate the landscape coefficient (K_L) by multiplying the three area characteristics, as shown in Equation 1.

Equation 1

$$K_L = k_s \times k_d \times k_{mc}$$

Determine the reference evapotranspiration rate (ET_o) for the region. This rate is a measurement of the total amount of water needed to grow a reference plant (such as grass or alfalfa), expressed in millimeters or inches. The values for ET_o in various regions throughout the United States can be found in regional agricultural data (see Resources). The ET_o for July is used in the calculation because this is typically the month with the greatest evapotranspiration effects and, therefore, the greatest irrigation demands.

Calculate the project-specific evapotranspiration rate (ET_L) for each landscape area by multiplying the ET_o by the K_L, as shown in Equation 2.

Equation 2

$$ET_L \text{ [in]} = ET_0 \times K_L$$

Determine the irrigation efficiency (IE) by listing the type of irrigation used for each landscape area and the corresponding efficiency. Table 2 lists irrigation efficiencies for two irrigation systems.

Table 2. Irrigation types and efficiencies

Type	Efficiency
Sprinkler	0.625
Drip	0.90

Determine, if applicable, the controller efficiency (CE), the percentage reduction in water use from any weather-based controllers or moisture sensor-based systems. This number must be supported by either manufacturer's documentation or detailed calculations by the landscape designer.

Determine, if applicable, the volume of reuse water (harvested rainwater, recycled graywater, or treated wastewater) available in July. Reuse water volumes may depend on rainfall volume and frequency, building-generated graywater and wastewater, and on-site storage capacity. On-site reuse systems must be modeled to predict volumes generated on a monthly basis as well as optimal storage capacity. For harvested stormwater calculations, the project team may use either the collected stormwater total for July based on historical average precipitation, or historical data for each month to model collection and reuse throughout the year. The latter method allows the team to determine what volume of water can be expected in the storage cistern at the beginning of July and add it to the expected stormwater volume collected during the month; it also allows the team to determine the optimal size of the stormwater cistern.

To calculate total water applied (TWA) and total potable water applied (TPWA) for each landscape area and the installed case, use Equations 3 and 4.

Equation 3

$$\text{Design case TWA (gal)} = \frac{\text{Area [sf]} \times ET_L \text{ [in]}}{IE} \times CE \times 0.6233 \text{ gal/sf/in}$$

Equation 4

$$\text{Design case TPWA (gal)} = \text{TWA (gal)} - \text{Reuse water (gal)}$$

Step 2. Create the baseline case.

In the baseline case, the k_s, k_d, and IE are set to average values representative of conventional equipment and design practices. The same k_{MC} and the reference ETo are used in both the design and the baseline cases. If the project substitutes low-water-using plants (such as shrubs) for high-water-using types (such as turf grass), the landscape areas can be reallocated in the baseline case, but the total landscape area must remain the same. The baseline cannot be 100% turf grass if typical landscaping practices in the region include trees, shrubs, and planting beds.

Calculate the TWA for the baseline case using Equation 5.

Equation 5

$$\text{Baseline case TWA (gal)} = \frac{\text{Area [sf]} \times ET_L \text{ [in]}}{IE} \times 0.6233 \text{ gal/sf/in}$$

Step 3. Calculate the percentage reduction in total irrigation water use (potable and reuse) and the percentage reduction of potable water use for irrigation.

Calculate the percentage reduction of potable water use according to Equation 6.

Equation 6

$$\% \text{ reduction of potable water} = \frac{1 - \text{design TPWA}}{\text{baseline TWA}} \times 100$$

If the percentage reduction of potable water use for irrigation achieved is 50% or more, the requirement for the credit is met.

7. Documentation Guidance

As a first step in preparing to complete the LEED-ND documentation requirements, work through the following measures. Refer to GBCI's website for the complete descriptions of all required documentation.

- Perform calculations of the baseline and design case to show the percentage reduction in water demand, and report what portion of irrigation will come from each nonpotable source (if any).
- Prepare a landscape plan showing a planting schedule and irrigation system.

8. Examples

A 2-acre mixed-use project in Austin, Texas, has 6,000 square feet of planted areas and three landscape types: shrubs, mixed vegetation, and turf grass. All are irrigated with a combination of potable water and graywater harvested from the building. The reference ET_o for Austin in July, obtained from the local agricultural service, is 8.12. The high-efficiency irrigation system uses drip irrigation with an efficiency of 90% and consumes an estimated 4,200 gallons of graywater during July. Table 3 shows the calculations to determine total potable water use for this design case.

The baseline case uses the same reference ET_o and total planted area but assumes sprinklers for irrigation (IE = 0.625), does not take advantage of graywater harvesting, and irrigates only shrubs and turf grass. Calculations to determine total water use for the baseline case are presented in Table 4.

The design case has an irrigation water demand of 14,632 gallons. Graywater reuse provides 4,200 gallons; this volume is treated as a credit in the water calculation. Thus, the total potable water use in July is 10,432 gallons. The baseline case has an irrigation demand of 38,967 gallons and uses no graywater. The project thus achieves a potable water savings of 73% and earns 1 point.

Table 3. Design case (July)

Landscape type	Area (sf)	Species factor (k_s)	Density factor (k_d)	Microclimate factor (k_{mc})	K_L	ET_L	IE	Total water applied (gal)
Shrubs	1,200	Low 0.2	Avg 1.0	High 1.3	0.26	2.11	Drip	1,755
Mixed	3,900	Low 0.2	Avg 1.1	High 1.4	0.31	2.50	Drip	6,755
Turf grass	900	Avg 0.7	Avg 1.0	High 1.2	0.84	6.82	Sprinkler	6,122
Subtotal water applied								14,632
July stormwater and graywater harvest								(4,200)
Total potable water applied								10,432

Table 4. Baseline case (July)

Landscape type	Area (sf)	Species factor (k_s)	Density factor (k_d)	Microclimate factor (k_{mc})	K_L	ET_L	IE	Total water applied (gal)
Shrubs	1,200	Avg 0.5	Avg 1.0	High 1.3	0.65	5.28	Sprinkler	6,316
Turf grass	4,800	Avg 0.7	Avg 1.0	High 1.2	0.84	6.82	Sprinkler	32,651
Total potable water applied								38,967

9. Exemplary Performance

Projects may earn an Innovation and Design Process credit for exemplary performance by reducing water consumption for outdoor landscape irrigation by 75% from a calculated midsummer baseline case.

10. Regional Variations

Much of the United States faces increasing demands on existing water supplies, making it important to landscape sites appropriately for the climate. Water-efficient landscaping varies by site and region. Consider the site's climate and microclimate, sun exposure, soil type, drainage, and topography.

In hot, dry climates, emphasize drought-tolerant plants and xeriscape designs. Reducing or eliminating turf grass will lessen the demand on potable water; rocks and stone can be incorporated into the landscape instead. If turf grass is desired, select a species that can endure drought.

In hot, humid, and temperate climates, select native plants and use rain or moisture sensors to avoid unnecessary watering in wet seasons. The use of captured stormwater can help eliminate the use of potable water for irrigation.

In cold climates, install native plants that will survive the winter months. Rain or moisture sensors will help prevent excessive watering.

11. Resources

Websites

American Rainwater Catchment Systems Association

www.arcsa.org

ARCSA was founded to promote rainwater catchment systems in the United States. Its website provides regional resources, suppliers, membership information, and publications, such as the *Texas Guide to Rainwater Harvesting*.

American Water Works Association, Water Wiser

www.awwa.org/waterwiser

This web clearinghouse provides articles, reference materials, and papers on all forms of water efficiency.

Center for Irrigation Technology

www.cati.csufresno.edu/cit/

CIT is an independent research and testing facility that provides information to designers, manufacturers, and users of irrigation equipment.

Irrigation Association

www.irrigation.org

This nonprofit organization focuses on promoting products that efficiently use water in irrigation applications.

National Oceanic and Atmospheric Administration, National Climatic Data Center

www.ncdc.noaa.gov/oa/ncdc.html

The NCDC website is useful for researching local climate information such as data for rainwater harvesting calculations, and it also includes links to state climate offices.

Rain Bird® ET Manager™ Scheduler

www.rainbird.com/landscape/products/controllers/etmanager.htm

This free software provides local evapotranspiration data for the United States and Canada; users can obtain data for the geographically closest or most climate-appropriate location.

Rocky Mountain Institute, graywater and rain collection

www.rmi.org

This on-line resource from the Rocky Mountain Institute provides general information and links to resources on rain collection and graywater systems.

Texas Water Development Board

www.twdb.state.tx.us

This website provides data from the state of Texas regarding water resources and services such as groundwater mapping and water availability modeling. The site also provides brochures on indoor and outdoor water efficiency strategies.

U.S. Environmental Protection Agency, water-efficient landscaping

www.epa.gov/watersense/docs/water-efficient_landscaping_508.pdf

Water Efficient Landscaping: Preventing Pollution and Using Resources Wisely provides information about reducing water consumption through creative landscaping techniques.

Print Media

Landscape Irrigation: Design and Management, by Stephen W. Smith (John Wiley & Sons, 1996).

Turf Irrigation Manual, fifth edition, by Richard B. Choate and Jim Watkins (Telsco Industries, 1994).

	GIB
ND	Credit 4

12. Definitions

existing present on the date of submission of LEED-ND certification documents; similarly, an element or condition that **exists** is present on the date that LEED-ND certification documents are submitted.

potable water water that meets or exceeds EPA's drinking water quality standards and is approved for human consumption by the state or local authorities having jurisdiction; it may be supplied from wells or municipal water systems.

project the land, water, and construction that constitutes the project application. A project applicant does not have to own or control all land or water within a project boundary, but all the area within the project boundary must comply with prerequisites and attempted credits.

EXISTING BUILDING REUSE

	ND
Credit	GIB Credit 5
Points	1 point

Intent

To extend the life cycle of *existing* building stock to conserve resources, reduce waste, and reduce adverse environmental effects of new buildings related to materials manufacturing and transport.

Requirements

Reuse the existing *habitable building* stock, achieving the greater of the following two benchmarks (based on surface area):

a. 50% of one existing building structure (including structural floor and roof decking) and envelope (including exterior skin and framing but excluding window assemblies and nonstructural roofing material).

b. 20% of the total existing building stock (including structure and envelope, as defined above).

Hazardous materials that are remediated as a part of the *project* scope must be excluded from the calculations.

AND

FOR ALL PROJECTS

Do not demolish any *historic buildings*, or portions thereof, or alter any *cultural landscapes* as part of the project.

An exception is granted only if such action has been approved by an appropriate review body. For buildings listed locally, approval must be granted by the local historic preservation review board, or equivalent. For buildings listed in a state register or in the National Register of Historic Places, approval must appear in a programmatic agreement with the State Historic Preservation Office.

1. Benefits and Issues to Consider

Environmental Issues

Building reuse is a very effective strategy for reducing the overall negative environmental consequences of construction. Reusing existing buildings significantly reduces the energy use associated with the demolition process as well as construction waste. Reuse strategies also reduce environmental effects associated with raw material extraction, manufacturing, and transportation.

Economic and Social Issues

Although retrofitting existing buildings to accommodate new programmatic and LEED requirements can add to the complexity of design and construction—reflected in the project's soft costs—reuse of existing components can reduce the cost of construction substantially.

Design the site such that existing buildings and cultural landscapes are preserved wherever possible, and emphasize retaining historic buildings and buildings that are important to the local community. Consider allotting time during community meetings to discuss the implications of, and solicit feedback on, any planned demolition of existing structures in the project. If feasible, have these conversations during the conceptual design phase, when modifications to the plan are still possible.

2. Related Credits

The strategies implemented to achieve this credit may also help achieve the following:

- GIB Credit 6, Historic Resource Preservation and Adaptive Use

3. Summary of Referenced Standards

There are no referenced standards for this credit.

4. Implementation

To ensure that no historic buildings are demolished and no cultural landscapes are altered, check with the local planning office, as well as the state historic preservation office and the National Register of Historic Places.

For buildings that will have new uses or major renovations, inventory existing conditions and develop a floor plan, sections, and elevations showing the location and sizes of existing structural and envelope components, including the foundation, structural walls, roof decks, and exterior walls (excluding windows). The drawings should provide the detail needed to determine the surface area of all these preexisting elements. Remove from the calculation any elements that pose contamination risk to building occupants.

Projects with multiple candidate buildings must achieve the greater of the two benchmarks in the credit requirement, reusing either 50% of one building or 20% of all buildings, whichever achieves the larger amount of reused building surface area.

5. Timeline and Team

During conceptual planning, the project team should identify existing buildings that may be suitable for reuse. Involve planners, architects, and structural, mechanical, and electrical engineers.

6. Calculations

For each existing building that is being reused, prepare a table showing the total and reused portions of building surface area (floors, ceilings, and walls). Exclude the following items from surface area:

- Nonstructural roofing materials.

- Window assemblies.

- Structural and envelope materials that are deemed structurally unsound.

- Structural and envelope materials that are considered hazardous or pose a health risk to building occupants.

- Contiguous or common walls with adjacent buildings to remain but not part of the project.

If the project has multiple common-wall buildings, count each common wall only once when calculating the total reuse percentage for all buildings.

Calculate the percentage of total building surface area represented by the reused surface area. Based on the results, determine whether 50% of one existing building structure or 20% of the total existing building stock is the higher benchmark. To achieve the credit, the project must meet the higher benchmark.

7. Documentation Guidance

As a first step in preparing to complete the LEED-ND documentation requirements, work through the following measures. Refer to GBCI's website for the complete descriptions of all required documentation.

- Obtain drawings of buildings to be reused and determine their surface area dimensions, or if drawings are not available, take field measurements.

- Retain documentation of any historic buildings or cultural landscapes; note whether any will be demolished as part of the project.

8. Examples

A project has four existing buildings on the site, described in Table 1.

Table 1. Example percentages of reused buildings

Building	Surface area of existing structure and envelope (sf)	Surface area of reused structure and envelope (sf)	Percentage reused
A	64,476	61,156	95
B	49,657	0	0
C	45,908	0	0
D	52,956	0	0
Total	212,997	61,156	

The components of Building A's structure and envelope reuse are listed in Table 2.

Table 2. Example determination of building structure and envelope reuse

Element	Existing surface area(sf)	Reused surface area (sf)	Percentage reused
Foundation (slab on grade)	11,520	11,520	100%
2nd-floor deck	11,520	10,000	87%
1st-floor interior structural walls	240	240	100%
2nd-floor interior structural walls	136	136	100%
Roof deck	11,520	11,520	100%
North exterior wall (excl. windows)	8,235	7,150	87%
South exterior wall (excl. windows)	8,235	8,235	100%
East exterior wall (excl. windows)	6,535	6,535	100%
West exterior wall (excl. windows)	6,535	5,820	81%
Total	64,476	61,156	95%

For this example, the project team first needs to determine whether it must achieve the credit requirements for (a) or (b). For credit requirement (a), 50% of one structure (based on surface area) must be reused, which in this case is 32,238 square feet (50% of 64,476 square feet). For credit requirement (b), 20% of the total existing building stock (based on surface area) must be reused, or 42,599 square feet (20% of 212,997). Because the project must achieve the greater of the two benchmarks, the team must meet the credit requirements for (b).

To determine the percentage of the existing building stock that will be reused, the team divides the square feet of building stock that will be reused by the total existing building square footage: (61,156 / 212,997) x 100 = 28%. The project exceeds the credit requirements threshold of 20%.

9. Exemplary Performance

Projects may earn an Innovation and Design process credit for exemplary performance by demonstrating either of the following significant improvements over the basic requirements:

- For requirement (a), reusing 75% of one existing building's structure and envelope.

- For requirement (b), reusing 40% of the total existing building stock.

10. Regional Variations

There are no regional variations associated with this credit.

11. Resources

Websites
Building Green
www.buildinggreen.com
This website offers a building reuse info clearinghouse of resources and links.

Print Media
Adaptive Reuse: Preserving Our Past, Building Our Future (Australian Department of the Environment, 2004)
Available at www.environment.gov.au/heritage/publications/adaptive/pubs/adaptive-reuse.pdf.

Building for Tomorrow, by Martin Pawley (Sierra Club Books, 1982).

Buildings Reborn: New Uses, Old Places, by Barbaralee Diamonstein (Harper & Row, 1978).

Ecologic Architecture, by Richard L. Crowther (Butterworth Architecture, 1992).

Guide to Resource Efficient Building Elements, fifth edition, by Tracy Mumma et al. (Center for Resourceful Building Technology, 1995).

Handbook of Architectural Technology, edited by Henry J. Cowan (VanNostrand Reinhold, 1991).

How Buildings Learn: What Happens after They're Built, by Stewart Brand (Viking Press, 1994).

How to Recycle Buildings, by Laurence E. Reiner (McGraw-Hill, 1979).

Re-Architecture: Old Buildings/New Uses, by Sherban Catacuzino (Abbeville Press, 1989).

Regenerative Design for Sustainable Development, by John Tillman Lyle (John Wiley, 1994).

Restoring Old Buildings for Contemporary Uses, by William C. Shopsin (Whitney Library of Design, 1989).

"Reusing Old Buildings," by Amita Baig, *Architecture + Design* XIII(1) (1996): 105–107.

12. Definitions

cultural landscape an officially designated geographic area that includes both cultural and natural resources associated with a historic event, activity, or person or that exhibits other significant cultural or aesthetic values.

existing present on the date of submission of LEED-ND certification documents; similarly, an element or condition that **exists** is present on the date that LEED-ND certification documents are submitted.

habitable building a structure intended for living, working, or other types of occupancy. Habitable structures do not include stand-alone garages and utility structures such as pump stations.

historic building a building or structure listed or determined to be eligible as a historic building or structure or as a contributing building or structure in a designated historic district, due to its historic, architectural, engineering, archeological, or cultural significance. The building or structure must be designated as historic by a local historic preservation review board or similar body, be listed in a state register of historic places, be listed in the National Register of Historic Places, or have been determined eligible for listing in the National Register.

project the land, water, and construction that constitutes the project application. A project applicant does not have to own or control all land or water within a project boundary, but all the area within the project boundary must comply with prerequisites and attempted credits.

HISTORIC RESOURCE PRESERVATION AND ADAPTIVE USE

	ND
Credit	GIB Credit 6
Points	1 point

Intent

To encourage the preservation and adaptive use of *historic buildings* and *cultural landscapes* that represent significant embodied energy and cultural value, in a manner that preserves historic materials and character-defining features.

Requirements

To achieve this credit, at least one historic building or cultural landscape must be present on the *project* site.

Do not demolish any historic buildings, or portions thereof, or alter any cultural landscapes as part of the project.

An exception is granted only if such action has been approved by an appropriate review body. For buildings or landscapes listed locally, approval must be granted by the local historic preservation review board, or equivalent. For buildings or landscapes listed in a state register or in the National Register of Historic Places, approval must appear in a programmatic agreement with the State Historic Preservation Office.

If any historic building in the project site is to be rehabilitated, rehabilitate in accordance with local review or federal standards for rehabilitation, whichever is more restrictive, using one of the following approaches:

a. Obtain approval, in the form of a "certificate of appropriateness," from a locally appointed historic preservation commission or architectural review board for any exterior alterations or additions.

b. If federal funds are used for the project, obtain confirmation from a state historic preservation office or the National Park Service that the rehabilitation satisfies the Secretary of the Interior's Standards for Rehabilitation.

c. If a building or site is listed in or determined eligible for the National Register of Historic Places but is not subject to federal or local review board review, include on the project team a preservation professional who meets the federal qualifications for historic architect and attests to conformance to the Secretary of the Interior's Standards for the Treatment of Historic Properties.

1. Benefits and Issues to Consider

Environmental Issues

The preservation of historic resources on a site, both buildings and cultural landscapes, can have important environmental benefits. Like the reuse of any building, historic building reuse or adaptive use reduces the overall environmental consequences of new construction and associated raw material extraction, manufacturing, and transportation. Reusing historic buildings significantly reduces the energy use associated with demolition as well as construction waste. The materials of all existing buildings have significant embodied energy, but this is especially apparent in older and historic buildings (those typically built before 1945), which were often constructed from materials, such as timber, brick, and concrete, that were far less energy consumptive than the components of more recent buildings. Materials from historic buildings are often more durable and have longer lifespans than newer materials.

Economic and Social Issues

A preserved and appropriately rehabilitated historic building or cultural landscape can give a project aesthetic value. Designating historic resources as local or state landmarks or listing them in the National Register of Historic Places can help educate the public about their significance and also ensure that the resources are preserved as valued assets. Rehabilitation may be costly, but the expense may be offset by the significant tax credits available for many rehab projects as well as savings on demolition and new construction fees. Consider contacting federal, state, and local preservation entities early in the design process to get an accurate sense of the value and potential of any historic resources in the project. For many historic resources, consultation with historic review boards or preservation organizations is required; it is also an important precaution against costly litigation or construction delays later in the project's development.

2. Related Credits

Meeting the requirements for GIB Credit 6 may also support achievement of the following credits:

- GIB Prerequisite 1, Certified Green Building
- GIB Credit 1, Certified Green Buildings
- GIB Credit 5, Existing Building Reuse

3. Summary of Referenced Standards

National Park Service, National Register of Historic Places
www.nps.gov/nr
The U.S. federal government designates historic buildings, sites, structures, objects, and districts through the National Park Service, an agency of the U.S. Department of Interior. A listing in the National Register places no obligations on private property owners and does not lead to public acquisition, require public access, or restrict what changes an owner may make. No listing is made if, for individual properties, the owner objects, or for districts, a majority of property owners object, but a property or district may still be determined "eligible." National Register listing does not automatically invoke local historic district zoning or local landmark designation.

National Park Service, Secretary of the Interior's Standards for Rehabilitation
www.cr.nps.gov/history/hps/tps/tax/rhb/
The Secretary of the Interior's Standards for Rehabilitation (Department of Interior regulations, 36 CFR Part 67), as described by the National Park Service's Technical Preservation Services, pertain to the rehabilitation of historic buildings of all materials, construction types, sizes, and occupancy. The standards describe the process of returning a property to a state of utility, through repair or alteration, that makes possible an efficient contemporary use while preserving those

portions and features of the property that are significant to its historic, architectural, and cultural values. They address the exterior and the interior, related landscape features, and the building's site and environment as well as attached, adjacent, or related new construction. The standards are designed for rehabilitation projects and take into consideration economic and technical feasibility.

National Park Service, Secretary of the Interior's Standards for the Treatment of Historic Properties with Guidelines for the Treatment of Cultural Landscapes
www.nps.gov/history/hps/hli/landscape_guidelines
These standards and guidelines provide guidance to cultural landscape owners, stewards and managers, landscape architects, preservation planners, architects, contractors, and project reviewers, both before and during the planning and implementation of project work.

4. Implementation

To achieve the credit, identify and document any historic buildings or cultural landscapes on the project site. This credit's Definitions section defines both historic buildings and cultural landscapes in detail. If the project has a historically significant building that has not been officially listed as historic, the project team can apply for local, state, or national listing, and if the building is designated, the project will be eligible for the credit.

To determine whether there are any historic buildings or cultural landscapes on the site, contact the local county historic preservation office (often part of the planning department), or consult the website of the state historic preservation office or the National Register of Historic Places. Specialists in historic preservation offer services, advice, and other resources for listing and rehabilitating historic buildings and can help determine whether an unlisted building would be eligible.

Cultural landscapes vary in size from less than 1 acre to thousands of acres. There are four types of cultural landscapes: (1) historic sites; (2) historic designed landscapes; (3) historic vernacular landscapes; and (4) ethnographic landscapes. To determine whether the site contains or is part of an officially designated cultural landscape, contact the local and state historic preservation offices or the National Park Service. To determine what activities are acceptable on a designated cultural landscape, consult the cultural landscape report prepared by the listing agency or other resources, such as the Secretary of the Interior's Standards with Guidelines for the Treatment of Cultural Landscapes.

Typically, municipal governments regulate the preservation and rehabilitation of historic buildings and sites through ordinances that establish zoning and historic districts and more specialized historic preservation ordinances. Local preservation laws vary greatly in their effectiveness and limitations on private owners' rights to alter historic properties, but commonly, all permits for demolitions and alterations to designated buildings must be approved by a historic preservation review board or commission, usually consisting of an uneven number of members appointed by the mayor or county supervisor. If approval for an alteration, addition to, or demolition of a historic building is granted, it is conveyed through a "certificate of appropriateness." Check with the local historic preservation office to make sure that all required processes and approvals are completed before beginning a rehabilitation project.

In addition to or instead of local designation, historic buildings and cultural landscapes may also be listed in a state register of historic places or the National Register of Historic Places. State and national listings do not have the same "teeth" as local preservation designations; they do not entail obtaining approval for alterations, additions, or demolition. The state historic preservation office maintains a state register of historic places and also submits applications to the National Park Service for listing in the National Register of Historic Places. National listing makes an income-producing property eligible for federal tax credits for rehabilitation. Many states also have separately administered tax credit programs for rehabilitation that can often be combined with federal incentives.

Whereas owners of locally designated resources are generally required to comply with the standards in local ordinances, resources listed in a state register or the national register are subject to review only in certain situations—for example, if a property is receiving federal funds, such as tax credits, if funding is coming from a federal or state agency, or if Section 106 actions are taking place. If the project involves rehabilitation of historic resources not subject to state or national review, consult with a preservation professional who can attest to conformance with the Secretary of the Interior's Standards for Rehabilitation. Project teams that are not applying for state or federal incentive programs should not contact the state historic preservation office or the National Park Service for a compliance review, since this is not a service they provide.

To earn this credit for rehabilitation of a historic building, the team must proceed in accordance with a local review or federal standards for rehabilitation, whichever is more restrictive. In addition, if the project involves demolishing any part of a historic building or altering a cultural landscape in any way, the team must first consult with the appropriate historic review body and receive prior approval. When rehabilitating a historic structure, the team should ideally work with a professional who has the federal qualifications to be a "historic architect"; this is required if the building is listed or determined eligible for the National Register of Historic Places. The National Park Service defines the necessary professional experience for historic architect (previously published in the Code of Federal Regulations, 36 CFR Part 61) as a professional degree in architecture or a state license to practice architecture, plus either (1) at least one year of graduate study in architectural preservation, American architectural history, preservation planning, or a closely related field; or (2) at least one year of full-time professional experience on historic preservation projects. The graduate study or experience must include detailed investigations of historic structures, preparation of historic structures reports, and preparation of plans and specifications for preservation projects.

For projects not reviewed by a state historic preservation office or the National Park Service, any demolition, rehabilitation, or alteration without approval from the appropriate review body or affirmed by a preservation professional disqualifies a project from achieving the credit.

5. Timeline and Team

The presence of historic resources at a project location should be a basic determinant in conceptualizing and planning the project. The project team's architectural and engineering capabilities should be supplemented by historic preservation specialists who have experience with the types of buildings or landscapes involved.

6. Calculations

There are no calculations for this credit.

7. Documentation Guidance

As a first step in preparing to complete the LEED-ND documentation requirements, work through the following measures. Refer to GBCI's website for the complete descriptions of all required documentation.

- Retain documentation regarding the listing or official designation of any historic buildings or cultural landscapes that are part of the project. Include historic buildings and cultural landscapes that were designated preproject, as well as any that have been listed or determined eligible as part of the project. Appropriate documentation may be completed National Register of Historic Places Registration forms with the signature of the Keeper, or Part 1, Evaluation of Significance of the Historic Preservation Certification Application.

- If the project will demolish any historic buildings or alter any cultural landscapes, document approval by the appropriate review body. This may consist of a Historic Preservation Certification Form (Part 2 or 3) with National Park Service signatures, or certificates of appropriateness issued by local architectural or preservation review boards.

- For rehabilitation of historic buildings, document approval with a Historic Preservation Certification Form (Part 2 or 3) with National Park Service signatures, or certificates of appropriateness issued by local architectural or preservation review boards.

8. Examples

There are no examples for this credit.

9. Exemplary Performance

Projects may earn an Innovation and Design process credit for exemplary performance by demonstrating either of the following significant improvements over the basic requirements:

- For projects with five or fewer historic properties, 100% of these buildings must be rehabilitated in accordance with the credit requirements. This does not apply to cultural landscapes.

- For projects with more than five historic properties, 90% of building square footage must be rehabilitated in accordance with the credit requirements. This does not apply to cultural landscapes.

10. Regional Variations

The prevalence and quality of historic buildings and districts vary greatly by region. Different local historic preservation review boards have different standards and review processes. Often, local requirements provide important insight into the area's cultural, architectural, and design priorities for historic preservation.

11. Resources

Websites
The Cultural Landscape Foundation
www.tclf.org
The Cultural Landscape Foundation is a nonprofit organization that aims to increase public awareness of the importance of cultural landscapes. They provide education, technical assistance, and other information about cultural landscapes.

National Park Service, Technical Preservation Service
www.nps.gov/history/hps/
The National Park Service offers many resources to help identify, evaluate, protect, and preserve historic resources throughout the United States. It offers many specific resources through its website beyond the standards for rehabilitation, described above, including information on conserving energy in historic buildings. Particularly useful publications available on-line include the *Illustrated Guidelines for Rehabilitating Historic Buildings, Preservation Briefs,* and *Preservation Tech Notes.*

National Park Service, historic preservation tax incentives
www.nps.gov/history/hps/tps/tax
This website provides guidance on the federal historic preservation tax incentives program as well as general guidance for applying the standards for rehabilitation, with case studies, and interpreting the standards bulletins. Specific guidance is available by topic at www.nps.gov/history/hps/tps/topics.

National Park Service, National Register of Historic Places

www.nps.gov/history/nr

The website for the National Register of Historic Placesexplains the register and links to a database with information on places listed in or determined eligible for theregister. Instructions for how to list a property are found at www.nps.gov/nr/national_register_fundamentals.htm.

National Conference of State Historic Preservation Officers

www.nps.gov/nr/shpolist.htm

This website provides a list of state historic preservation offices, which survey, evaluate, and nominate buildings and sites for the state and national registers of historic places. The state offices can provide information about their nomination processes and give general guidance concerning the rehabilitation of buildings.

National Park Service, National Historic Landmarks Program

www.nps.gov/history/nhl

This website provides general information about national historic landmarks as well as a link to a searchable database. National historic landmarks are designated for their exceptional value in illustrating or interpreting the heritage of the United States.

National Trust for Historic Preservation

www.preservationnation.org/

This is a nonprofit organization dedicated to preserving historic structures and places in the United States. The website contains an extensive list of resources and publications.

Print Media

Adaptive Reuse: Preserving Our Past, Building Our Future (Australian Department of the Environment, 2004), available at www.environment.gov.au/heritage/publications/adaptive/pubs/adaptive-reuse.pdf.

Buildings Reborn: New Uses, Old Places, by Barbaralee Diamonstein (Harper & Row, 1978).

Historic Preservation: Curatorial Management of the Built World, by James Marston Fitch (University Press of Virginia, 1990).

Keeping Time: The History and Theory of Preservation in America, by William J. Murtagh (Sterling Publishing, 1990).

Preservation Brief 36: Protecting Cultural Landscapes: Planning, Treatment and Management of Historic Landscapes, by Charles A. Birnbaum (National Park Service, 1994), available at www.nps.gov/history/hps/TPS/briefs/brief36.htm.

Re-Architecture: Old Buildings/New Uses, by Sherban Catacuzino (Abbeville Press, 1989).

Respectful Rehabilitation, by National Trust for Historic Preservation (Preservation Press, 1986).

Restoring Old Buildings for Contemporary Uses, by William C. Shopsin (Whitney Library of Design, 1989).

"Reusing Old Buildings," by Amita Baig, *Architecture +Design* XIII(1) (1996): 105–107.

Many helpful publications produced by the National Park Service, including almost 50 preservation briefs, are available in print format. Some are free; others require a small fee. Instructions for ordering are available at www.nps.gov/history/nps/bookstore.

12. Definitions

cultural landscape an officially designated geographic area that includes both cultural and natural resources associated with a historic event, activity, or person or that exhibits other significant cultural or aesthetic values.

historic building a building or structure listed or determined to be eligible as a historic building or structure or as a contributing building or structure in a designated historic district, due to its historic, architectural, engineering, archeological, or cultural significance. The building or structure must be designated as historic by a local historic preservation review board or similar body, be listed in a state register of historic places, be listed in the National Register of Historic Places, or have been determined eligible for listing in the National Register.

project the land, water, and construction that constitutes the project application. A project *applicant* does not have to own or control all land or water within a *project boundary*, but all the area within the project boundary must comply with prerequisites and attempted credits.

MINIMIZED SITE DISTURBANCE IN DESIGN AND CONSTRUCTION

GIB CREDIT 7

	ND
Credit	GIB Credit 7
Points	1 point

Intent

To preserve *existing* noninvasive trees, *native plants*, and pervious surfaces.

Requirements

OPTION 1. Development Footprint on Previously Developed Land

Locate 100% of the *development footprint* on areas that are *previously developed* and for which 100% of the c*onstruction impact zone* is previously developed.

OR

OPTION 2. Undeveloped Portion of Project Left Undisturbed

Depending on the *density* of the *project*, do not develop or disturb a portion of the land that has not been previously developed on the site, exclusive of any land preserved by codified law or a prerequisite of LEED for Neighborhood Development; or exempt areas designated as nonbuildable in land-use comprehensive plans and stipulate in *covenants, conditions, and restrictions* (CC&R) or other binding documents that the undisturbed area will be protected from development in perpetuity. Densities and minimum percentages are as follows (mixed-use projects must use the lowest applicable density or calculate a weighted average per the methodology in NPD Credit 2, Compact Development):

Table 1. Minimum undeveloped area, by project density

Residential density (DU/acre)	Nonresidential density (FAR)	Minimum area left undisturbed
< 15	< .50	20%
15 – 21	.50 – 1.0	15%
> 21	> 1.0	10%
DU = dwelling unit; FAR = floor-area ratio.		

For portions of the site that are not previously developed, identify construction impact zones that limit disturbance to a minimum of 40 feet beyond the building perimeter; 10 feet beyond surface walkways, patios, surface parking and utilities less than 12 inches in diameter; 15 feet beyond *street* curbs and main utility branch trenches; and 25 feet beyond constructed areas with permeable surfaces (such as pervious paving areas, stormwater retention facilities, and playing fields) that require additional staging areas to limit compaction in the constructed zone.

AND

FOR ALL PROJECTS

Survey the site to identify the following:

    a. Trees in good or excellent condition, as determined by an arborist certified by the International Society of Arboriculture (ISA).

b. Any heritage or champion trees of special importance to the community because of their age, size, type, historical association, or horticultural value, as defined by a government forester.

c. All trees larger than 6 inches in diameter at breast height (dbh, 4 feet 6 inches above ground).

d. Any *invasive* tree species present on the site, and whether those trees threaten the health of other trees to be preserved on the site, as determined by an ISA-certified arborist.

Preserve the following trees that are also identified as in good or excellent condition:

a. All heritage or champion trees and trees whose dbh exceeds 50% of the state champion dbh for the species.

b. A minimum of 75% of all noninvasive trees (including the above) larger than 18 inches dbh.

c. A minimum of 25% of all noninvasive trees (including the above) larger than 12 inches dbh if deciduous, and 6 inches dbh if coniferous.

Tree condition ratings must be based on assessment by an ISA-certified arborist using ISA-approved assessment measures.

Develop a plan, in consultation with and approved by an ISA-certified arborist, for the health of the trees, including fertilization and pruning, and for their protection during construction. The plan must include protective fencing located 1 foot for each 1-inch caliper from the trunk or at the tree drip line, whichever is larger, and specify that if trenching or other disturbance is necessary within the protected zone, this work must be done by hand. If disturbance includes a permanent excavation of 3 feet or deeper, the excavation must start from a point not closer than 15 feet from the tree's drip line. If an ISA-certified arborist has determined that any trees to be preserved are threatened by invasive vegetation, develop a plan to reduce the invasive vegetation to the maximum extent possible. Stipulate in CC&R or other binding documents that the undisturbed area of the preserved trees will be protected from development in perpetuity.

1. Benefits and Issues to Consider

Environmental Issues

Careful inventory and preservation of existing site features make the most efficient use of a project site. Limiting the development footprint and construction impact zone to previously developed land is the simplest way to ensure that construction activities do not harm undeveloped areas. Construction activities, particularly when close to undeveloped areas, can be very disruptive to the ecological community. Wildlife, plant communities, wetlands, and water bodies may all be affected.

Mature trees are an important natural asset of a site, especially when little green space is planned for the project. Trees provide shade and habitat for a variety of species and may act as a catchment system for rainwater. Consider how preserved trees can be part of a stormwater management plan.

Economic and Social Issues

Placing limits on construction impact zones can be inconvenient, but cost and time savings may result from clearly delineating areas to be left undisturbed. The closer that construction gets to undeveloped areas, the more complicated and costly various protection plans, such as the erosion and sedimentation control plan, may become. If feasible, the most cost-effective way to guarantee that land remains undisturbed is to limit the development footprint and construction impact zone to previously developed land.

Mature or locally significant trees are a valuable asset. Trees provide beauty and encourage project residents and visitors to linger and enjoy outdoor spaces. By removing some air pollutants, trees can deliver important public health benefits, especially for individuals with asthma and other respiratory illnesses.

2. Related Credits

Limiting the development footprint, minimizing construction impact zones, and preserving land that has not been previously developed may reduce the need for erosion and sedimentation control measures and allow stormwater to infiltrate and evapotranspire. Meeting the requirements for this credit may therefore assist in achieving the following related credits:

- GIB Prerequisite 4, Construction Activity Pollution Prevention
- GIB Credit 8, Stormwater Management

If the undisturbed land that is preserved under this credit is significant habitat, wetlands or water bodies, or steep slopes, then earning this credit may assist in earning the following related credits:

- SLL Credit 6, Steep Slope Protection
- SLL Credit 7, Site Design for Habitat or Wetland and Water Body Conservation
- SLL Credit 8, Restoration of Habitat or Wetlands and Water Bodies

3. Summary of Referenced Standards

International Society of Arboriculture, certified arborist
www.isa-arbor.com
ISA certification was developed to provide the public and government officials with a means to identify professional arborists who have demonstrated, through an exam and education program, that they have a thorough knowledge of tree care practices.

4. Implementation

For Option 1, build on parts of the project site that are previously developed so as not to disturb areas that are currently undeveloped. Locate and design the development footprint to minimize disturbance to the existing ecosystem.

For Option 2, reduce footprints by clustering development and using multistory buildings. Conduct a thorough environmental site assessment and avoid development and construction that will directly or indirectly harm sensitive areas. Option 2 requirements can still be met if habitat restoration activities are planned for areas that will be preserved; that is, habitat restoration is not considered disturbance. Note that deed restrictions or other CC&Rs used to preserve land under this credit are not adequate to achieve SLL Credit 7, Site Design for Habitat or Wetland and Water Body Conservation, or SLL Credit 8, Restoration of Habitat or Wetlands and Water Bodies, which require preservation by donating or selling the land or selling a conservation easement on the land to an accredited land trust or relevant public agency.

During the construction process, clearly mark construction and disturbance boundaries and note these site protection requirements in construction documents. Delineate lay-down, recycling, and disposal areas, and use paved areas for staging activities. Erect construction fencing around the dripline of existing trees to protect them from damage and soil compaction by construction vehicles. Establish contractual penalties for any destruction of protected areas outside the construction boundaries. Coordinate infrastructure construction to minimize disruption of the site, and work with existing topography to limit cut-and-fill activities.

For the tree protection portion of the credit, work with a local arborist to evaluate all trees on the site and identify those that meet the credit's preservation criteria. To identify heritage or champion trees, contact the jurisdiction's arborist or regional or state agencies; preserve them as required. Develop a tree preservation management plan that is approved by an ISA-certified arborist. If a certified arborist determines that preserved trees are threatened by invasive plants, the plan must also include reducing the invasive vegetation to the maximum extent possible. Invasive vegetation reduction strategies usually include baseline monitoring, rapid response to incipient infestations of new invaders, and control or suppression of established invaders.

5. Timeline and Team

The project team should work to minimize site disturbance once the project design is sufficiently advanced to identify physical impacts and determine mitigation measures. Important contributors will be architects, civil engineers, specialists in erosion and sedimentation control, and certified arborists.

6. Calculations

For Option 2, the credit requires a determination of the minimum amount of previously undeveloped land that must remain undisturbed by the development footprint and construction impact zone, depending on the project's residential and/or nonresidential densities. Mixed-use projects can determine the minimum area in either of two ways; for each approach, refer to Table 2.

1. Use whichever density—residential (column 1) or nonresidential (column 2)—corresponds to the greater percentage of area to be left undisturbed (column 4).

2. Based on the mixed-use density calculation method from NPD Credit 2, Compact Development, take the number of points earned under NPD Credit 2 (column 3) and use the corresponding percentage of area to be left undisturbed (column 4).

Table 2. Determination of undisturbed area for mixed-use projects, by project density

Residential density (DU/acre)	Nonresidential density (FAR)	Points earned under NPD Credit 2	Minimum area left undisturbed
< 15	< .50	1	20%
15–21	.50 – 1.0	2	15%
> 21	> 1.0	3, 4, 5, 6	10%

7. Documentation Guidance

As a first step in preparing to complete the LEED-ND documentation requirements, work through the following measures. Refer to GBCI's website for the complete descriptions of all required documentation.

- Draft a tree preservation plan that identifies all trees to be preserved and includes the required CC&Rs.

- Map the construction impact zone; it must conform to the dimensions stipulated in the credit requirements.

8. Examples

A project has a residential density of 20 dwelling units per acre, plus nonresidential space with a density of 1.2 FAR. The team refers to Table 2 to determine what minimum percentage of the undeveloped area must remain undisturbed. The project's residential density corresponds to 15%, and the nonresidential density indicates 10%. The team must use the density that corresponds to the higher percentage and thus leave 15% undeveloped.

Alternatively, the team could have used its score under NPD Credit 2, Compact Development, to find the minimum percentage. Assuming the project earned 2 points for its weighted density under NPD Credit 2, the team would look across row 2 in Table 2 and see that 15% of the undeveloped area must remain undisturbed.

9. Exemplary Performance

This credit is not eligible for exemplary performance under Innovation and Design Process.

10. Regional Variations

Some regions and communities have traditionally had tree-lined streets and well-established urban forests; in other areas of the country, street trees are less common or impractical because of drought. Project teams should be sensitive to local expectations.

11. Resources

Websites
American Forests, urban forests
www.americanforests.org/graytogreen/air/
The American Forests website has resources on the value of urban forests and a tool to help calculate the amount of air pollutants that a city's trees can remove each year.

Forest Service, urban and community forestry
www.fs.fed.us
The Forest Service, an agency of the U.S. Department of Agriculture, provides information and links on preservation of trees.

North American Native Plant Society

www.nanps.org

This nonprofit association is dedicated to the study, conservation, cultivation, and restoration of native plants. The website contains links to state and provincial associations.

Soil and Water Conservation Society

www.swcs.org

This nonprofit science and educational organization is focused on fostering the science and art of managing soil, water, and related natural resources for sustainability.

Print Media

Best Development Practice, by Reid Ewing (APA Planners Press, 1996).

Beyond Preservation: Restoring and Inventing Landscapes, by A. Dwight Baldwin et al. (University of Minnesota Press, 1994).

Design for Human Ecosystems: Landscape, Land Use, and Natural Resources, by John Tillman Lyle and Joan Woodward (Milldale Press, 1999).

Design with Nature, by Ian McHarg (Doubleday & Company, 1971).

Green Development: Integrating Ecology and Real Estate, by Alex Wilson et al. (John Wiley & Sons, 1998).

Landscape Planning: Environmental Application, by William Marsh (J.W. Wiley, 1991).

Landscape Restoration Handbook, by Donald Harker (Lewis Publishers, 1999).

The Practice of Watershed Protection, by Thomas Schueler Center for Watershed Protection, 2000).

12. Definitions

construction impact zone the project's development footprint plus the areas around the improvement where construction crews, equipment, and/or materials are staged and moved during construction.

covenants, conditions, and restrictions limitations that may be placed on a property and its use and are made a condition of holding title or lease.

density the amount of building structures constructed on the project site, measured for residential buildings as dwelling units per acre of buildable land available for residential uses, and for non-residential buildings as the floor-area ratio of buildable land area available for nonresidential uses. In both cases, structured parking is excluded.

development footprint the total land area of a project site covered by buildings, streets, parking areas, and other typically impermeable surfaces constructed as part of the project.

existing present on the date of submission of LEED-ND certification documents; similarly, an element or condition that **exists** is present on the date that LEED-ND certification documents are submitted.

invasive plant either an indigenous or nonindigenous species or strain that is characteristically adaptable, aggressive, has a high reproductive capacity, and tends to overrun the ecosystems it inhabits.

native (or indigenous) plant a plant species that did or would have occurred on the site or within the subject county prior to the widespread land alterations that accompanied European settlement. Cultivars of native plants may be considered native plants.

previously developed altered by paving, construction, and/or land use that would typically have required regulatory permitting to have been initiated (alterations may exist now or in the past). Previously developed land includes a platted lot on which a building was constructed if the lot is no more than 1 acre; previous development on lots larger than 1 acre is defined as the development footprint and land alterations associated with the footprint. Land that is not previously developed and altered landscapes resulting from current or historical clearing or filling, agricultural or forestry use, or preserved natural area use are considered undeveloped land. The date of previous development permit issuance constitutes the date of previous development, but permit issuance in itself does not constitute previous development.

project the land, water, and construction that constitutes the project application. A project applicant does not have to own or control all land or water within a project boundary, but all the area within the project boundary must comply with prerequisites and attempted credits.

street a dedicated right-of-way that can accommodate one or more modes of travel, excluding alleys and paseos. A street is suitable for primary entrances and provides access to the front and/ or sides of buildings and lots. A street may be privately owned as long as it is deeded in perpetuity for general public use. A street must be an addressable thoroughfare (for mail purposes) under the standards of the applicable regulating authority.

STORMWATER MANAGEMENT

	ND
Credit	GIB Credit 8
Points	1-4 points

Intent

To reduce pollution and hydrologic instability from stormwater, reduce flooding, promote aquifer recharge, and improve water quality by emulating natural hydrologic conditions.

Requirements

Implement a comprehensive stormwater management plan for the *project* that retains on-site, through infiltration, evapotranspiration, and/or reuse, the rainfall volumes listed in Table 1. Rainfall volume is based on the project's *development footprint*, any other areas that have been graded so as to be effectively impervious, and any pollution-generating pervious surfaces, such as landscaping, that will receive treatments of fertilizers or pesticides.

The percentile rainfall event (Table 1) is the total rainfall on a given day in the record that is greater than or equal to X percent of all rainfall events over a 20- to 40+-year period. For example, a 95th percentile event in a particular region might be 1.5 inches, which would then be the volume to retain. To determine the volume to be retained, projects may use NOAA's published national rainfall data, run an approved stormwater model, or independently gather local rain gauge data and rank rainfall events. One hundred percent of the water volume from rainfall events up to the X percentile event must not be discharged to surface waters unless the harvested and reused runoff is authorized for discharge or allowed to be discharged into sanitary treatment systems.

Table 1. Points for retaining stormwater on-site

Percentile rainfall event (total volume to be retained)	Points
80%	1
85%	2
90%	3
95%	4

Projects that earn at least 2 points under this credit may earn 1 additional point by meeting each of the following site characteristics:

a. The project is located on a *previously developed site* (1 point).

b. The project is located on a site that meets the definition of *brownfield* in SLL Credit 2, Brownfields Redevelopment (1 point).

c. The project is designed to be transit ready by achieving the following (1 point):

- At least 2 points under NPD Credit 1, Walkable Streets.

- At least 2 points under NPD Credit 2, Compact Development.

- At least 2 points under NPD Credit 3, Mixed-Use Neighborhood Centers.

The BMPs for the comprehensive stormwater management plan must be selected from the *Washington State Department of Ecology's Stormwater Management Manual for Western Washington, Volume V, Runoff Treatment* (2005 edition), or locally approved equivalent, whichever is more stringent, and must comply with all federal, state, and local regulations. The plan must include season-specific maintenance that ensures continuous performance of the stormwater management system.

For stormwater reuse systems not on a combined stormwater and sewer system, the total water reused for indoor use must not exceed 90% of the average annual rainfall.

Stormwater BMPs (except cisterns) must be designed to drain down within 72 hours.

1. Benefits and Issues to Consider

Environmental Issues

Stormwater is a major source of pollution for all types of water bodies in the United States.[12] Soil compaction caused by site development, roads, and parking lots produces stormwater runoff that contains sediment and other contaminants, including atmospheric deposition, pesticides, fertilizers, vehicle fluid leaks, and mechanical equipment waste, and harms species that depend on water bodies for habitat.

Increased stormwater runoff can overload pipes and sewers and damage water quality, affecting navigation and recreation. Furthermore, municipal systems that convey and treat runoff volumes require significant infrastructure and maintenance.

The health of streams is closely linked to stormwater runoff velocities and volumes. Increases in the frequency and magnitude of stormwater runoff due to development can increase bank-full events, trigger erosion, widen channels, and cause downcutting in streams. Effective on-site management practices let stormwater infiltrate the ground, thereby reducing the volume and intensity of stormwater flows.[13] Additionally, reducing stormwater runoff helps maintain the natural aquifer recharge cycle and restore depleted stream base flows.

Economic and Social Issues

If natural drainage systems are designed and implemented at the beginning of site planning, they can be integrated economically into the overall development. Water retention features require investments for design, installation, and maintenance; these features can also add significant value as site amenities, and costs can be minimized if systems are planned early in the design. Certain features, such as vegetated swales, can also reduce costs for landscape irrigation. The use of pervious pavement as part of an infiltration strategy may reduce the need for expensive and space-consuming retention options as well as the infrastructure needed to support conveyance. Using stormwater for nonpotable purposes, such as flushing urinals and toilets, custodial applications, and building equipment uses, lowers costs for potable water.

Even small stormwater collection and treatment systems lessen the burden on municipalities for maintenance and repair, resulting in a more affordable and stable tax base. Where public utilities provide stormwater collection and conveyance service, projects that manage stormwater on-site may be eligible for reduced stormwater fees. Check with the local stormwater utility for fee reduction programs.

2. Related Credits

Several credits are referenced in the Requirements. Additionally, techniques used to infiltrate, reuse, or evapotranspire stormwater may help projects achieve these other credits:

- SLL Credit 7, Site Design for Habitat or Wetland and Water Body Conservation
- SLL Credit 8, Restoration of Habitat or Wetlands and Water Bodies
- NPD Credit 5, Reduced Parking Footprint
- NPD Credit 14, Tree-Lined and Shaded Streets
- GIB Credit 3, Building Water Efficiency
- GIB Credit 4, Water-Efficient Landscaping
- GIB Credit 9, Heat Island Reduction

12 U.S. Environmental Protection Agency, "Reducing Stormwater Costs through Low Impact Development (LID) Strategies and Practices." 2007. www.epa.gov/owow/nps/lid/costs07/factsheet.html (accessed May 2008).
13 Ibid.

3. Summary of Referenced Standards

National Oceanic and Atmospheric Administration, rainfall data

www.ncdc.noaa.gov

NOAA's National Climatic Data Center provides information on rainfall measured at weather stations across the United States.

Washington State Department of Ecology, Stormwater Management Manual for Western Washington: Volume 5, Runoff Treatment Best Management Practices

www.ecy.wa.gov/programs/wq/stormwater/manual.html

This manual lists best management practices that can be used to meet the credit requirements to infiltrate, reuse, and evapotranspirate stormwater. The manual provides guidance on which BMPs are most appropriate for different types of sites and development.

4. Implementation

Conventional stormwater controls, such as stormwater ponds, fail to adequately protect streams, lakes, and coastal water bodies; such strategies do not meet the credit requirements. Instead, use an integrated approach to evaluate and select designs and technologies that minimize the project's effects on water resources. Consider the following factors and approaches: potable water use, groundwater withdrawals for water supply, aquifer recharge, stormwater management goals, runoff harvest and reuse, infiltration and evapotranspiration, and wastewater and graywater treatment and reuse.

Because of the high cost of building and maintaining conventional stormwater collection and treatment systems, communities across the nation are using on-site solutions to manage their stormwater, on the assumption that it is better to capture and deal with runoff close to the site where it originates. These solutions—commonly referred to as low-impact development (LID), conservation design, zero-impact development, or natural approaches—decentralize the management of stormwater by using natural systems (vegetation, soils) to treat runoff, minimizing the impervious area footprint, infiltrating runoff, harvesting runoff for reuse, and using vegetation to evapotranspire runoff.

Appropriate measures and strategies depend on local hydrologic characteristics. A full range of measures should be considered and evaluated, both those that are basic and low in cost and those that require more complex engineering: minimized building footprint; clustered development; natural systems that provide overland filtration and infiltration, such as soils with high infiltration rates; bioretention systems or rain gardens; porous pavement or pavers; green roofs; urban forests or expanded tree canopy; wetland restoration; bioswales; infiltration systems; rainwater cisterns or other systems that harvest stormwater for reuse in irrigation or building systems; vegetated filter strips; preservation of natural areas, such as forests, floodplains, riparian zones, and wetlands; and constructed wetlands and extended-retention vegetated ponds.

Refer to the *Washington State Department of Ecology Stormwater Management Manual for Western Washington: Volume 5, Runoff Treatment Best Management Practices* for detailed descriptions of BMPs and recommended approaches for different types of sites. Compare BMPs from locally approved manuals or regulations with those in the Washington State manual and choose the more stringent measures. If the recommended BMPs are comparable in stringency, choose the BMPs that are most appropriate to the project site and region.

If the site has not been previously developed, preserve its existing hydrology—site runoff volumes, velocities, and pollutant loadings—as much as possible. Evaluate site characteristics, such as local rainfall patterns, soils, geology, topography, and existing vegetative cover and species composition.

Projects on previously developed sites and brownfield sites have an opportunity to improve stormwater management compared with existing conditions and therefore receive an additional point under this credit if they have BMPs that manage stormwater for the 85th percentile rainfall event. Stormwater management can be particularly challenging on brownfield sites because of concerns about leakage from contaminated soils. Infiltration can actually enhance remediation of such sites if "natural attenuation" has been identified as part of the cleanup, but good stormwater management may be critical if the cleanup strategy involves a cap or other containment measure. Implementing these strategies can also be challenging in urban settings with little open space available for filtration; explore innovative stormwater management techniques. High-density, transit-oriented projects with stormwater management BMPs also receive an additional point because they contribute to regional stormwater management and water quality goals by concentrating development within the watershed and reducing development pressure on sites that are not previously developed.

Municipal, county, and state governments have various regulations on where stormwater may be captured and used, how long it can be held in a cistern, how it must be treated before reuse, and other design requirements. Check with the governing authority to find out about the requirements for collection, use, and distribution of captured stormwater. For this credit, only the harvested and reused water that is authorized to be discharged into sanitary treatment systems can be released; all other stormwater volume that is equal to or less than the local percentile rainfall event must be managed on-site.

5. Timeline and Team
Stormwater management should be an integral part of site planning at the outset of project conceptualization. The project team should include specialists experienced and certified in stormwater best management practices, including civil engineers and landscape architects. During the conceptual design phase, the developer should work with the urban planner, environmental consultant, civil engineer, and landscape architect on a holistic stormwater management strategy that is mindful of walkability and integrated with other goals of environmental stewardship. During preliminary design, the civil engineer and landscape architect should design the stormwater management system and perform preliminary calculations to confirm compliance with this credit. During construction, the project team should confirm proper installation and operation of the stormwater management system by reviewing the contractor's as-built drawings, and draft season-specific maintenance plans.

6. Calculations
Daily rainfall data can be downloaded from the National Climatic Data Center (NCDC) website (the URL and instructions below were accurate as of December 2009):

- Go to the NCDC website (www.ncdc.noaa.gov/oa/mpp/digitalfiles.html).
- Select the "1. 3200-3210/CDO" dataset.
- Select "Continue with SIMPLIFIED Options."
- Select "Specific Station," select the state, and select "Continue."
- Scroll down to click on a list of all weather stations and select the one nearest the project site; select "Continue."
- Specify the date range (at least the most recent 20 years) and select "Continue."
- Review the information, select "Add to Shopping Cart," and complete the checkout process.
- Import the ASCII file into Excel.
- Remove all nonstorm events (all days with no reported rainfall) from the data set.
- Use the Excel percentile function to determine the percentiles of rainfall events.

Step 1. Using the rainfall data from NCDC or other approved sources, as described in the credit requirements, calculate the percentile rainfall event in Excel, using the percentile function. Use the inches of rainfall corresponding to the 80%, 85%, 90%, and 95% percentile rainfall events to determine the amount of rainfall that must be managed to meet point thresholds.

Step 2. Delineate the development footprint, other areas that have been graded so as to be effectively impervious, and any pollution-generating pervious surfaces. Calculate the square footage of all such areas. The total is the developed area.

Step 3. Determine the volume of rainfall that must be retained by multiplying the square footage of areas delineated in Step 2 by the inches of rainfall (converted to cubic feet, cf) calculated in Step 1. See Equation 1.

Equation 1

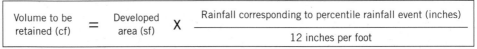

$$\text{Volume to be retained (cf)} = \text{Developed area (sf)} \times \frac{\text{Rainfall corresponding to percentile rainfall event (inches)}}{12 \text{ inches per foot}}$$

Step 4. Determine the amount of rainfall infiltrated, reused, or evapotranspired as a result of the comprehensive stormwater management plan. It may be necessary to sum the volumes of multiple BMPs.

Volumes of stormwater captured by cisterns for reuse may be combined unless the drawdown rate for a cistern is less than the minimum drawdown rate to ensure that the cistern does not overflow. Use Equation 2 to determine the amount of captured stormwater and Equation 3 to determine the minimum drawdown rate necessary to empty the tank prior to the next rainfall event. If the actual drawdown rate is less than the minimum drawdown rate, the volume of stormwater presumed to be captured by the system must be reduced accordingly.

Equation 2

$$\text{Stormwater volume captured (cf)} = \frac{\text{Rainfall event (inches)} \times R \times \text{collection surface area (sf)}}{12 \text{ inches}}$$

Where R = 0.05 + (0.009 x I), and I = percentage of collection surface that is impervious.

Equation 3

$$\text{Minimum drawdown rate (cf/second)} = \frac{\text{Tank capacity (cf)}}{\text{Rainfall event interval (seconds)}}$$

The number of points earned is based on the rainfall volume thresholds calculated in Step 3; refer to Table 1.

7. Documentation Guidance

As a first step in preparing to complete the LEED-ND documentation requirements, work through the following measures. Refer to GBCI's website for the complete descriptions of all required documentation.

- Obtain NOAA rainfall data, or equivalent, for the project location.

- Prepare a stormwater management plan that addresses infiltration, evapotransporation, or reuse.

- List stormwater best management practices to be used and quantify the volume of stormwater that each component of the plan is designed to retain.

8. Examples

A 15-acre project has 10 acres that are impervious or pollution-generating pervious surfaces, and the team converts this area to square feet by multiplying by 43,560 square feet per acre, for a total impervious area of 435,600 square feet. Next, the team obtains local meteorological data to calculate the amounts of rainfall per rainfall event. Thirty years' worth of NOAA data are entered into an Excel spreadsheet column of rainfall per day, where each row is a different day's rainfall total. The days with zero rainfall are deleted. Using the Excel percentile function, the team determines that the 80th percentile rainfall event equals 0.72 inches and then calculates the volume of rainfall to be retained, using Equation 1: 435,600 x .72 / 12 = 26,136 cubic feet. The volume of rainfall for rainfall events in other percentiles is calculated the same way, and the team lists the results (Table 2).

Table 2. Example rainfall volumes to be retained, by percentile event

Percentile rainfall event	Rainfall (in)	Rainfall volume to be retained (cf)
80th	0.72	26,136
85th	0.94	34,122
90th	1.20	43,560
95th	1.70	61,710

Most of the project buildings have cisterns to collect stormwater, and the drawdown rate for reusing this stormwater exceeds the minimum. The total capacity of the cisterns is 23,500 cubic feet of water. In addition, the project has pervious pavement for parking lots and sidewalks, and the civil engineer calculates that this pervious pavement will infiltrate 3,884 cubic feet of water. Therefore, the project will reuse and infiltrate 27,384 cubic feet of water, which corresponds to the 80th percentile rainfall event, and earns 1 point.

9. Exemplary Performance

Projects on previously developed sites may earn an Innovation and Design Process credit for exemplary performance by effectively managing the 97th percentile storm event in the manner suggested by this credit.

10. Regional Variations

The approach to this credit varies dramatically across regions and climate zones. Local stormwater management requirements also differ. The strategies employed in an urban environment where water is discharged to a municipal stormwater system will be different from the approach for a rural project that discharges to streams or lakes with high water quality standards.

11. Resources

Websites
Center for Watershed Protection
www.cwp.org
A nonprofit dedicated to disseminating watershed protection information to community leaders and watershed managers, the center offers on-line resources, training seminars, and watershed protection techniques.

Natural Resources Defense Council, stormwater management
www.nrdc.org/water/pollution
NRDC's website contains resources on urban stormwater practices including documents titled "Urban Stormwater Solutions" and "Rooftops to Rivers: Green Strategies for Controlling Stormwater and Combined Sewer Overflows."

Stormwater Manager's Resource Center
www.stormwatercenter.net
This site, for practitioners and local government officials, provides technical assistance on stormwater management.

U.S. Environmental Protection Agency, Office of Wetlands, Oceans, and Watersheds
www.epa.gov/owow
This website offers watershed management tools, resource protection strategies, and regulatory information, plus publications on water conservation and landscaping practices.

U.S. Environmental Protection Agency, stormwater management
www.cfpub.epa.gov/npdes/stormwater/menuofbmps/index.cfm
This EPA website provides information about catch basins as a tool for sediment control following construction in new developments and redevelopments.

Whole Building Design Guide, low-impact development
www.wbdg.org/resources/lidsitedesign.php
"Achieving Sustainable Design through Low Impact Development Practices" describes low-impact development practices, design goals, design strategies, site planning processes, case studies, and links to resources.

Websites of Local Examples and Guidance

City of Portland, Oregon
www.portlandonline.com/bds/index.cfm
This resource for stormwater planners provides techniques used throughout the city. Photographs and information are available on-line.

North Carolina Cooperative Extension
www.bae.ncsu.edu/topic/raingarden/Building.htm
This resource for rain gardens provides a sample calculation for sizing rain gardens.

Pennsylvania Department of Environmental Protection, stormwater management
www.dep.state.pa.us/dep/subject/advcoun/stormwater/stormwatercomm.htm
This website contains a draft of the *Pennsylvania Stormwater Best Management Practices Manual*.

Georgia Stormwater Management Manual
www.georgiastormwater.com/
This website contains a manual on techniques for managing stormwater.

Maryland Department of the Environment, stormwater management
www.mde.state.md.us/Programs/WaterPrograms/SedimentandStormwater/stormwater_design/index.asp
The *Maryland Stormwater Design Manual*, Volumes I and II was designed in an effort to incorporate experiences gained by the State of Maryland's stormwater community and achieve much-needed improvements for managing urban runoff. The state provides design standards and environmental incentives to produce better methods of managing stormwater by relying less on single BMPs for all development projects and more on mimicking existing hydrology through total site design policies.

Minnesota Pollution Control Agency, stormwater management
www.pca.state.mn.us/water/pubs/sw-bmpmanual.html
Protecting Water Quality in Urban Areas—A Manual contains information on best management practices, stormwater systems and retention ponds, erosion prevention and sediment control, and modeling.

New Jersey Department of Environmental Protection, stormwater management

www.njstormwater.org/bmp_manual2.htm

New Jersey Stormwater Best Management Practices Manual was developed to provide guidance on the standards in the state's proposed stormwater management rules, N.J.A.C. 7:8. The manual provides examples of ways to meet the standards, includes computations for stormwater runoff rates and volumes, and discusses structural stormwater management measures.

Prince George's County, Maryland, low-impact development

www.epa.gov/owow/nps/lid/lidnatl.pdf

Low-Impact Development Design Strategies: An Integrated Design Approach discusses LID site planning, hydrologic analysis, integrated management, sediment control, and public outreach.

San Francisco Bay Area, Stormwater Management Agencies Association

www.cleanwaterprogram.org/uploads/SAS_Manual_index.pdf

www.basmaa.org/AboutBASMAA/tabid/55/Default.aspx

Start at the Source: Design Guidance Manual for Stormwater Quality Protection discusses planning and zoning, site design, drainage systems, and design details about permeable pavements, streets, parking lots, driveways, buildings, landscapes, and outdoor work areas. It also provides residential, commercial, and industrial case studies.

Town of Franklin, Massachusetts, stormwater management

www.town.franklin.ma.us/Pages/FranklinMA_Planning/initiatives/bestdevelopment.pdf

Best Development Practices Guidebook contains information about stormwater management, erosion and sediment control, landscape design, and site planning.

Printed Media

Stormwater Best Management Practice Design Guide, by Michael Clar, Billy Barfield, and Thomas O'Connor (Environmental Protection Agency, 2004).

www.epa.gov/ORD/NRMRL/pubs/600r04121/600r04121a.pdf

12. Definitions

brownfield real property, the expansion, redevelopment, or reuse of which may be complicated by the presence or possible presence of a hazardous substance, pollutant, or contaminate.

development footprint the total land area of a project site covered by buildings, streets, parking areas, and other typically impermeable surfaces constructed as part of the project.

previously developed site a site that, preproject, consisted of at least 75% **previously developed** land.

project the land, water, and construction that constitutes the project application. A project applicant does not have to own or control all land or water within a project boundary, but all the area within the project boundary must comply with prerequisites and attempted credits.

HEAT ISLAND REDUCTION

	ND
Credit	GIB Credit 9
Points	1 point

Intent

To reduce heat islands to minimize effects on the microclimate and human and wildlife habitat.

Requirements

OPTION 1. Nonroof Measures

Use any combination of the following strategies for 50% of the nonroof site hardscape (including roads, sidewalks, courtyards, parking lots, parking structures, and driveways):

    a. Provide shade from open structures, such as those supporting solar photovoltaic panels, canopied walkways, and vine pergolas, all with a solar reflectance index (SRI) of at least 29.

    b. Use paving materials with an SRI of at least 29.

    c. Install an open-grid pavement system that is at least 50% pervious.

    d. Provide shade from tree canopy (within ten years of landscape installation).

OR

OPTION 2. High-Reflectance and Vegetated Roofs

Use roofing materials that have an SRI equal to or greater than the values in Table 1 for a minimum of 75% of the roof area of all new buildings within the *project*; or install a vegetated ("green") roof for at least 50% of the roof area of all new buildings within the project. Combinations of SRI-compliant and vegetated roofs can be used provided they collectively cover 75% of the roof area of all new buildings (use the equation in Option 3).

Table 1. Minimum solar reflectance index value, by roof slope

Roof slope	SRI
Low (≤ 2:12)	78
Steep (> 2:12)	29

OR

OPTION 3. Mixed Nonroof and Roof Measures

Use any of the strategies listed under Options 1 and 2 that in combination meet the following criterion:

$$\frac{\text{Area of Nonroof Measures}}{0.5} + \frac{\text{Area of SRI Roof}}{0.75} + \frac{\text{Area of Vegetated Roof}}{0.5} \geq \text{Total Site Hardscape Area} + \text{Total Roof Area}$$

1. Benefits and Issues to Consider

Environmental Issues

The use of dark, nonreflective surfaces for roofs, parking, walkways, and other hardscapes contributes to the heat island effect by absorbing the sun's warmth, which then radiates into the surroundings. Because of heat island effects, ambient temperatures in urban areas are artificially elevated by 2° to 10°F compared with surrounding suburban and undeveloped areas.[14] The resulting increased summer cooling loads require larger heating, ventilating, and air-conditioning (HVAC) equipment and greater electricity consumption, both of which generate greenhouse gases and pollution. Heat islands are detrimental to site habitat, wildlife, and animal migration corridors. Plants and animals are also sensitive to large fluctuations in daytime and nighttime temperatures and may not thrive in areas affected by heat islands. Projects that earn GIB Credit 9 by providing vegetated roofs contribute to increased habitat areas for birds, insects, and other wildlife.

Economic and Social Issues

The energy used to cool a building represents a substantial portion of the operating budget over its lifetime. Reducing heat islands can significantly lower cooling costs. According to the Department of Energy's Lawrence Berkeley National Laboratory, the annual energy savings potential of heat island reduction measures, studied in the metropolitan areas of Sacramento, Baton Rouge, and Salt Lake City, range from $4 million to $15 million.[15]

Vegetated roofs and roof surfaces with high solar reflectance index (SRI) values can reduce costs associated with HVAC equipment. Vegetated roofs typically require additional investment; cool roofs that reflect the sun's energy could cost the same as more conventional roofing systems. Any upfront investment is likely to be recouped in energy cost savings throughout the life cycle of the project. According to U.S. Environmental Protection Agency researchers who monitored 10 buildings in California and Florida, cool roofs save residents and building owners 20% to 70% in annual cooling energy costs.[16]

Site measures to reduce heat islands may also raise initial costs for additional landscaping, open-grid paving, or architectural shading devices. However, these items have an acceptable payback when integrated into a syst ems approach to maximizing energy savings. Some high-reflectance pavements, such as concrete made with white cement, may cost up to twice as much as those made with gray cement, but some blended cements (for example, slag) are very light in color and cost the same as or slightly less than Portland-only gray cement.[17] High-reflectance pavements also increase overall light levels and may enable a building to use fewer site lighting fixtures. Owners should assess the cost of installing highly reflective pavements or coatings against possible energy savings from reduced site lighting.

2. Related Credits

Reducing the heat island effect on a neighborhood scale may assist in achieving the following:

- NPD Credit 14, Tree-Lined and Shaded Streets

- GIB Prerequisite 2, Minimum Building Energy Efficiency

- GIB Credit 2, Building Energy Efficiency

14 U.S. Environmental Protection Agency, "Heat Island Effect." www.epa.gov/heatisland/index.htm (accessed November 2008).

15 U.S. Environmental Protection Agency, "Heat Island Effect: Urban Heat Island Pilot Project(UHIPP)." www.epa.gov/hiri/pilot/index.html (accessed November 2008).

16 U.S. Environmental Protection Agency, "Heat Island Effect: Cool Roofs." www.epa.gov/heatisld/strategies/coolroofs.html (accessed May 2008).

17 American Concrete Pavement Association," Albedo: A Measure of Pavement Surface Reflectance."2002. www.pavement.com/Downloads/RT/RT3.05.pdf.

3. Summary of Referenced Standards

There are no standards referenced in this credit.

4. Implementation

Reducing the heat island effect is the focus of this credit, which encourages greater reflectivity and vegetation. Strategically planted trees and light-colored hardscapes have the potential to noticeably reduce energy use for building cooling, lower electric bills, and cut emissions from electricity generation.

Using detailed site plans showing buildings and parking locations, identify roof and nonroof surfaces and the portions that can be shaded or have high reflectivity. For the credit, roofs can be either vegetated or covered with material having a solar reflectance index (SRI) rating of 29 or higher.

The credit uses the SRI to quantify the reflectivity of materials. The index is a measure of the roof's ability to reject solar heat, as shown by a small temperature rise. It is defined such that a standard black (reflectance 0.05, emittance 0.90) is 0 and a standard white (reflectance 0.80, emittance 0.90) is 100 (see Table 1). For example, the standard black has a temperature rise of 90°F (50°C) in full sun, and the standard white has a temperature rise of 14.6° F (8.1°C). Once the maximum temperature rise of a given material has been computed, the index value can be computed by interpolating between the values for white and black. Materials with the highest SRI values are the coolest choices for roofing. Because of the way SRI is defined, particularly hot materials can have slightly negative values, and particularly cool materials can exceed 100.

In addition to high-reflectance materials, roofs can also be vegetated. A "green" roof has layers of drainage materials and planting media on a high-quality waterproof membrane. Green roofs require consideration of the load-bearing capacity of roof decks, the moisture and root penetration resistance of the roof membrane, hydraulics, and wind shear. These considerations apply to designing new construction as well as retrofitting existing roofs.

The project's nonroof hardscapes, including sidewalks, streets, and parking lots, can achieve the credit through shading, materials with high SRI values, or open-grid paving systems. Shading with trees can be especially effective. Trees affect climate, cool buildings, and reduce building energy use both directly, by shading surfaces and keeping them and ambient temperatures cooler, and indirectly, by reducing the air temperature around buildings through evapotranspiration. A nonroof alternative to shading and high-SRI material is paving that is porous or has an open grid. Open-grid systems provide structural capacity for vehicle traffic while providing permeability and infiltration benefits for stormwater runoff.

5. Timeline and Team

Heat island reduction should be taken into consideration once project planning has reached the site design phase. As rights-of-way and buildings are laid out, the project design team should begin to assess the heat island effects of hardscape features and respond with appropriate design measures. Architects, landscape architects, and energy efficiency specialists can contribute to heat island reduction strategies.

6. Calculations

OPTION 1. Nonroof Measures

Use the percentage of total nonroof hardscape covered by the four heat reduction measures listed in the credit requirements. For tree shade calculations, tree canopy size should be the estimated size ten years after landscape installation. All shade coverage must be calculated at 10 a.m., 12 noon, and 3 p.m. on the summer solstice. The arithmetic mean of these three values is the effective shaded area. Shade calculations should be consistent with shade calculations for NPD Credit 14, Tree-Lined and Shaded Streets. For parking lots, sidewalks, and other hardscape, refer to the SRI values in Table 2. Hardscape areas cannot be double-counted; for example, a square foot of shaded, open-grid pavement can be counted as either open-grid pavement or shaded hardscape, but not both.

Table 2. Solar reflectance index (SRI) for standard paving materials

Material	Emissivity	Reflectance	SRI
Typical new gray concrete	0.9	0.35	35
Typical weathered* gray concrete	0.9	0.20	19
Typical new white concrete	0.9	0.7	86
Typical weathered* white concrete	0.9	0.4	45
New asphalt	0.9	.05	0
Weathered asphalt	0.9	.10	6
* Reflectance of surfaces can be maintained with cleaning. Typical pressure washing of cementitious materials can restore reflectance close to original value. Weathered values are based on no cleaning.			

OPTION 2. High-Reflectance and Vegetated Roofs

Step 1. Determine the total roof surface area of the project's buildings, in square feet.

Step 2. Determine the area of the roofs covered by mechanical equipment, solar energy panels, and appurtenances, and deduct these areas from the total roof surface area.

Step 3. Determine whether the areas of qualifying reflective and vegetative roofing are adequate to meet the credit requirements, using Equation 1. If more than one type of low-slope or steep-slope material is used, determine the weighted rooftop SRI average and verify that 75% or more of the roof areas comply with the credit requirements.

Equation 1

$$\left[\frac{\text{Area of low-slope SRI material}}{78 \times \frac{.75}{\text{SRI value}}} + \frac{\text{Area of steep-slope SRI material}}{29 \times \frac{.75}{\text{SRI value}}} + \frac{\text{Vegetated roof area}}{.5} \right] \geq \text{Total roof area} - \text{Deducted area}$$

OPTION 3. Mixed Roof and Nonroof Measures

Follow the instructions for Options 1 and 2 to calculate the nonroof hardscape area, roof area, deducted roof area, and areas covered by heat reduction strategies. Use Equation 2 to determine whether the Option 3 threshold is met.

Equation 2

$$\left[\frac{\text{Area of nonroof measures}}{.5} + \frac{\text{Area of low-slope SRI material}}{78 \times \frac{.75}{\text{SRI value}}} + \frac{\text{Area of steep-slope SRI material}}{29 \times \frac{.75}{\text{SRI value}}} + \frac{\text{Vegetated roof area}}{.5}\right] \geq \frac{\text{Total}}{\text{hardscape area}} + \frac{\text{Total}}{\text{roof area}} - \frac{\text{Deducted}}{\text{area}}$$

7. Documentation Guidance

As a first step in preparing to complete the LEED-ND documentation requirements, work through the following measures. Refer to GBCI's website for the complete descriptions of all required documentation.

- Prepare a site plan that highlights all roof conditions and nonroof hardscape areas. Clearly label each portion of roof and hardscape that counts toward credit achievement, and list material information about the compliant surfaces (e.g., SRI values of materials, open-grid paving).

- If parking spaces are placed under cover, determine the total number of parking spaces and the portion covered. If applicable, assemble SRI values for structures that cover parking areas.

8. Examples

A project pursuing Option 3 has the following site characteristics:

Nonroof	Area (sf)
Hardscape with SRI ≥ 29	2,572
Shaded hardscape	8,203
Total	10,775

	Green roof (sf)	Total area (sf)	Deducted area (sf)	Total area to be treated (sf)
Roof A	18,544	46,777	8,750	38,027
Roof B	20,560	42,345	8,345	34,000
Roof C	21,895	53,690	9,035	44,655
Total	60,999	142,812	26,130	116,682

The team prepares the left side of Equation 2:

$$\frac{2,572 + 8,203}{.5} + \frac{0}{78 \times \frac{.75}{\text{SRI value}}} + \frac{0}{29 \times \frac{.75}{\text{SRI value}}} + \frac{60,999}{.5} = 143,548$$

The right side of Equation 2 is as follows:

$$10,775 + 142,812 - 26,130 = 127,457$$

Because 143,548 > 127,457, the Option 3 threshold is met.

9. Exemplary Performance

Projects may earn an Innovation and Design Process credit for exemplary performance by demonstrating one of the following:

OPTION 1. Nonroof Measures

Any combination of Option 1 strategies is applied to 100% of the nonroof site hardscape.

OPTION 2. High-Reflectance and Vegetated Roofs

100% of the roof area of new buildings either is made of materials with SRI values equal to or greater than the values in Table 1, or consists of a vegetated roof system.

OPTION 3. Mixed Nonroof and Roof Measures

100% of the roof area either is made of materials with SRI values equal to or greater than the values in Table 1, or consists of a vegetated roof system.

10. Regional Variations

Heat island intensities depend on an area's weather and climate, proximity to water bodies, and topography.[18] Buildings in very cold climates or at high latitudes may not experience the same rise in surface and ambient temperatures. Buildings in urban areas and those in climate zones 1, 2, and 3 (as defined by ASNI/ASHRAE/IESNA Standard 90.1–2007) are most affected by heat islands and are likely to benefit from measures to decrease cooling loads by avoiding additional heat absorption. In sunny climates, teams may need to shade reflective pavements to mitigate glare inside buildings.

11. Resources

Websites

American Concrete Pavement Association

www.pavement.com

This national association represents concrete pavement contractors, cement companies, equipment and material manufacturers, and suppliers. See "Albedo: A Measure of Pavement Surface Reflectance," *R&T Update* (3.05) (June 2002), available at www.pavement.com/Downloads/RT/RT3.05.pdf.

Lawrence Berkeley National Laboratory, Heat Island Group

www.eetd.lbl.gov/HeatIsland/

Lawrence Berkeley National Laboratory conducts heat island research to find, analyze, and implement solutions to minimize heat island effect. Current research efforts focus on the study and development of more reflective surfaces for roadways and buildings.

U.S. Environmental Protection Agency, heat island effect

www.epa.gov/heatisland/index.htm

EPA offers basic information about heat island effect, its social and environmental costs, and reduction strategies.

18 U.S. Environmental Protection Agency, "Heat Island Effect: Basic Information." www.epa.gov.gov/hiri/about/index.html (accessed November 2008).

12. Definitions

heat island thermal gradient differences between developed and undeveloped areas.

project the land, water, and construction that constitutes the project application. A project applicant does not have to own or control all land or water within a project boundary, but all the area within the project boundary must comply with prerequisites and attempted credits.

SOLAR ORIENTATION

	ND
Credit	GIB Credit 10
Points	1 point

Intent

To encourage energy efficiency by creating optimum conditions for the use of passive and active solar strategies.

Requirements

OPTION 1. Block Orientation (For Projects Earning at Least 2 Points Under NPD Credit 2, Compact Development)

Locate the *project* on *existing block*s or design and orient the project such that 75% or more of the blocks have one axis within plus or minus 15 degrees of geographical east-west, and the east-west lengths of those blocks are at least as long as the north-south lengths of the blocks.

Earn at least 2 points under NPD Credit 2, Compact Development.

Figure 1. Solar-oriented blocks with east-west lengths equal to or greater than north-south lengths, and east-west axis within 15 degrees of geographic east-west

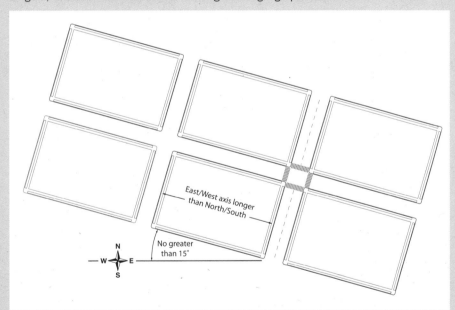

OR

OPTION 2. Building Orientation (Available For All Projects)

Design and orient 75% or more of the project's total building square footage (excluding existing buildings) such that one axis of each qualifying building is at least 1.5 times longer than the other, and the longer axis is within 15 degrees of geographical east-west. The length-to-width ratio applies only to walls enclosing conditioned spaces; walls enclosing unconditioned spaces, such as garages, arcades, or porches, cannot contribute to credit achievement. The surface area of equator-facing vertical surfaces and slopes of roofs of buildings counting toward credit achievement must not be more than 25% shaded at the time of initial occupancy, measured at noon on the winter solstice.

Figure 2. Solar-oriented buildings with longer axis (at least 1.5 times length of other axis) within 15 degrees of geographic east-west

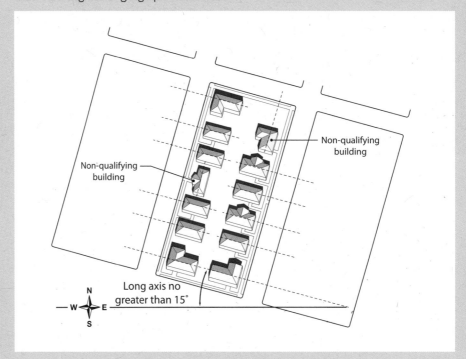

1. Benefits and Issues to Consider

A building's orientation to the sun affects its ability to provide natural lighting, use the sun for passive heating, offer protection from overheating, and deploy photovoltaic or other solar power sources. Proper building orientation on the site can also enhance daylight and views, which improve the comfort and mental health for building occupants while reducing energy demand for lighting.

If incorporated into the design of the project early on, orienting buildings for solar efficiency can be one of the most cost-effective energy-saving measures used in a project, depending on the level of design flexibility available. Existing buildings or streets in the project may make solar orientation more challenging, however.

2. Related Credits

Orienting blocks or buildings for solar efficiency may affect strategies that contribute to the following related credits:

- NPD Credit 2, Compact Development
- NPD Credit 6, Street Network
- NPD Credit 14, Tree-Lined and Shaded Streets
- GIB Credit 2, Building Energy Efficiency
- GIB Credit 11, On-Site Renewable Energy Sources

3. Summary of Referenced Standards

There are no standards referenced for this credit.

4. Implementation

Solar orientation contributes directly to a building's overall energy use, and building orientation is an input for most building energy simulation modeling, necessary for GIB Credit 2, Building Energy Efficiency. An integrated design approach to creating the site plan enables proper building orientation through its street network and open space placement.

This credit encourages long buildings and blocks that face true north or true south. Only blocks containing buildable land can count toward the orientation threshold; any area dedicated in perpetuity to nondevelopment should be excluded.

Option 1 is available only for dense development (projects earning 2 or more points under NPD Credit 2, Compact Development), where the block frontage is more likely than individual buildings to be exposed to the sun. In the Northern Hemisphere, especially for locations north of 35 degrees latitude, true-north and true-south building faces have different design considerations. North building faces can provide consistent indirect daylight without glare and excessive heat gain. If natural light will be provided through glazing on a north building face, a narrow north-south axis means daylight does not need to reach as far into the building to illuminate the interior, making it easier to use daylighting for a greater portion.

Buildings that face true south receive consistent direct sunlight. This can be filtered or shaded to reduce heat and glare for natural lighting, or it can be used for heat in colder climates, and it is optimal for photovoltaic cells, solar water heaters, and other active solar applications. If a building has a pitched roof, a long east-west building axis creates a large south-facing roof and thus opportunities for active solar applications. Buildings that face true east or west, in contrast, receive changing amounts of light and heat from the sun throughout the day and are not recommended for achieving the full potential of active or passive solar systems.

Site Design for Solar Orientation

Conduct a preliminary assessment of the site's potential for taking advantage of the sun's energy. First, assess the site for the overall availability of sunlight and the extent of shading. This includes shading from trees, existing buildings, or other features, as well as local weather or climate. In addition, assess the site's implicit ability to moderate the local climate with vegetation, open space, or large bodies of water. This can affect the efficiency of passive and active solar designs as well as buildings' heating and cooling demand.

If solar energy options are feasible, follow a three-step process for incorporating optimal solar orientation into the site design. First, assess the maximum solar access available, based on the preliminary assessment of sunlight, shading, and site features. Next, assess local regulations for any impediments to solar applications. Finally, develop a base map of site constraints and opportunities, and create or adjust the site plan to achieve optimal solar orientation.

Sometimes waterfront, wetlands, topography, existing buildings and infrastructure, or an existing street network may constrain a project's ability to achieve solar orientation that meets the credit requirements. In other cases, projects can modify the existing street network to achieve the credit. For example, a site with long block lengths could pursue Option 1 by adding through-streets running true north-south, which would also enhance walkability. For sites with existing buildings, it may still be possible to achieve the credit by ensuring that the equator-facing side of any new building is not shaded by existing buildings.

Individual Building Orientation

With new construction, additions, and major renovation to existing buildings, project teams should take advantage of the opportunity to design optimal building orientation. This is important for both passive and active solar applications and can improve occupants' comfort as well as building energy efficiency. Considerations include the slopes and orientation of roofs, the locations of windows and overhangs, the placement of landscaping, nearby existing and planned trees and buildings, the need for any light-shielding devices like canopies, and the use of thermal mass.

5. Timeline and Team

The project's building energy modeler should work with the urban designers or architects who lay out the blocks and buildings. It may be useful to hire a solar design specialist to assess the potential of the site and make recommendations. To make the best potential use of solar energy, address solar orientation as early as the conceptual site plan, since it is increasingly difficult to change street orientations as the project progresses.

6. Calculations

OPTION 1. Block Orientation

Step 1. Count the blocks in the project.

Step 2. Count the blocks with both of the following characteristics: (1) one axis is within plus or minus 15 degrees of true east-west; and (2) the true east-west axis length is at least as long as the true north-south axis length.

Step 3. Calculate the percentage of blocks with optimal orientation, according to Equation 1.

Equation 1

$$\% \text{ blocks with optimal orientation} = \frac{\text{Blocks with optimal orientation}}{\text{Total blocks}}$$

OPTION 2. Building Orientation

Step 1. Determine the total square footage of all new buildings in the project.

Step 2. Identify all new buildings in the project where one axis is at least 1.5 times longer than the other and the longer axis is within 15 degrees of true east-west. For nonrectangular buildings with variable axis lengths, use the average length of the two exterior walls for each axis. For buildings in which the east-west axis is variable, use the average degrees from east-west of the north and south exterior walls. Determine whether existing or planned buildings, other structures, or trees with foliage on the winter solstice will shade any portion of equator-facing building sides. If so, then for each such building, calculate the surface area of the equator-facing wall and sloped roof, calculate the surface area that will be shaded at noon on the winter solstice, and determine whether more than 25% of the surface area will be shaded. If more than 25% will be shaded, exclude that building from the list of buildings with solar orientation. Sum the total square footage of solar-oriented buildings that meet the minimal shading requirement.

Step 3. Calculate the percentage of building square footage with optimal orientation, according to Equation 2.

Equation 2

$$\text{\% building area with optimal orientation} = \frac{\text{Area of qualifying buildings}}{\text{Total area of all buildings}}$$

7. Documentation Guidance

As a first step in preparing to complete the LEED-ND documentation requirements, work through the following measures. Refer to GBCI's website for the complete descriptions of all required documentation.

- For the block orientation option, prepare a site plan showing the street network and the location of all buildings and blocks.

- Measure the degree orientation of each block or building on the site plan.

- For the building orientation option, determine the square footage of every qualifying new building in the project, and determine the total square footage of all new building space.

- For the building orientation option, create a cross-section drawing showing any shading that would affect solar access for relevant buildings.

8. Examples

Refer to Figures 1 and 2 in the Rating System.

9. Exemplary Performance

Projects may earn an Innovation and Design Process credit for exemplary performance by achieving one of the following thresholds:

OPTION 1. Block Orientation

95% or more of the blocks have the optimal orientation specified in the requirements.

OPTION 2. Building Orientation

95% or more of the project's total building square footage has the optimal orientation specified in the requirements.

10. Regional Variations

Variations in weather, climactic conditions, and local regulations will affect the feasibility of active and passive solar applications. Design considerations for north or south faces of buildings, described in the Implementation section, apply to the Northern Hemisphere. In the Southern Hemisphere, they are the opposite. Some benefits of the solar orientation required in the credit may become less effective at project locations below 35 degrees latitude, since the location of the sun in the sky is increasingly overhead as one nears the equator, minimizing the difference between north and south building faces.

11. Resources

Print Media

Design with Climate: A Bioclimatic Approach to Architectural Regionalism, by Victor Olgyay (Van Nostrand Reinhold, 1992).

Energy Design Handbook (American Institute of Architects, 1993).

Implementing Energy-Efficient Land-Use (Oregon Department of Energy, 1980).

Protecting Solar Access for Residential Development: A Guide Book for Planning Officials (American Planning Association and U.S. Department of Housing and Urban Development, 1979).

Site for Solar Access: A Guide Book for Residential Developers and Site Planners (American Planning Association and U.S. Department of Housing and Urban Development, 1979).

12. Definitions

block land bounded by the project boundary, transportation or utility rights-of-way that may be publicly dedicated or privately owned and deeded in perpetuity for general public use, waterfront, and/or comparable land division features.

existing present on the date of submission of LEED-ND certification documents; similarly, an element or condition that **exists** is present on the date that LEED-ND certification documents are submitted.

project the land, water, and construction that constitutes the project application. A project applicant does not have to own or control all land or water within a project boundary, but all the area within the project boundary must comply with prerequisites and attempted credits.

ON-SITE RENEWABLE ENERGY SOURCES

	ND
Credit	GIB Credit 11
Points	1-3 points

Intent

To encourage on-site renewable energy production to reduce the adverse environmental and economic effects associated with fossil fuel energy production and use.

Requirements

Incorporate on-site nonpolluting renewable energy generation, such as solar, wind, geothermal, small-scale or micro hydroelectric, and/or biomass, with production capacity of at least 5% of the *project's* annual electrical and thermal energy cost (exclusive of *existing* buildings), as established through an accepted building energy performance simulation tool. Points are awarded as listed in Table 1.

Table 1. Points for on-site renewable energy generation

Percentage of annual electrical and thermal energy cost	Points
5%	1
12.5%	2
20%	3

1. Benefits and Issues to Consider

Environmental Issues

Use of renewable energy instead of fossil fuel–based energy can dramatically improve outdoor environmental quality. Use of renewable energy means reductions in air and water pollution, benefiting all community members. Energy production from traditional, fossil fuel–based sources is a significant contributor to air pollution in the United States, releasing such pollutants as sulfur dioxide, nitrogen oxide, and carbon dioxide, which have widespread and adverse effects on human health, especially respiratory health, and contribute to acid precipitation, smog, and concentrations of greenhouse gases.

The overall environmental benefit of renewable energy depends on the source of energy and the process by which it is extracted. For example, using biomass can reduce the estimated 136 million tons of woody construction, demolition, and land-clearing waste annually sent to landfills,[19] but if these wastes are not processed properly, their combustion could degrade air quality. Although renewably generated electricity is not entirely benign, it greatly lessens the negative environmental impacts of power generation. Generating renewable energy on-site is an excellent way for owners to reduce the negative environmental effects of a project's energy use.

Economic and Social Issues

Using on-site renewable energy technologies can result in cost savings. Utility rebates are often available to reduce first costs of renewable energy equipment. The initial costs of installing or providing renewable energy sources on-site can be offset by future savings. A life-cycle cost analysis of the potential savings can help project teams in their decision-making process. In some states, initial costs can also be offset by net metering, in which excess energy is sold back to the utility, and through programs that provide incentives for using renewable energy. Project teams should ascertain whether these options are available locally, particularly for the type of renewable energy they plan to use. Research on the available technologies is essential; consider climatic, geographical, and other regional factors that influence the appropriateness of an on-site renewable source for the building's energy use.

Renewable energy benefits rural communities in particular; siting and operating wind farms and biomass conversion facilities in rural areas enhances economic development. Rural wind generation is providing new sources of income for American farmers, Native Americans, and other rural landowners while meeting the growing demand for clean sources of electricity. However, care must be taken to minimize undesirable noise and bird kills on wind farms and emissions from combustion at biomass conversion facilities.

2. Related Credits

The installation of renewable energy systems usually has only a small effect on the achievement of other energy-related credits. However, it may change the energy performance of project buildings and should therefore be considered alongside other energy efficiency measures. See the following related credits:

- GIB Credit 1, Certified Green Buildings
- GIB Credit 2, Building Energy Efficiency
- GIB Credit 12, District Heating and Cooling
- GIB Credit 13, Infrastructure Energy Efficiency

---

19 U.S. Environmental Protection Agency, Office of Solid Waste, "Wastes—Non-Hazardous Waste—Industrial Waste: Basic Information." www.epa.gov/osw/nonhaz/industrial/cd/basic.htm (accessed November 2008).

3. Summary of Referenced Standard

There are no standards referenced in the credit.

4. Implementation

Conduct a thorough site inventory and feasibility survey of renewable energy opportunities for providing clean, affordable energy to project residents and workers. On-site renewable energy technologies eligible for the credit include the following:

- Solar power systems.
- Solar thermal systems.
- Wind energy systems.
- Biomass thermal systems.
- Biofuel-based electrical systems (see list of eligible biofuels, below).
- Geothermal heating systems.
- Geothermal electric systems.
- Small-scale or micro hydroelectric power systems.
- Wave and tidal power systems.

Systems producing on-site renewable electrical power should be designed to facilitate net metering back to the grid for periods when the renewable energy system output exceeds the site demand. Ask local utilities and electric service providers about incentive and rebate programs.

Some restrictions apply. Geothermal energy systems that use deep-earth water or steam sources to produce electric power or provide thermal energy may be eligible for this credit; those that use vapor compression systems for heat transfer are not eligible. Active solar thermal energy systems that employ collection panels, heat transfer mechanical components (such as pumps or fans), and defined heat storage systems (such as hot water tanks) are eligible. Thermosiphon solar and storage tank "batch heaters" are also eligible.

The following biofuels are considered renewable energy under this credit:

- Untreated wood waste, including mill residues.
- Agricultural crops or waste.
- Animal waste and other organic waste.
- Landfill gas.

These types of on-site systems are not eligible for this credit:

- Architectural features.
- Passive solar strategies.
- Daylighting strategies.
- Geoexchange systems (ground-source heat pumps).

Energy production based on the following biofuels is not eligible for this credit:

- Combustion of municipal solid waste.
- Forestry biomass waste other than mill residue.
- Wood coated with paints, plastics, or laminates like Formica.

- Wood treated for preservation with materials containing halogens, chlorine compounds, halide compounds, chromated copper arsenate, or arsenic. If more than 1% of the wood fuel has been treated with these compounds, the energy system is ineligible.

For projects with renewable energy resources that supply district energy systems, also see the Implementation section under GIB Credit 12, District Heating and Cooling.

5. Timeline and Team

The project team should consider on-site renewable energy during early planning phases and designate and protect areas with favorable resource conditions, such as solar access and wind exposure. Once project plans have advanced enough to support building details, the total amount of power and thermal energy demand can be used to scope and analyze potential renewable supplies. Important team contributors will be mechanical and electrical engineers, architects, and specialists in solar, wind, or other renewables.

6. Calculations

Determine the percentage of the project's total annual electric and thermal cost (exclusive of existing buildings) provided by the renewable energy system. Energy costs are expressed in dollars per energy unit. Use the renewable system's capacity, expressed in energy units, to determine the renewable's percentage of the total. Annual energy costs must be estimated using an accepted building energy performance simulation tool.

7. Documentation Guidance

As a first step in preparing to complete the LEED-ND documentation requirements, work through the following measure. Refer to GBCI's website for the complete descriptions of all required documentation.

- Assemble an estimate of the project's total annual electric and thermal energy cost.

8. Example

There are no examples for this credit.

9. Exemplary Performance

Projects may earn an Innovation and Design Process credit for exemplary performance by demonstrating that 27.5% of the annual electrical and thermal energy cost is covered by on-site, nonpolluting, renewable energy generation technologies.

10. Regional Variations

The availability and appropriateness of renewable energy technologies for neighborhoods and buildings vary by region. Factors like climate, geography, and location can greatly affect the choice of the best renewable source. For example, although solar energy is available across the United States, it is most abundant—and thus solar-based energy generation is most efficient—in the Southwest.

Similarly, biomass is likely to be more cost-effective in agricultural regions, and wind power in coastal regions. More information on regional variation of renewable energy sources can be found at www1.eere.energy.gov/maps_data.

11. Resources

Websites

American Wind Energy Association

www.awea.org

This national trade association represents wind power plant developers, wind turbine manufacturers, utilities, consultants, insurers, financiers, researchers, and others involved in the wind energy industry.

ENERGY Guide, green power

www.energyguide.com

This website provides information on green power and other sources of energy, as well as general information on energy efficiency and tools for selecting power providers based on economic, environmental, and other criteria.

National Center for Photovoltaics

www.nrel.gov/ncpv/

NCPV provides clearinghouse information on all aspects of photovoltaic systems.

North Carolina Solar Center, state incentives for renewable energy

www.dsireusa.org

The center's database, known as DSIRE, collects information on state financial and regulatory incentives (e.g., tax credits, grants, and special utility rates) to promote the application of renewable energy technologies. The incentives can be searched by state.

U.S. Department of Energy, Green Power Network

www.apps3.eere.energy.gov/greenpower/

The Green Power Network provides news and information on green power markets and related activities. It contains up-to-date information on providers, product offerings, and consumer issues, plus in-depth analyses of issues and policies affecting green power markets. The website is maintained by the National Renewable Energy Laboratory for DOE.

U.S. Department of Energy, National Renewable Energy Laboratory

www.nrel.gov

NREL is a leader in DOE's effort to secure for the nation an energy future that is environmentally and economically sustainable.

U.S. Department of Energy, Office of Energy Efficiency and Renewable Energy

www.eere.energy.gov/

This website is a comprehensive resource for information on energy efficiency and renewable energy and provides access to energy links and downloadable documents. The maps and data section of the EERE website (www1.eere.energy.gov/maps_data) provide information on regional distribution of renewable energy sources and technologies in the United States.

U.S. Department of Energy, Wind Powering America

www.windpoweringamerica.gov/

This initiative seeks to increase the use of wind energy in the United States while generating new sources of income for American farmers, Native Americans, and other rural landowners.

U.S. Environmental Protection Agency, Green Power Partnership

www.epa.gov/greenpower/index.htm

EPA's Green Power Partnership provides assistance and recognition to organizations that demonstrate environmental leadership by choosing green power. It includes a buyer's guide with lists of green power providers in each state.

Print Media

Wind and Solar Power Systems, by Mukund Patel (CRC Press, 1999).

Wind Energy Comes of Age, by Paul Gipe (John Wiley & Sons, 1995).

12. Definitions

existing present on the date of submission of LEED-ND certification documents; similarly, an element or condition that **exists** is present on the date that LEED-ND certification documents are submitted.

project the land, water, and construction that constitutes the project application. A project applicant does not have to own or control all land or water within a project boundary, but all the area within the project boundary must comply with prerequisites and attempted credits.

DISTRICT HEATING AND COOLING

	ND
Credit	GIB Credit 12
Points	2 points

Intent

To encourage the development of energy-efficient neighborhoods by employing district heating and cooling strategies that reduce energy use and adverse energy-related environmental effects.

Requirements

Incorporate a district heating and/or cooling system for space conditioning and/or water heating of new buildings (at least two buildings total) such that at least 80% of the *project's* annual heating and/or cooling consumption is provided by the district plant. *Single-family residential* buildings and *existing* buildings of any type may be excluded from the calculation.

Each system component that is addressed by ANSI/ASHRAE/IESNA Standard 90.1–2007 must have an overall efficiency performance at least 10% better than that specified by the standard's prescriptive requirements. Additionally, annual district pumping energy consumption that exceeds 2.5% of the annual thermal energy output of the heating and cooling plant (with 1 kWh of electricity equal to 3,413 Btus) must be offset by increases in the component's efficiency beyond the specified 10% improvement. Combined heat and power (CHP) district systems can achieve this credit by demonstrating equivalent performance.

1. Benefits and Issues to Consider

Environmental Issues

Building heating and cooling needs consume substantial amounts of energy, stressing municipal energy infrastructure and resulting in sizable carbon emissions. District heating and cooling (DHC) infrastructure is often more energy efficient than individual building boilers and chiller systems, reducing the burden on infrastructure. Because most traditional energy generation facilities are powered by petroleum-based products, DHC also reduces the depletion of these resources and limits the associated carbon emissions. Maximum efficiency can be achieved if a DHC system is connected to a renewable energy source. Combined heat and power, a specific kind of DHC in which waste heat is captured during energy generation, is another way to maximize efficiency.

Economic and Social Issues

To be cost-effective, a DHC system needs to be incorporated into a project early in the design phase. Careful consideration of the upfront costs versus the return potential is required with DHC, since not all projects are necessarily good candidates for the technology. A project that is designed compactly and comprises several multiunit residences and multistory nonresidential buildings is the most likely candidate for a DHC system.

2. Related Credits

DHC systems can use renewable energy resources and improve the overall energy efficiency of a project, contributing to achievement of the following:

- GIB Credit 2, Building Energy Efficiency

- GIB Credit 10, Solar Orientation

- GIB Credit 11, On-Site Renewable Energy Sources

- GIB Credit 13, Infrastructure Energy Efficiency

3. Summary of Referenced Standards

ANSI/ASHRAE/IESNA Standard 90.1–2007, Energy Standard for Buildings Except Low-Rise Residential

www.ashrae.org

This standard was formulated by American Society of Heating, Refrigerating and Air-Conditioning Engineers (ASHRAE) with the Illuminating Engineering Society of North America (IESNA) under an American National Standards Institute (ANSI) consensus process. It establishes minimum requirements for the energy-efficient design of buildings with these exceptions: single-family houses, multiunit structures of three habitable stories or fewer above grade, manufactured houses (mobile and modular homes), buildings that do not use electricity or fossil fuel, and equipment and building systems that use energy primarily for industrial, manufacturing, or commercial processes). Building envelope requirements are provided for semiheated spaces, such as warehouses. The standard addresses the following categories:

- Section 5. Building envelope (including semiheated spaces, such as warehouses).

- Section 6. Heating, ventilation, and air-conditioning (including parking garage ventilation, freeze protection, exhaust air recovery, and condenser heat recovery for service water heating).

- Section 7. Service water heating (including swimming pools).

- Section 8. Power (including all building power distribution systems).

- Section 9. Lighting (including exit signs, building exterior, grounds, and parking garages).
- Section 10. Other equipment (including all permanently wired electrical motors).

Within each section are mandatory provisions and additional prescriptive requirements. Some sections also contain performance alternatives. The energy cost budget method allows certain prescriptive requirements to be exceeded, provided energy cost savings are made in other areas. However, in all cases, the mandatory provisions must still be met.

4. Implementation

District heating and cooling systems are thermal energy networks that distribute hot water, chilled water, and/or steam from a single energy source to multiple recipients via underground pipes. The district energy supply may come from a conventional boiler or chiller, geothermal wells, a water body such as a lake or river, or waste heat captured from industrial processes or electrical generation (combined heat and power). DHC technology is particularly well suited to areas of high density and mixed use because it lowers distribution costs and increases system efficiency with peak load diversity.

DHC is generally better suited for projects with large amounts of building square footage and mixed uses that can capture economies of scale and energy efficiencies. However, even modest-sized projects of a few buildings on a single bock can sometime use DHC advantageously. In some cases, smaller LEED-ND projects may be able to connect to existing DHC systems.

Calculate the space-conditioning and domestic hot water needs of project buildings and compare the cost-effectiveness of DHC service with individual building systems. If DHC is competitive, system plans will need to be developed concurrent with other project infrastructure, particularly the central plant location and the streets and other rights-of-way to be used for distribution pipelines.

Detached single-family residences may not be feasible DHC customers because of the higher distribution costs of reaching dispersed buildings with small loads, and existing buildings may be difficult to retrofit to DHC. For these reasons, single-family dwellings and existing buildings of any kind do not need to be included in the calculation of the total project's annual thermal load (of which DHC must provide at least 80%). However, if such buildings are connected to a system, their loads become part of the calculation. At least two buildings must be connected to the DHC system.

All components of a DHC system regulated by ASHRAE Standard 90.1–2007 must be 10% more efficient than the standard's prescriptive requirements, and if annual DHC pumping energy exceeds 2.5% of the system's annual thermal output, that excess must be offset by efficiency beyond the minimum 10% improvement. If electricity is also being generated in a combined heat and power system, power equivalencies to the thermal criteria can be used to demonstrate compliance.

5. Timeline and Team

DHC feasibility analysis can begin when project building plans are sufficiently advanced to support estimation of space conditioning and domestic hot water loads, and DHC design should progress in concert with other neighborhood-scale infrastructure. Project team contributors will include architects, mechanical and electrical engineers, and energy efficiency specialists with DHC experience. The energy modeling that often accompanies building design will be the first opportunity to characterize the potential DHC load. The team's mechanical, electrical, and energy efficiency members can prepare a comparison of DHC with individual building systems, and if the life-cycle results favor DHC, the team's architects and civil engineers can plan distribution pipeline routes and connections to buildings.

6. Calculations

There are no calculations for this credit.

7. Documentation Guidance

As a first step in preparing to complete the LEED-ND documentation requirements, work through the following measures. Refer to GBCI's website for the complete descriptions of all required documentation.

- List the ASHRAE-regulated components in the DHC system and their efficiency ratings.

- Identify which project buildings will be served by the system.

- Estimate total annual project thermal load, DHC annual thermal output, and DHC annual pumping power requirements.

8. Examples

There are no examples for this credit.

9. Exemplary Performance

Projects may earn an Innovation and Design Process credit for exemplary performance by demonstrating that at least 95% of the project's annual heating and/or cooling consumption is provided by the district plant and that the efficiency of each system component addressed by ANSI/ASHRAE/IESNA Standard 90.1–2007 has an overall efficiency performance at least 20% better than the standard.

10. Regional Variations

There are no regional variations associated with this credit.

11. Resources

Websites

International District Energy Association
www.districtenergy.org
IDEA is a nonprofit trade association that provides reliable, economical, efficient, and environmentally sound district energy services.

International Energy Agency, district energy
www.iea-dhc.org
IEA provides information about district heating and cooling and conducts research on district energy technology, materials, and efficiency. It also provides reports and case studies on district heating and cooling in cities in the United States and throughout the world.

Print Media

The District Heating Handbook, fourth edition (International District Energy Association, 1998).

12. Definitions

existing present on the date of submission of LEED-ND certification documents; similarly, an element or condition that **exists** is present on the date that LEED-ND certification documents are submitted.

project the land, water, and construction that constitutes the project application. A project applicant does not have to own or control all land or water within a project boundary, but all the area within the project boundary must comply with prerequisites and attempted credits.

single-family residential any residential unit other than multiunit residential, including single, duplex, triplex, row house, townhouse and semiattached residential building types.

INFRASTRUCTURE ENERGY EFFICIENCY

	ND
Credit	GIB Credit 13
Points	1 point

Intent

To reduce adverse environmental effects from energy used for operating public infrastructure.

Requirements

Design, purchase, or work with the municipality to install all new infrastructure, including but not limited to traffic lights, *street* lights, and water and wastewater pumps, to achieve a 15% annual energy reduction below an estimated baseline energy use for this infrastructure. The baseline is calculated with the assumed use of lowest first-cost infrastructure items.

1. Benefits and Issues to Consider

Environmental Issues

A project's overall energy efficiency is determined not just by the systems inside its buildings but also by the energy-consuming components of its infrastructure. Since many energy-efficient products also have longer service lives, numerous secondary positive effects may follow, such as reduced traffic congestion during replacement of lighting fixtures.

Consider how renewable technologies, such as solar-powered street lamps, can be incorporated into the new infrastructure features to further reduce energy consumption from the local grid.

Economic and Social Issues

Using more efficient infrastructure in a project can reduce the burden on municipal systems, which are often under enormous pressure to provide consistent service and reasonable prices.

Whereas savings resulting from energy-efficient buildings usually accrue to the building owner, savings on efficient infrastructure may be realized by several parties, including the municipality. These savings may be passed along to residents in the form of lower service fees or increased funding for civic activities and spaces.

2. Related Credits

Infrastructure that is energy efficient may include district heating and cooling facilities and transit facilities; see the following related credits:

- NPD Credit 7, Transit Facilities
- GIB Credit 12, District Heating and Cooling

3. Summary of Referenced Standards

There are no referenced standards for this credit.

4. Implementation

Neighborhood infrastructure components are increasingly available with energy-efficient features that reduce consumption and extend useful lives and therefore have low life-cycle costs. To achieve this credit, project applicants do not need to install or pay for the infrastructure themselves; this may be done for the project by the municipality. The credit is only for new infrastructure; if no new infrastructure is constructed as part of the project, the project cannot earn this credit.

Infrastructure includes any energy-using equipment outside the building, such as street lights, traffic lights, water and wastewater pumps, utility systems, pumps for fountains, centralized parking meters, bus stop lighting, and signage lighting. Any energy-consuming components of district heating and cooling systems, such as pumps, are included, but energy-producing components, such as combined heat and power plants, are not.

To determine the 15% annual energy reduction, first identify and list all types of new infrastructure that will be needed for the project. The credit does not require that all infrastructure be replaced with new infrastructure, only that any new infrastructure installed must meet the requirements. Next, identify the infrastructure components (traffic lights, pumps, etc.), including brand, model number, and energy specification, that have the lowest first cost to install. Usually, items with the lowest first cost are the least efficient. Calculate the total amount of energy use that would be expected if the lowest-first-cost infrastructure were installed (see Calculations, below). This is the baseline. Then identify energy-efficient models of the same equipment that will be installed as a part of the project and calculate their total expected energy use. The project team must demonstrate, at minimum, a 15% reduction in energy use over the baseline from this new infrastructure. The 15% reduction requirement is for all new infrastructure within the project boundary on an annual basis, not for each individual piece of equipment.

5. Timeline and Team

Infrastructure energy efficiency is considered when the project design is sufficiently advanced that infrastructure items can be specified. During the detailed site design process, the project's architects, mechanical and electrical engineers, and energy efficiency specialists should select the components and identify and calculate their energy use. As part of the process, project applicants should consult with community public works officials about local experiences and preferences for certain infrastructure components.

6. Calculations

Calculate the project's annual energy reduction from a baseline, using Equation 1. This credit addresses new infrastructure only; existing infrastructure that is not being replaced is excluded from the calculation and does not factor into the numerator or the denominator. The baseline case is the energy used by the lowest-first-cost infrastructure.

Equation 1

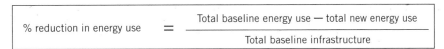

$$\% \text{ reduction in energy use} = \frac{\text{Total baseline energy use} - \text{total new energy use}}{\text{Total baseline infrastructure}}$$

The result must indicate that the project reduces energy use by at least 15%.

7. Documentation Guidance

As a first step in preparing to complete the LEED-ND documentation requirements, work through the following measures. Refer to GBCI's website for the complete descriptions of all required documentation.

- List all energy-consuming infrastructure equipment and the number of each needed for the project.

- Document make, model, and energy specification of the lowest-first-cost versions of new on-site infrastructure.

- Document make, model, and energy specification of the new on-site infrastructure that will actually be installed.

8. Examples

There are no examples for this credit.

9. Exemplary Performance

Projects may earn an Innovation and Design Process credit for exemplary performance by demonstrating a 30% annual energy reduction below an estimated baseline energy use for the infrastructure described in this credit.

10. Regional Variations

There are no regional variations associated with this credit.

11. Resources

Websites

American Society of Heating, Refrigerating, and Air-Conditioning Engineers

www.ashrae.org

The ASHRAE website contains information on HVAC technologies. ·

Illuminating Engineering Society of North America

www.iesna.org

The mission of IESNA is to benefit society by promoting knowledge and disseminating information for the improvement of the lighted environment. The society's website lists technical documents on illumination available through the on-line bookstore, plus lighting-related publications that encourage good lighting design.

American Council for an Energy-Efficient Economy

www.aceee.org

ACEEE is a nonprofit organization dedicated to advancing energy efficiency by conducting technical and policy assessments; advising policymakers and program managers; collaborating with businesses, public interest groups, and other organizations; and providing education and outreach through conferences, workshops, and publications.

12. Definitions

street a dedicated right-of-way that can accommodate one or more modes of travel, excluding alleys and paseos. A street is suitable for primary entrances and provides access to the front and/ or sides of buildings and lots. A street may be privately owned as long as it is deeded in perpetuity for general public use. A street must be an addressable thoroughfare (for mail purposes) under the standards of the applicable regulating authority.

WASTEWATER MANAGEMENT

	ND
Credit	GIB Credit 14
Points	1-2 points

Intent

To reduce pollution from wastewater and encourage water reuse.

Requirements

Design and construct the *project* to retain on-site at least 25% of the average annual wastewater generated by the project (exclusive of *existing* buildings), and reuse that wastewater to replace *potable water*. An additional point may be awarded for retaining and reusing 50%. Provide on-site treatment to a quality required by state and local regulations for the proposed reuse. The percentage of wastewater diverted and reused is calculated by determining the total wastewater flow using the design case after the GIB Prerequisite 3 calculations, and determining how much of that volume is reused on-site.

Table 1. Points for reusing wastewater

Percentage of wastewater reused	Points
25%	1
50%	2

1. Benefits and Issues to Consider

Environmental Issues

Reducing or eliminating the volume of sewage that leaves a site reduces public infrastructure, chemical inputs, energy use, and emissions at municipal water treatment works. Water reuse can greatly reduce negative environmental effects.

On-site wastewater treatment systems transform waste into resources that can be used on the building site, such as soil nutrients and treated water for potable and nonpotable use. The systems can also provide opportunities to enhance occupants' understanding of nutrient cycles.

Economic Issues

Wastewater treatment systems and water recovery systems require initial capital investment in addition to regular maintenance. Project teams must balance these costs with the anticipated savings in water and sewer bills.

Projects that generate large amounts of wastewater can realize considerable savings by recycling graywater. However, dual sanitary and graywater distribution piping doubles construction piping costs. In addition, local codes requiring filtration, disinfection treatment, overflow protection, and other measures add to the cost of construction, operation, and maintenance. In some systems, pumps are required for distribution, incurring additional energy costs for operation. If a graywater system is anticipated, project teams should install dual plumbing lines during the initial construction to avoid the substantial costs and difficulty of adding them later.

Compare the available reclaimed wastewater supply with the amount of water demand projected for a typical year. This analysis can help determine storage capacity and, if treatment is necessary, the cost of water treatment systems. Conducting this type of analysis early in the design process can help identify synergies that reduce the cost of infrastructure, as well as the extent of site disturbance. For example, water storage can be located beneath a parking lot and may prove more economical if installed when the site is graded. Water storage may also be economically feasible if a cistern to collect rainwater is added to a stormwater detention system.

Water treatment can be incorporated into natural or constructed wetlands and add value as a site enhancement. Currently, packaged biological wastewater systems have a high initial cost, relative to the overall building cost, because of the novelty of the technology. Evaluate such systems carefully to determine whether cost savings or educational value justify the purchase.

2. Related Credits

Since improved building water efficiency may reduce the amount of wastewater generated by the project, the following are related:

- GIB Prerequisite 3, Minimum Building Water Efficiency
- GIB Credit 3, Building Water Efficiency

3. Summary of Referenced Standards

There are no referenced standards for this credit.

4. Implementation

This credit applies only to new construction and major renovations of existing buildings.

The feasibility of wastewater reuse and treatment depends on the project's size and location. Consult with local wastewater officials and environmental regulatory agencies to determine applicable codes and standards for on-site wastewater treatment and reuse. Determine wastewater reuse goals, and then evaluate appropriate strategies for on-site reuse. The team should coordinate water conservation strategies with wastewater reuse goals using a water budget, for example.

The graywater portion of project wastewater flows should be identified by type, volume, and location on the project site. In turn, eligible reuse applications need to be characterized, and conveyance systems designed. A variety of systems may be used for on-site treatment and reuse; options include constructed wetlands, mechanical recirculating sand filters, and anaerobic biological treatment facilities. EPA's Office of Water (www.epa.gov/OW-OWM.html/mtb/mtbfact.htm) maintains detailed fact sheets for municipal wastewater technologies.

5. Timeline and Team

During predesign, setting water goals and strategy involves the owner, architect, and engineers. During schematic design, mechanical and civil engineers can help establish a water budget with estimated volumes for end uses of nonpotable water (flush fixtures, irrigation, process loads). Investigate various wastewater sources for potential supply.

A water budget enables comparison of trade-offs for water conservation strategies and evaluation of the impact of water infrastructure on other systems. In early design stages, architects and engineers can determine the area required for wastewater harvesting and treatment to meet specific end-use demands. Estimate the feasibility and cost of different reuse and treatment strategies and compare environmental effects of on-site with off-site water supply. Water goals and strategy can then be confirmed or reassessed.

6. Calculations

This credit requires calculating the percentage of average annual wastewater generated that is reused on-site to replace potable water use. The percentage of wastewater retained and reused is calculated by determining the total wastewater flow of the design case; refer to the Calculations section under GIB Prerequisite 3, Minimum Building Water Efficiency. The results must indicate that 25% or more of that volume is reused on-site.

For new multiunit residential buildings three stories or fewer and new single-family residential buildings, total wastewater flow is determined by estimating total water consumption based on the design case measures employed. Enter design case fixture values in the GIB Prerequisite 3 calculator to obtain total estimated water consumption and total wastewater flow for applicable buildings. Proceed as above to calculate the percentage of wastewater volume that is reused on-site.

7. Documentation Guidance

As a first step in preparing to complete the LEED-ND documentation requirements, work through the following measures. Refer to GBCI's website for the complete descriptions of all required documentation.

- Retain a description of the on-site wastewater reuse system.

- Calculate the percentage of total wastewater reused on-site, based on the design case calculations for GIB Prerequisite 3, Minimum Building Water Efficiency.

- Obtain confirmation that reuse complies with any applicable regulations.

8. Examples

There are no examples for this credit.

9. Exemplary Performance

Projects may earn an Innovation and Design Process credit for exemplary performance by demonstrating that 75% of the project's average annual wastewater is reused.

10. Regional Variations

Depending on seasonal precipitation patterns, rainwater harvesting for on-site use may require a storage strategy.

Climate also affects the viability of on-site treatment options. For example, biological treatment in hot, humid climates is more efficient and effective and requires less surface area than in a cold climate. When considering an on-site wastewater reclamation system, first check with local government agencies for regulations and required permits. Each state has its own standards and requirements for the installation and operation of such systems. Codes for the treatment of wastewater from alternative plumbing fixtures may also differ. Confirm the legality of nontraditional approaches with code officials before committing to specific wastewater reuse strategies.

11. Resources

Websites

Rocky Mountain Institute, water efficiency

www.rmi.org/sitepages/pid128.php

This portion of RMI's website is devoted to water conservation and efficiency. The site contains information on watershed management and commercial, industrial, and institutional water use and articles on policy and implementation.

U.S. Environmental Protection Agency, WaterSense

www.epa.gov/watersense

The WaterSense program helps U.S. consumers save water and protect the environment by labeling high-quality, water-efficient products that do not require a change in lifestyle. Businesses and organizations can partner with WaterSense.

U.S. Environmental Protection Agency, water conservation

www.epa.gov/OWOW/nps/chap3.html

How to Conserve Water and Use It Effectively provides guidance for commercial, industrial, and residential water users on saving water and reducing sewage volumes.

U.S. Environmental Protection Agency, wastewater treatment

www.epa.gov/nrmrl/pubs/625r00008/html/625R00008.htm

EPA's *Onsite Wastewater Treatment Systems Manual* provides a focused and performance-based approach to on-site wastewater treatment and system management and offers information on on-site sewage treatment options.

Water Reuse Association

www.watereuse.org/?assoc&wra

An introduction to water reuse with resources for learning more.

Print Media

Constructed Wetlands for Wastewater Treatment and Wildlife Habitat: 17 Case Studies, Publication 832/B-93-005 (U.S. Environmental Protection Agency, 1993)
Available at www.epa.gov/owow/wetlands/construc/.

Mechanical & Electrical Equipment for Buildings, eighth edition, by Benjamin Stein and John Reynolds (John Wiley & Sons, 1992).

Sustainable Building Technical Manual (Public Technology, 1996)
Available at www.pti.org.

"Water: Doing More with Less," by Alex Wilson, *Environmental Building News*
Available at www.buildinggreen.com/auth/article.cfm/2008/2/3/Water-Doing-More-With-Less/.

"Water Reuse: Issues, Technologies, and Applications," by Metcalf & Eddy, Inc., an AECOM Company, Takashi Asano, Franklin Burton, Harold Leverenz, Ryujiro Tsuchihashi, and George Tchobanoglous (Metcalf & Eddy, 2007).

Water, Sanitary and Waste Services for Buildings, fourth edition, by A. Wise and J. Swaffield (Longman Scientific & Technical, 1995).

12. Definitions

existing present on the date of submission of LEED-ND certification documents; similarly, an element or condition that **exists** is present on the date that LEED-ND certification documents are submitted.

potable water water that meets or exceeds EPA's drinking water quality standards and is approved for human consumption by the state or local authorities having jurisdiction; it may be supplied from wells or municipal water systems.

project the land, water, and construction that constitutes the project application. A project applicant does not have to own or control all land or water within a project boundary, but all the area within the project boundary must comply with prerequisites and attempted credits.

LEED 2009 FOR NEIGHBORHOOD DEVELOPMENT

RECYCLED CONTENT IN INFRASTRUCTURE

	ND
Credit	GIB Credit 15
Points	1 point

Intent

To use recycled and reclaimed materials to reduce the adverse environmental effects of extracting and processing virgin materials.

Requirements

Use materials for new infrastructure such that the sum of *postconsumer* recycled content, in-place reclaimed materials, and one-half of the *preconsumer* recycled content constitutes at least 50% of the total mass of infrastructure materials.

Count materials in all of the following infrastructure items as applicable to the *project*:

  a. Roadways, parking lots, sidewalks, unit paving, and curbs.

  b. Water retention tanks and vaults.

  c. Base and subbase materials for the above.

  d. Stormwater, sanitary sewer, steam energy distribution, and water piping.

Recycled content is defined in accordance with ISO/IEC 14021, Environmental labels and declaration, Self-declared environmental claims (Type II environmental labeling).

1. Benefits and Issues to Consider

Environmental Issues

Products with recycled content reduce virgin materials use and solid waste volumes. As the number of products containing recycled content grows, the marketplace for recycled materials develops.

Postconsumer recycled content is derived from materials that can no longer be used for their original purpose, and preconsumer recycled content consists of raw material diverted from the waste stream during the manufacturing process. Although the use of both types of recycled content is encouraged, postconsumer recycled content is accorded greater value because of its increased environmental benefit over the life cycle of the product.

Economic and Social Issues

Many commonly used products are now available with recycled content. Research all recycled-content materials for economic considerations. For example, if the recycled-content product is not as durable as its conventional counterpart, the need for more frequent replacement will add to costs. Most recycled-content products, however, exhibit performance similar to products containing only virgin materials and can be incorporated into construction projects with ease and little to no cost premium.

2. Related Credits

There are no related credits.

3. Summary of Referenced Standards

International Organization for Standardization, ISO Standard 14021-1999, Environmental Labels and Declarations—Self-Declared Environmental Claims (Type II Environmental Labeling)

www.iso.org

This standard specifies requirements for self-declared environmental product claims, including statements, symbols, and graphics. It further describes selected terms commonly used in environmental claims and gives qualifications for their use. It also describes a general evaluation and verification methodology for self-declared environmental claims and specific evaluation and verification methods.

4. Implementation

This credit applies to new and renovated infrastructure.

The overall percentage of recycled infrastructure materials is determined by combining the recycled content of new infrastructure items with in-place reclaimed materials (materials used in infrastructure that exists before the project and will remain in use after the project is completed). Research may be required to determine the percentages of recycled content that can realistically be expected in specific products and materials. ISO Type II environmental labeling provides information about a product's environmental characteristics, including recycled content, which may assist project teams in making product purchases. Many standard materials in the marketplace contain recycled content as a matter of course because of the nature and economics of their manufacture. For other materials, research may be required to identify those with high levels of recycled content.

Identify products that contain recycled content and pursue documentation from suppliers, manufacturers, and vendors directly or through subcontractors to confirm the actual recycled content for each product. Recycled content determinations must be made according to Type II environmental labeling standards as defined in ISO 14021 Environmental Labels and Declarations Package.

5. Timeline and Team

Recycled content goals for infrastructure should be established during the design phase. Members of the design and construction teams should assist with determining the recycled content of materials to be purchased and documenting the actual levels of recycled content in the materials used.

6. Calculations

Postconsumer recycled content is consumer waste, much of which comes from residential curbside recycling programs. Other postconsumer content is generated when construction and demolition debris is recycled.

Preconsumer (or postindustrial) recycled content comes from process waste that an industry has sold or traded with another. This definition does not include in-house industrial scrap or trimmings, which are normally fed back into the same manufacturing process. In the calculations that follows, preconsumer recycled content is accorded half the value of postconsumer recycled content.

Step 1. Calculate the total recycled content for each infrastructure material, by mass, according to Equation 1.

Equation 1

$$\text{Total recycled content} = \text{Postconsumer recycled content of new materials} + \frac{\text{preconsumer recycled content of new materials}}{2} + \text{in-place reclaimed materials}$$

Step 2. Calculate the percentage recycled content for infrastructure materials, by mass, according to Equation 2.

Equation 2

$$\% \text{ recycled content} = \frac{\text{Total recycled content}}{\text{total materials}} \times 100$$

The results must indicate that 50% of the mass of all infrastructure materials is recycled.

7. Documentation Guidance

As a first step in preparing to complete the LEED-ND documentation requirements, work through the following measures. Refer to GBCI's website for the complete descriptions of all required documentation.

- For each infrastructure category, maintain records of the materials used and their postconsumer and preconsumer recycled content levels.
- Obtain estimates for mass of in-place reclaimed materials for each infrastructure category.

8. Examples

There are no examples for this credit.

9. Exemplary Performance

Projects may earn an Innovation and Design Process credit for exemplary performance by using the recycled and reclaimed materials listed in the requirements for at least 75% of the total mass of infrastructure materials.

10. Regional Variations

There are no regional variations associated with this credit.

11. Resources

Websites

BuildingGreen, Inc., GreenSpec

www.buildinggreen.com/menus/index.cfm

GreenSpec contains detailed listings for more than 1,900 green building products, including environmental data, manufacturer information and links to additional resources.

Print Media

Industrial Materials Recycling: Managing Resources for Tomorrow (U.S. Environmental Protection Agency, 2004).

12. Definitions

postconsumer generated by households or commercial, industrial, or institutional facilities in their role as end-users of a product, which can no longer be used for its intended purpose.

preconsumer diverted from the waste stream during the manufacturing process. It does not include the reutilization of materials such as rework, regrind or scrap generated in a process and capable of being reclaimed within the same process that generated it.

project the land, water, and construction that constitutes the project application. A project applicant does not have to own or control all land or water within a project boundary, but all the area within the project boundary must comply with prerequisites and attempted credits.

SOLID WASTE MANAGEMENT INFRASTRUCTURE

	ND
Credit	GIB Credit 16
Points	1 point

Intent

To reduce the volume of waste deposited in landfills. To promote the proper disposal of hazardous wastes.

Requirements

Meet at least four of the following five requirements and publicize their availability and benefits:

a. Include as part of the *project* at least one recycling or reuse station, available to all project occupants, dedicated to the separation, collection, and storage of materials for recycling; or locate the project in a local government jurisdiction that provides recycling services. The recyclable materials must include, at a minimum, materials paper, corrugated cardboard, glass, plastics and metals.

b. Include as part of the project at least one drop-off point, available to all project occupants, for potentially hazardous office or household wastes; or locate the project in a local government jurisdiction that provides collection services. Examples of potentially hazardous wastes include paints, solvents, oil, and batteries. If a plan for postcollection disposal or use does not exist, establish one;

c. Include as part of the project at least one compost station or location, available to all project occupants, dedicated to the collection and composting of food and yard wastes; or locate the project in a local government jurisdiction that provides composting services. If a plan for postcollection use does not exist, establish one.

d. On every mixed-use or nonresidential *block* or at least every 800 feet, whichever is shorter, include recycling containers adjacent to other receptacles or recycling containers integrated into the design of the receptacle.

e. Recycle and/or salvage at least 50% of nonhazardous construction and demolition debris. Develop and implement a construction waste management plan that, at a minimum, identifies the materials to be diverted from disposal and specifies whether the materials will be stored on-site or commingled. Excavated soil and land-clearing debris do not contribute to this credit. Calculations can be done by weight or volume but must be consistent throughout.

1. Benefits and Issues to Consider

Environmental Issues

Construction and demolition generate enormous quantities of solid waste. The U.S. Environmental Protection Agency estimates that 136 million tons of such debris was generated in 1996, 57% of it from nonresidential sources.[20] Commercial construction generates between 2 and 2.5 pounds of solid waste per square foot, and the majority of this waste could be recycled.[21] Recycling of construction and demolition debris reduces demand for virgin resources and reduces the environmental impacts associated with resource extraction, processing, and in many cases, transportation.

Throughout a project's lifetime, a substantial amount of solid waste will be generated by construction debris, residents, employees, and visitors. Creating a management system as an integral part of the project design is the best way to ensure that waste will be dealt with responsibly for years to come.

By creating convenient recycling opportunities, a significant portion of the solid waste stream can be diverted from landfills. Recycling of paper, metals, glass, cardboard, and plastics reduces the need to extract virgin natural resources. For example, recycling 1 ton of paper avoids the processing of 17 trees and saves 3 cubic yards of landfill space.[22] Recycled aluminum requires only 5% of the energy required to produce virgin aluminum from bauxite, its raw material form.[23] The disposal of hazardous wastes in landfills can be prevented by diverting toxic materials to a specially designed facility.

Compost facilities are an excellent way to both dispose of waste and produce a useful product that can be used to fertilize a community garden or landscaped open spaces. Some municipalities have composting programs and green waste collection services; their requirements for acceptable materials may differ. For example, not all collection programs accept food waste and compostable cutlery.

Economic and Social Issues

Community recycling efforts return valuable resources to local production processes and may spur increases in employment in the recycling industry. Community-wide participation results in higher recycling rates and, in turn, more stable markets for recycled materials. The economics of recycling has improved in recent years as international competition for both raw and recycled materials has heated up and conventional disposal costs have increased. More stringent waste disposal regulations coupled with ever-decreasing landfill capacity have changed the waste management equation.

Waste management plans require time and money to draft and implement; in the long term, however, they provide guidance to achieve substantial savings throughout the construction process. Recyclable materials have differing market values, depending on the presence of local recycling facilities, reprocessing costs, and the availability of virgin materials on the market. In general, it is economically beneficial to recycle metals, concrete, asphalt, and cardboard. Market

20 U.S. Environmental Protection Agency, Office of Solid Waste, "Municipal Solid Waste Generation, Recycling, and Disposal in the United States: Facts and Figures for 2006." 2007. www.epa.gov/epawaste/nonhaz/municipal/pubs/msw06.pdf (accessed November 2008).

21 Wisconsin Department of Natural Resources, Northeast Region, "Building Green at DNR—Northeast Region Headquarters Construction Waste & Recycling." www.dnr.wi.gov/org/land/facilities/greenbldg/gbhqwaste.html (accessed November 2008).

22 Oberlin College Recycling Program, "Recycling Facts."www.oberlin.edu/recycle/facts.html (accessed November 2008).

23 The Aluminum Association, "Aluminum Industry Vision." www1.eere.energy.gov/industry/aluminum/pdfs/alum_vision.pdf (accessed November 2008).

values fluctuate from month to month, so track the values and project different cost recapturing scenarios. Even when no revenue is received for materials, as is often the case for scrap wood and gypsum wallboard, recycling construction waste can reduce project costs by significantly reducing landfill tipping fees.

2. Related Credits

Renovating existing historic or other buildings and recycling and salvaging demolition and construction debris are addressed in these related credits:

- GIB Credit 5, Existing Building Reuse
- GIB Credit 6, Historic Resource Preservation and Adaptive Use

3. Summary of Referenced Standards

There are no standards referenced for this credit.

4. Implementation

Consider selecting a project site within a jurisdiction that provides recycling or reuse facilities, hazardous waste disposal facilities, or compost facilities. If such services are not available for the site, incorporate recycling or reuse stations into the project design. Recycling or reuse facilities should be located and designed to ensure access for all occupants. For potentially hazardous wastes, locate drop-off points in a secured facility or structure, away from residential units, schools, parks and recreation facilities, and senior care facilities to prevent harm.

To create a compost station as part of the project, designate an area that occupants can easily reach and encourage their involvement. Neighborhood farms and gardens are particularly good locations for compost stations. Since composting facilities may need approvals or permits from state or local agencies, check with the state or local government and provide them with a plan before investing significant time and resources.

Design considerations for litter receptacles and integrated recycling receptacles should include protection from the elements and signage to discourage contamination.

Consider developing and implementing a construction waste management plan for the project's nonhazardous construction and demolition debris, such as cardboard, metal, brick, acoustical tile, concrete, plastic, clean wood, glass, gypsum wallboard, carpet, and insulation. Designate specific areas on the construction site for segregated or commingled collection of recyclable materials, and track recycling efforts throughout the construction process.

Identify construction haulers and recyclers to handle the designated materials; they can be valuable partners in this effort. Make sure jobsite personnel understand and participate in the program, and provide updates throughout the construction process. Obtain records (waste haul receipts, waste management reports, spreadsheets, etc.) to verify that the diverted materials have been recycled or salvaged as intended. Diversion may include donations to reuse centers and other nonprofit organizations, such as Habitat for Humanity.

The recyclability of a material often depends on the extent of its contamination. Demolished wood, for instance, is often not reusable or recyclable unless it is deconstructed and denailed. Other materials cannot be recycled if they have absorbed liquids. To prevent contamination, install clear signage, educate all on-site personnel, and inspect bins regularly. Ways to publicize recycling services to residents and employees of the project include mailings, flyers, posters, a website, and neighborhood associations. For new residents, the information could be part of a welcome package.

5. Timeline and Team

During the design phase, the project team should determine the availability of applicable solid waste management infrastructure and plan for any facilities needed on-site. The project team should consult with state and local governments as early as possible to determine what regulations apply to compost stations and other facilities. The team also should reserve space in mixed-use areas for litter and recycling receptacles. During the design phase, the project team should plan for recycling or salvage of nonhazardous construction and demolition debris. During construction, the project team should ensure that construction waste management plan is implemented according to plan.

6. Calculations

Calculations for construction waste are based on the amount of waste diverted from the landfill or incineration compared with the total amount of waste generated on-site. Convert all materials to either volume or weight; if the latter, use the solid waste conversion factors in Table 1 or another defensible conversion metric. Exclude from the calculations hazardous waste, excavated soil, and land clearing debris, which should be disposed of appropriately, according to relevant regulations. Projects that crush and reuse existing concrete, masonry, or asphalt on-site should include the weight or volume of these materials in the calculations.

Calculate the percentage of total construction and demolition debris that is recycled and/or salvaged.

Table 1. Solid waste conversion factors

Material	Density (lbs / cubic yard)
Cardboard	100
Gypsum wallboard	500
Mixed waste	350
Rubble	1,400
Steel	1,000
Wood	300

7. Documentation Guidance

As a first step in preparing to complete the LEED-ND documentation requirements, work through the following measures. Refer to GBCI's website for the complete descriptions of all required documentation.

- Prepare a site map showing the locations of solid waste management infrastructure, whether provided by the local government or the developer.

- Retain product cutsheets or other evidence showing that litter receptacles have integrated recycling receptacles.

- Maintain a summary of the construction waste management plan, including material types and volume calculations.

8. Examples

A developer is preparing for partial demolition of a 0.25-acre shopping center prior to redevelopment. The developer intends to salvage some of the crushed asphalt but will remove the rest of the existing structures. The contractor has developed a construction waste management plan to aid in the demolition and construction process. The plan outlines the staging of waste materials during demolition to be sorted within the building before being delivered to local recycling facilities. (If the contractor were commingling the recycled materials rather than separating them on-site, diversion rates would be required from the recycler.)

Table 2 shows the waste diversion calculation. Because exact material weights were not available, the contractor used the conversion factors from Table 1 to estimate the weight of construction waste.

Table 2. Example construction waste management summary

	Diversion destination	Quantity (tons/cy)
Concrete	ABC Recycling	138.0
Wood	Z-Construction Reuse	10.2
Gypsum wallboard	ABC Recycling	6.3
Steel	Re-Cycle Steel Collectors	1.1
Crushed asphalt	On-site reuse	98.2
Masonry	ABC Recycling	6.8
Cardboard	ABC Recycling	1.6
Total diverted from landfill		**262.2**
General mixed waste sent to landfill		**52.3**
Total construction waste		**314.5**

Having totaled the amounts of individual materials, the team determines what percentage of total construction waste is diverted from landfills:

$$\frac{262.2}{314.5} \quad X \quad 100 \quad = \quad 83.4\%$$

9. Exemplary Performance

This credit is not eligible for exemplary performance under Innovation and Design Process.

10. Regional Variations

Recycling opportunities are expanding rapidly in many communities. Recycling of metal, vegetation, concrete, and asphalt has long been available and economical in most communities. Paper, corrugated cardboard, plastics, and clean wood markets vary by regional and local recycling infrastructure but are recycled in most communities.

In urban areas, recycling resources are typically well developed, and teams can choose whether to separate waste on-site or hire a commingled waste recycler. Commingled recycling may increase recycling costs but will simplify the waste management effort on-site and increase diversion rates. This option is especially useful for projects that have tight site constraints and no room for multiple collection bins. In rural areas, recyclers may be harder to find. The environmental benefits of recycling in these cases need to be balanced against the environmental consequences of transporting waste long distances to recycling centers.

11. Resources

Websites

Construction Materials Recycling Association

www.cdrecycling.org

This nonprofit organization is dedicated to information exchange within the North American construction waste and demolition debris processing and recycling industries.

U.S. Environmental Protection Agency, composting

www.epa.gov/epaoswer/non-hw/composting/index.htm

This website contains information about laws and statutes related to composting, methods of composting, and a downloadable version of Chapter 7 of EPA's *Decision-Maker's Guide to Solid Waste Management.*

Earth 911

www.earth911.org/master.asp

This website contains information and education programs on recycling as well as regional links to recyclers. It also includes information about household hazardous waste and links to municipal HHW programs, facilities, and events.

Resource Venture, construction waste management

www.resourceventure.org/free-resources/get-started/green-building-publications/green-building-publications-1#construction-waste-management

This website provides publications on construction waste management.

Print Media

Composting and Recycling Municipal Solid Waste, by Luis Diaz et al. (CRC Press, 1993).

McGraw-Hill Recycling Handbook, by Herbert F. Lund (McGraw-Hill, 2000).

12. Definitions

block land bounded by the project boundary, transportation or utility rights-of-way that may be publicly dedicated or privately owned and deeded in perpetuity for general public use, waterfront, and/or comparable land division features.

project the land, water, and construction that constitutes the project application. A project applicant does not have to own or control all land or water within a project boundary, but all the area within the project boundary must comply with prerequisites and attempted credits.

LIGHT POLLUTION REDUCTION

	ND
Credit	GIB Credit 17
Points	1 point

Intent

To minimize light trespass from *project* sites, reduce sky-glow to increase night sky access, improve nighttime visibility through glare reduction, and reduce adverse effects on wildlife environments.

Requirements

"Shared areas" of a project are spaces and facilities dedicated to common use (publicly or privately owned).

In residential areas, at least 50% of the external luminaires must have fixture-integrated lighting controls that use motion sensors to reduce light levels by at least 50% when no activity has been detected for 15 minutes.

AND

In all shared areas, install automatic controls that turn off exterior lighting when sufficient daylight is available and when the lighting is not required during nighttime hours; these lights must meet the total exterior lighting power allowance requirements in Table 3.

AND

Document which lighting zone or zones (Table 1) describe the project, and for all shared areas, follow the requirements in Table 2. If two or more different zones border the project, use the most stringent uplight requirements, and use light trespass requirements for the adjacent zone. Roadway lighting that is part of the project must meet the requirements for the appropriate zone.

For illuminance generated from a single luminaire placed at the intersection of a private vehicular driveway and public roadway accessing the site, project teams may use the centerline of the public roadway as the site boundary for a length of two times the driveway width centered at the centerline of the driveway when complying with the trespass requirements.

Compliance with the light trespass requirements may alternatively be met by using only luminaires that comply with Table 4 ratings for backlight and glare.

AND

Stipulate *covenants, conditions, and restrictions* (CC&R) or other binding documents to require continued adherence to the requirements.

Table 1. Lighting zones

Zone	Definition
LZ0	Undeveloped areas within national parks, state parks, forest land and rural areas and sites immediately adjacent to areas officially recognized as ecologically sensitive by the local zoning authority.
LZ1	Developed areas within national parks, state parks, forest land and rural areas.
LZ2	Areas predominantly consisting of residential zoning, neighborhood business districts, light industrial with limited nighttime use, and residential mixed-use areas.
LZ3	All other areas not included in LZ0, LZ1, LZ2, or LZ4 (including commercial-industrial and high-density residential).
LZ4	High-activity commercial districts in major metropolitan areas (as designated by local jurisdiction, such as local zoning authority).

Table 2. Allowable light trespass and uplight, by lighting zone

Lighting zone	Maximum horizontal and vertical illuminance (fc) at site boundary	Maximum horizontal and vertical illuminance (fc) at specified distance beyond site boundary	Maximum percentage of fixture lumens emitted above 90° or higher from nadir (straight down)
LZ0	0	0 at 0 ft.	0%
LZ1	0.01	.01 at 0 ft.	0%
LZ2*	0.10	.02 at 10 ft.	1%
LZ3*	0.20	.05 at 15 ft.	2%
LZ4*	0.60	.05 at 15 ft.	5%

fc = footcandle.
* In LZ2, LZ3, and LZ4, for project boundaries that abut public rights-of-way, light trespass requirements may be met relative to the curb line instead of the project boundary.

Table 3. Allowable lighting power densities, by lighting zone

	Lighting zone				
	LZ0	LZ1	LZ2	LZ3	LZ4
All exterior improved areas (except those listed below)	0.04 W/sf	0.04 W/sf	0.06 W/sf	0.10 W/sf	0.13 W/sf
Walkways	0.7 W/lf	0.7 W/lf	0.7 W/lf	0.8 W/lf	1.0 W/lf
Landscaping	No allowance	0.04 W/sf	0.05 W/sf	0.05 W/sf	0.05 W/sf
Entrance door (per linear foot of doorway)	20W	20W	20W	30W	30W
Entry canopy	0.25 W/sf	0.25 W/sf	0.25 W/sf	0.40 W/sf	0.40 W/sf
Illuminated building façade	No allowance	No allowance	2.5W/lf	3.75W/lf	5.0W/lf

sf = square feet; lf = linear feet.
Note: The total exterior lighting power density allowance for all shared exterior applications is the sum of the specified allowances for individual illuminated areas. The following lighting is exempted when its controls meet the above requirements and are independent of the controls for nonexempt lighting:
   a. Specialized signal, directional, and marker lighting associated with transportation.
   b. Advertising and directional signage.
   c. Lighting integral to equipment or instrumentation and installed by its manufacturer.
   d. Lighting for theatrical purposes, including performance, stage, film, and video.
   e. Lighting for athletic playing fields.
   f. Temporary lighting (installed for no more than 30 days and then removed for at least 30 days).
   g. Lighting for industrial production, material handling, transportation sites, and associated storage areas.
   h. Theme elements in theme or amusement parks.
   i. Lighting to highlight features of public monuments and registered *historic buildings* or landmark structures.

Alternative method for meeting light trespass requirements in Table 2

A luminaire may be used if it is rated as follows according to the lighting zone of the site. If the luminaire is installed in other than the intended manner, the rating must account for the actual photometric geometry. An exception applies if at least 98% of a luminaire's emitted lumens are intercepted by man-made structures within the project. In either case, luminaires equipped with adjustable mounting devices permitting alteration of luminaire aiming in the field are not permitted.

Table 4. Allowable backlight and glare, by lighting zone

	Lighting zone				
Backlight luminaire rating	LZ0	LZ1	LZ2	LZ3	LZ4
> 2 mounting heights from property line	B0	B1	B2	B3	B4
1 to 2 mounting heights from property line and properly oriented*	B0	B1	B2	B3	B3
0.5 to 1 mounting height to property line and properly oriented*	B0	B0	B1	B2	B2
< 0.5 mounting height to property line adjacent to street and properly oriented*	B0	B0	B1	B2	B2
< 0.5 mounting height to property line and properly oriented*	B0	B0	B0	B1	B2
Glare luminaire rating	G0	G1	G2	G3	G4

* The luminaire must be mounted with backlight toward the property line.
Note: Backlight and glare ratings are defined based on specific lumen limits for IESNA TM-15-07 solid angles, Addendum A.

1. Benefits and Issues to Consider

Environmental Issues

Light trespass from poorly designed outdoor lighting systems can affect a site's nocturnal ecosystem, and light pollution can limit night sky observations. Placing too much light on the site and lighting at inappropriate times can exacerbate both of these issues. Through thoughtful design and careful maintenance, outdoor lighting can address site illumination requirements while minimizing negative effects on the environment.

Properly designed lighting systems can promote a unique appreciation for a project at night. Yet even with the best of luminaires—those designed to reduce light pollution and requiring the lowest wattage—the light from these fixtures will be reflected off surfaces and into the atmosphere. Using the minimum amount of lighting equipment, limiting or eliminating all aesthetic lighting, and avoiding light pollution through the careful selection of lighting equipment and controls enable nocturnal life to thrive while still allowing human nighttime activity.

Economic and Social Issues

Outdoor lighting is important for human safety and security. Illuminating community gathering places, sidewalks between buildings, and support facilities, such as parking lots and roadways, is necessary for twilight and nighttime use.

The initial cost and ongoing operational costs for exterior lighting can be greatly reduced by eliminating luminaires that do not directly enhance safety or security. Additionally, using the most efficacious light sources, luminaires, and controls will further reduce the energy costs of these systems. Long-life lamps can further increase operational savings by requiring a less frequent relamping cycle. However, the initial cost per luminaire can be somewhat higher because of increased costs associated with internal reflectors and shielding, more efficient lamp and ballast combinations, and controls.

2. Related Credits

There are no related credits.

3. Summary of Referenced Standards

Illuminating Engineering Society of North America, Addendum A for IESNA TM-15-07, Backlight, Uplight, and Glare (BUG) Ratings

www.iesna.org/PDF/Erratas/TM-15-07BUGRatingsAddendum.pdf

This IESNA standard provides ratings to evaluate luminaire optical performance related to light trespass, sky glow, and high-angle brightness control.

Illuminating Engineering Society of North America, IESNA RP-33-99, Lighting for Exterior Environments

www.iesna.org

This IESNA standard is not cited explicitly in the credit, but it is the source of the lighting zones listed in Table 1 of the credit requirements. These zones determine the allowable light trespass and uplight for a project or portion of a project.

4. Implementation

Achieving this credit requires six actions.

1. Use automatic controls for at least 50% of all exterior luminaires used in residential areas.

   In all residential areas, determine the total number of light fixtures. Ensure that at least 50% of the fixtures include integrated motions sensors, and ensure that the sensors reduce lighting levels by at least 50% when no activity has been detected in the area for 15 minutes.

2. Determine the correct lighting zones for the project site and all adjacent properties.

Use Table 1 to determine the applicable lighting zone for each area within the project site and immediately adjacent to it. Lighting zone 4 can be used only if the area has been defined as LZ4 by the local zoning authority.

3. Use automatic controls for all shared areas.

Design exterior lighting in all shared areas such that automatic controls will turn off the exterior lighting either when there is sufficient daylight or when it is not required during nighttime hours. Areas that are designed to be illuminated for dusk-to-dawn operation should be controlled by either an astronomical time switch or a photosensor. All other areas should be controlled by either a combination of a photosensor and a time switch or an astronomical time switch. All time switches should be capable of retaining programming and the time setting during a loss of power for at least ten hours.

4. Meet light trespass and uplight requirements for all shared areas.

Refer to Table 2. For each shared area, according to its lighting zone, look up (1) the maximum allowed horizontal and vertical illuminance at the boundary of the shared area; (2) the maximum allowed horizontal and vertical illuminance at the specified distance beyond the boundary of the shared area; and (3) the maximum uplight. For light trespass along the edge of a shared area, use the lighting zone of the adjacent area (whether on or off the project site). For uplight, use the most stringent (lowest) zone found either within or directly adjacent to the project.

Next, determine the actual illuminance and uplight from the fixtures selected for the project, using software or manual calculations (see the Calculations section). Compute (1) the maximum horizontal and vertical illuminance at the boundary of the shared area; (2) the maximum horizontal and vertical illuminance at the specified distance beyond the boundary of the shared area; and (3) the percentage uplight. The results must not exceed the maximums listed in Table 2.

As an alternative method of showing compliance for light trespass for the entire project, the project team may choose to use only luminaires meeting both the backlight and the glare requirements shown in Table 4. These ratings may be available on product literature (refer to the B and G portions of the BUG rating) or can be computed using Addendum A of IESNA TM-15, referenced above. For each luminaire, (1) determine the backlight rating based on the distance (in units of mounting heights) of the luminaire from the closest edge of the shared area and the direction it faces relative to that edge, then (2) look up the glare rating (Table 4).

5. Meet lighting power density requirements for all shared areas.

Refer to Table 3. Compute the total watts used by all nonexempt lighting (exempted lighting is listed in the note to Table 3). For each type of shared area, determine the maximum allowed lighting power density (Table 3) based on the area type specified in the first column and the lighting zone for the areas immediately adjacent to the shared area under consideration. Use the lighting zone that is most prevalent. "Areas immediately adjacent" may be on or off the actual project site. Use the lighting power density to determine the watts allowed for this area. Add the total watts allowed for the composite for all shared areas. Then confirm that the total watts used by all nonexempt lighting do not exceed the total watts allowed.

6. Provide CC&Rs or other binding documents that require continued adherence to standards defined in the requirement.

General Considerations

In primarily dark environments (LZ0 and LZ1), no landscape features should be illuminated, and architectural lighting should be included only when other strategies cannot provide the minimum amount of required lighting. In places with medium or high ambient brightness (LZ2 through LZ4), some low-level lighting of features, façades, or landscape areas may be appropriate in pedestrian areas, or for identifying and marking pedestrian paths in areas where light trespass is not likely to be an issue. However, even in areas of high ambient brightness, all nonessential lighting (including landscape and architectural lighting) should be minimized or turned off after hours. All adjustable luminaires should be properly aimed so that their light does not cross project boundaries. Use automatic controls wherever possible to turn off nonessential lighting after normal operating hours or after curfew.

At a minimum, consider the following strategies when designing the exterior lighted environment:

- Employ a lighting professional to assess the project's lighting needs and provide recommendations based specifically on lighting for a sustainable built environment.

- Carefully review and respond to any applicable lighting ordinances or bylaws that might affect the lighting design for the project site.

- In most cases, it is better to have two luminaires with lower light output and good glare control than one higher-output luminaire.

- Select all lighting equipment carefully. Any type of luminaire, whether it is full cutoff, semicutoff or noncutoff, can produce excessive brightness in the form of glare. For example, horizontal lamp positions in full-cutoff luminaires tend to produce less glare than vertical lamps,

- Design exterior lighting to produce minimal upward illumination from the luminaire and minimal reflected light off adjacent surfaces. Select luminaire locations carefully to control glare and contain light within the design area. Pay special attention near the property line to ensure that minimal measurable light from the project's luminaires crosses the boundary. Use shielded fixtures to minimize light trespass and sky-glow.

Figure 1. Unshielded light fixture

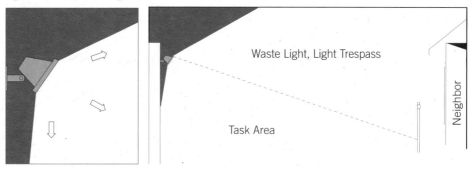

Figure 2. Shielded light fixture

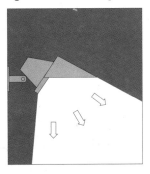
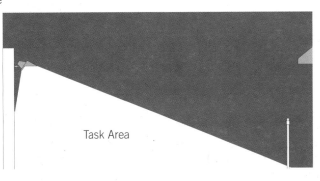

Task Area

- Use the minimum amount of light needed.

- Develop a control scheme to lower light levels as appropriate and to turn lighting off after hours or after curfew.

- Create a computer model of the proposed electric lighting design and simulate system performance. Use this model to calculate the specified illuminances demonstrating that illuminance values are as required at the project site boundary and at the required distance beyond the site boundary. Calculate the vertical light levels along and above the site boundary to a height of at least the highest luminaire on the site.

- After the lighting system is constructed, commission it to make sure that it is installed and operating properly. Perform maintenance on the system on a regular basis to make sure that it continues to operate properly and that light pollution is minimized.

5. Timeline and Team

During the design phase, the project team should determine the lighting zones for the project and adjacent properties, consider strategies that eliminate lighting areas not essential to safety or security, and look for opportunities to illuminate areas at lower lighting power densities than the maximums allowed in the requirement. A qualified lighting engineer should be contracted to assist with exterior lighting design and document light trespass, power densities, backlight, uplight, and glare levels.

6. Calculations

Compliance with this credit involves calculations for light trespass, uplight, and lighting power density.

Light Trespass

The light trespass requirement includes making computations of horizontal and vertical illuminance at the edge of each shared area and a specified distance beyond that edge. For most projects, the number of luminaires and corresponding computations make performing this analysis manually impractical. A variety of software packages, available from both product manufacturers and third-party sources, can do the computations rapidly and accurately.

The following formulas demonstrate how to compute the illuminances at any one point:

$$E_h \quad \sum_{i=1}^{N} \frac{Ii \times (\cos(\Theta_i))}{D_i^2}$$

where

E_h = the horizontal illuminance at a single point.

N = the number of luminaires contributing lighting to this point.

I_i = the luminous intensity from each luminaire in the direction of the point.

Θ_i = the angle between a ray drawn from the luminaire to the point and a ray pointing straight up from the point.

D_i = the distance from the point to the luminaire.

$$E_v \quad \sum_{i=1}^{N} \frac{I_i \times (cos(\Phi_i))}{D_i^2}$$

where

Ev = the vertical illuminance at a single point.

N = the number of luminaires contributing lighting to this point.

Ii = the luminous intensity from each luminaire in the direction of the point.

Φi = the angle between a ray drawn from the luminaire to the point and a ray pointing straight out from the point, perpendicular to the vertical plane of points.

Di = the distance from the point to the luminaire.

The calculation model should show the entire site and all installed exterior lighting fixtures. A horizontal calculation grid is set up to measure the site illumination at the ground plane, and a vertical calculation grid is set at the property boundary and at the extents of the lighting zone requirements (10 feet beyond the site boundary for LZ2, and 15 feet beyond the site boundary for LZ3 and LZ4) to measure vertical illumination. All vertical calculation grids extend from grade to the height of the tallest exterior luminaire in the project.

The spacing of all calculation grids is a maximum of 10 by 10 feet and excludes building interior areas. The calculated illuminances are then compared with the values in Table 2, for the correct lighting zone. For light trespass along the edge of any one shared area, use the lighting zone of the adjacent area, whether that adjacent area is inside or outside the boundary.

Uplight

Using manufacturer's data for each fixture, determine the initial lamp lumens for each luminaire. From photometric data, determine the number of initial lamp lumens that are emitted at or above 90 degrees from nadir and their percentage of the total. This percentage must be less than or equal to the value in the last column of Table 2 for the site's lighting zone. For uplight, use the most stringent (lowest) zone found either within or directly adjacent to the project.

Luminaires without photometric distribution data are assumed to have 100% of their initial lamp lumens at or above 90 degrees. Luminaires with limited field adjustability are assumed to have maximum tilt applied, and lumens at or above 90 degrees are calculated from the maximum tilted orientation. Luminaires with a full range of field adjustability (those that can be aimed in any vertical direction) are assumed to have lumens at or above 90 degrees and should be calculated at the tilt orientation that has the most lumens in that range.

Lighting Power Density (LPD)

Software packages can automate much of this process; the following steps demonstrate how a manual calculation would be performed.

Step 1. Identify the nonexempt lighting for each shared area (exempted lighting is listed in the note to Table 3).

Step 2. Determine the input power, in watts, for each nonexempt luminaire, and add the watts to determine the total input watts that will be used by the project lighting for each area.

Step 3. Refer Table 3. Identify the area's type (column 1) and lighting zone and find the corresponding allowed watts per square foot or linear foot.

Step 4. For all exterior improved areas and illuminated landscape areas, measure the area, in square feet, and multiply it by the allowed LPD, according to Equation 1.

Equation 1

| Allowed watts | = | Area (sf) | X | Allowed LPD |

Step 5. For walkways and illuminated building façades, measure the length of the walkway or façade, in linear feet, and multiply it by the allowed LPD, according to Equation 2.

Equation 2

| Allowed watts | = | Façade or walkway length (lf) | X | Allowed LPD |

Step 6. For building entrances, measure the width of the doorway, in linear feet. Measure the area of any canopy over the door, in square feet. Multiply each by the allowed LPD and sum the results, according to Equation 3.

Equation 3

| Allowed watts | = | [Door width (lf) X allowed LPD] | + | [Canopy area (sf) X allowed LPD] |

Sum the results of the above equations to determine the total allowed watts for the shared area. The actual watts used by the project lighting must not exceed the allowed watts.

7. Documentation Guidance

As a first step in preparing to complete the LEED-ND documentation requirements, work through the following measures. Refer to GBCI's website for the complete descriptions of all required documentation.

- Map the shared areas of the project, residential areas, and lighting zones.

- Maintain records for lighting fixtures, such as product cutsheets, that document lighting power densities, integrated motion sensors, and automatic daylight shut-off controls.

- Obtain photometric analysis for all lighting fixtures to assist in determining light trespass, backlight, uplight, and glare levels.

- Retain a copy of CC&Rs or other binding documents that require continued adherence to the requirements.

8. Examples

The following examples illustrate a fairly simple project, with three calculation areas within one shared area. The project as a whole has been classified as LZ3. Adjacent properties are also LZ3 except for one LZ2 edge along a low-density residential area. The project parking lot is along this zone.

Luminaire Schedule

The project team lists the luminaires used in this shared area, along with their input watts and quantities (Table 5); none are exempt (Table 3, note).

Table 5. Example luminaire schedule

Label	Catalog number	Description	Lamp	Quantity	Input watts	Total wattage	Uplight (%)	B rating	G rating
A	MRP 70M SR5S DBL	Omero post top	70-watt clear ED17 ceramic metal halide	32	85.5	2,736	0.2%	B2	G2
B	MRBX 32TRT ASY	Omero architectural bollard	32-watt TRT compact fluorescent	6	35	210	1.1%	B0	G1
C	TWA 35S	GP building mounted	35-watt clear ED-17 HPS	5	46	230	3.6%	B0	G1
Total						3,176			

Light Trespass

This table shows the details for a shared area that is adjacent to two different lighting zones. Referring to Table 2, the team records the values for maximum allowable light trespass, shown in columns 3 and 4 of Table 6. Using commercial lighting software, the team calculates the light trespass for the shared area (columns 5 and 6).

Table 6. Example determination for light trespass

Area	Lighting zone	Max allowed E_h/E_v at edge[2]	Max allowed E_h/E_v beyond edge[2]	Max calculated E_h/E_v at edge[3]	Max calculated E_h/E_v beyond edge[3]
Shared area[1]	LZ2	0.10	0.02 at 10 feet	0.08	0.01 at 10 feet
	LZ3	0.20	0.05 at 15 feet	0.18	0.05 at 15 feet

[1] This shared area is adjacent to two different lighting zones.
[2] These values are from table 2.
[3] These values have been calculated using a commercially available lighting program.

The illuminance does not exceed the maximums, so the project is in compliance with the light trespass requirements.

Alternative Determination for Light Trespass

The bollards and the building-mounted luminaires are both rated B0-G1. Since the most stringent lighting zone on this project is LZ2, these would both easily pass, based on the specifications in Table 4. The post-top unit is rated B2-G2 and must be mounted at least one mounting height from the nearest edge of the area and oriented away from that same edge.

Uplight

Table 7 lists the data needed to compute compliance.

Table 7. Example determination for uplight

Label	Catalog number	Quantity	Rated lumens	Uplight (%)	Total uplight lumens
A	MRP 70M SR5S DBL	32	6,000	0.2	384
B	MRBX 32TRT ASY	6	2,400	1.1	158.4
C	TWA 35S	5	2,250	3.6	405
Total			217,650		947.4

The most stringent lighting zone either in or adjacent to the site is LZ2. Referring to Table 2, the project team finds that is it allowed 1% of the total 217,650 uplight lumens, or 2,175. Since the luminaires emit a total of 947.4 uplight lumens, the project is in compliance.

LPD for Individual Areas

Referring to Table 3, the team categorizes each of the three calculation areas and finds the allowable wattage for its lighting zone. Although the parking lot is next to a low-density residential area (LZ2), the greater part of its edge is adjacent to an LZ3 area; the team therefore uses LZ3. Table 8 shows the results.

Table 8. Example site characteristics within shared area

Area	Description	Category (from Table 3)	Lighting zone	LPD (from Table 3)	Area or length	Allowed Watts
1	Parking lot	Exterior improved area	LZ3	0.10 W/sf	30,000 sf	3,000
2	Walkway	Walkways	LZ3	0.8 W/lf	180 lf	144
3	Doorway with canopy	Entrance door	LZ3	30 W/lf	6 lf	180
		Canopy	LZ3	0.40 W/sf	360 sf	144
Total						3,468

Since the total watts used (3,176) is less than the total watts allowed (3,468), the project complies with the lighting power density requirement.

9. Exemplary Performance

This credit is not eligible for exemplary performance under Innovation and Design Process.

10. Regional Variations

There are no regional variations associated with this credit.

11. Resources

Websites

Illuminating Engineering Society of North America

www.iesna.org

The mission of IESNA is to benefit society by promoting knowledge and disseminating information for the improvement of the lighted environment. The society's website lists technical documents on illumination available through the on-line bookstore, plus lighting-related publications that encourage good lighting design.

International Dark-Sky Association

www.darksky.org/

This nonprofit educational agency is dedicated to finding solutions to light pollution.

Rensselaer Polytechnic Institute, Lighting Research Center

www.lrc.rpi.edu

This leading university-based research center provides objective information about lighting technologies, applications, and products.

Sky and Telescope

www.skyandtelescope.com

This site includes facts on light pollution and its effect on astronomy and offers information on fixtures that minimize light pollution.

Print Media

Concepts in Practice Lighting: Lighting Design in Architecture, by Torquil Barker (B.T. Batsford, 1997).

The Design of Lighting, by Peter Tregenza and David Loe (E & FN Spon, 1998).

The IESNA Lighting Handbook, ninth edition, edited by Mark S. Rea (Illuminating Engineering Society of North America, 2000).

Lighting for Exterior Environments RP-33-99, by IESNA Outdoor Environment Lighting Committee (Illuminating Engineering Society of North America, 1999).

12. Definitions

covenants, conditions, and restrictions limitations that may be placed on a property and its use and are made a condition of holding title or lease.

historic building a building or structure listed or determined to be eligible as a historic building or structure or as a contributing building or structure in a designated historic district, due to its historic, architectural, engineering, archeological, or cultural significance. The building or structure must be designated as historic by a local historic preservation review board or similar body, be listed in a state register of historic places, be listed in the National Register of Historic Places, or have been determined eligible for listing in the National Register.

project the land, water, and construction that constitutes the project application. A project applicant does not have to own or control all land or water within a project boundary, but all the area within the project boundary must comply with prerequisites and attempted credits.

project boundary the platted property line of the project defining land and water within it. Projects located on publicly owned campuses that do not have internal property lines must delineate a sphere-of-influence line to be used instead. *Project site* is equivalent to the land and water inside the project boundary. The project must not contain noncontiguous parcels, but parcels can be separated by public rights-of-way. Projects may also have enclaves of nonproject properties that are not subject to the rating system, but such enclaves cannot exceed 2% of the total project area and cannot be described as certified.

INNOVATION AND EXEMPLARY PERFORMANCE

	ND
Credit	IDP Credit 1
Points	1-5 points

Intent

To encourage exemplary performance above the requirements set by the LEED for Neighborhood Development Rating System and/or innovative performance in green building, smart growth, or new urbanist categories not specifically addressed by the LEED for Neighborhood Development Rating System.

Requirements

In writing, identify the intent of the proposed innovation credit, the proposed requirement for compliance, the proposed submittals to demonstrate compliance, and the design approach and strategies that might be used to meet the requirements.

One point is awarded for each IDP Credit 1 earned, up to a total of 5. No more than 3 exemplary performance credits will be awarded in the Innovation and Design Process category.

IDP	
ND	Credit 1

1. Benefits and Issues to Consider

Sustainable neighborhood planning and development come from innovative strategies and thinking. Institutional measures to reward such thinking—like the achievement of this credit—benefit our physical and social environment. Recognition of the exceptional will spur further innovation.

2. Related Credits

Any LEED-ND credit can inspire ideas for innovative proposals and strategies. Refer to the credits' Exemplary Performance sections to determine whether the project may be able to earn additional points under Innovation and Design Process by exceeding the required performance. Consider also proposals and strategies that may be outside the scope of LEED-ND credits.

3. Summary of Referenced Standards

There are no referenced standards for this credit. Please refer to the Summary of Referenced Standards section in each credit for any relevant standards.

4. Implementation

Credits in this section may be earned by documenting environmental and social benefits in one of two ways:

Exemplary Performance Proposals

Exemplary performance strategies deliver performance that greatly exceeds the level or scope required by LEED-ND credits. Typically, IDP credits for exemplary performance are awarded for doubling the credit requirements and/or achieving the next incremental percentage threshold. For instance, to achieve exemplary performance for GIB Credit 13, Infrastructure Energy Efficiency, infrastructure energy savings must meet a threshold of 30% (as opposed to the required 15%).

Exemplary performance is not available for all credits in LEED-ND. Credits that allow exemplary performance through a predetermined approach are noted throughout this reference guide and the LEED-ND documentation forms. A maximum of 3 IDP points can be earned for exemplary performance.

Innovation Proposals

Innovation proposals are substantive innovations related to a credit or measures and strategies not addressed by existing credits. There are three basic criteria for achieving an innovation credit:

1. The project must demonstrate quantitative performance improvements for environmental or social benefit (establishing a baseline of standard performance for comparison with the final plan and design).

2. The process or specification must be comprehensive. Measures that address a limited portion of a project or are otherwise not comprehensive are not eligible.

3. The concept the project team develops for the innovation credit must be applicable to other projects and be significantly better than standard sustainable design practices.

IDP credits are not awarded for the use of a particular product or design strategy if the technology aids in the achievement of an existing LEED credit.

IDP credits awarded for one project do not constitute automatic approval for similar strategies in a future project. Previously approved IDP credits may be pursued by any LEED-ND project, but the project team must sufficiently document the achievement.

5. Timeline and Team

Innovation ideally begins at a project's conception, but it can enter at any step of the process and come from any member of the project team. Open-mindedness, creativity, and follow-through are critical ingredients. Options for innovation may come from technology—for example, infrastructure for electric vehicles—or be more general, such as educational outreach measures. Thus, team members with a variety of skills and interests can contribute to the achievement of this credit.

6. Calculations

For exemplary performance, please refer to the Calculations section within each applicable credit.

7. Documentation Guidance

As a first step in preparing to complete the LEED-ND documentation requirements, work through the following measures. Refer to GBCI's website for the complete descriptions of all required documentation.

- Document the process by which the project team has worked to develop and/or implement environmental or social benefits beyond the requirements set by the LEED-ND Rating System or innovative performance in other areas.

- Track development and implementation of the specific exceptional and innovative strategies used.

8. Examples

The level of effort involved in achieving an IDP credit should be extraordinary. For example, installing a single green product is not a sufficient level of effort, nor is an environmental educational program consisting of only neighborhood signage. Conversely, a neighborhood visitors' center with interactive displays, if coupled with an educational website and video highlighting the project's environmental strategies, could be eligible for an IDP credit.

It is the responsibility of the project team to determine the feasibility of possible IDP-related initiatives, develop and execute the program so that it yields a meaningful environmental or social benefit, and provide documentation and calculations that substantiate the validity of the project team's approach and implementation. Teams are encouraged to explore the full range of innovative opportunities within their projects. The following list provides examples only and does not constitute formal approval of any similar proposals.

Educational program. Provide an educational program on the environmental and human health benefits of sustainable neighborhoods and how residents and workers can help improve green performance. Evaluate results and refine the program to increase its impact and audience as appropriate. The program must be actively instructional and comprise at least two instructional initiatives that have ongoing components, such as the following:

- A comprehensive signage program or displays throughout the project to educate occupants and the public on the benefits of sustainable neighborhoods. Examples include windows to view energy-saving mechanical equipment in the buildings, signs that call attention to water-conserving landscape features, and digital screens showing real-time energy consumption or building performance data.

- A case study highlighting the successes of the LEED-ND project that could be used to inform the operations of other neighborhoods.

- Guided tours focusing on sustainability, using the project as an example.

- An educational outreach program that engages occupants or the public through periodic events covering sustainable neighborhood topics.

- A website or electronic newsletter that informs project occupants and the public about the project's features and green strategies they can practice at home.

Life-cycle assessment. Evaluate a substantial quantity of products or materials being used (or being considered for use in the project) on the basis of an ISO 14040 life-cycle assessment.

Electronics recycling. Provide a collection and recycling program that allows all project occupants (both commercial and residential) to recycle end-of-life electronic equipment.

Jobs and housing. Conduct a joint demonstration of affordable housing design and construction with low-income job training using local university architectural and engineering students in collaboration with a community-based job training service and the project developer.

9. Regional Variations

IDP credits may have regional content. For example, measures to reduce the heat island effect would be appropriate for cooling-dominant climatic zones. Neighborhood and streetscape designs that use the regional vernacular in building types and architecture are other examples.

LEED ACCREDITED PROFESSIONAL

	ND
Credit	IDP Credit 2
Points	1 point

Intent

To support the integrated planning and design required for a LEED for Neighborhood Development *project* and to streamline the application and certification process.

Requirements

At least one principal member of the project team must be a LEED Accredited Professional.

OR

At least one principal member of the project design team must be a professional who is credentialed in smart growth as determined by the Natural Resources Defense Council in consultation with Smart Growth America.

OR

At least one principal member of the project design team must be a professional who is credentialed in new urbanism as determined by the Congress for the New Urbanism.

Note: A separate LEED Accredited Professional exam track for professionals wanting to specialize in the LEED for Neighborhood Development Rating System will be available in early 2010; this IDP credit can be achieved if a principal member of the project design team is accredited as a result of passing the exam.

IDP	
ND	Credit 2

1. Benefits and Issues to Consider

This credit is available for professionals who are accredited by GBCI for LEED, have the smart growth qualifications defined by the Natural Resources Defense Council, or have the New Urbanism qualifications defined by the Congress for the New Urbanism.

Professionals meeting those requirements have the expertise required to plan and design neighborhood projects to LEED-ND standards and coordinate the documentation process necessary for LEED certification. The accredited professional understands the importance of integrated design and the interactions between prerequisites and credits and their respective criteria. Planners, architects, engineers, owners, and others who have a strong interest in sustainable neighborhoods are all appropriate candidates for accreditation or qualification. Such professionals should manage the project's LEED application and can also educate other team members about LEED and green neighborhood design.

2. Related Credits

There are no related credits.

3. Summary of Referenced Standards

LEED Accredited Professional (AP) Green Building Certification Institute
www.gbci.org
Individuals who successfully complete the LEED professional accreditation exam are Accredited Professionals. Accreditation certifies that the individual has the knowledge and skills necessary to participate in the LEED application and certification process, holds a firm understanding of green building practices and principles, and is familiar with LEED requirements, resources, and processes. The Green Building Certification Institute (GBCI), established with the support of the U.S. Green Building Council (USGBC), handles exam development and delivery to ensure objective and balanced management of the credentialing program.

4. Implementation

There are three compliance paths for the credit: LEED AP credentialing from GBCI, smart growth qualifications as defined by the Natural Resources Defense Council (NRDC), and New Urbanism qualifications as defined by the Congress for the New Urbanism (CNU).

Obtaining LEED AP credentialing is accomplished by successfully completing the AP test administered by GBCI. At present, any AP may earn the credit. In 2010 GBCI will offer a LEED for Neighborhood Development exam and credential; a project team member who is credentialed in LEED-ND will also earn the credit.

For the smart growth compliance path, individuals must possess at least three of the following qualifications:

- Significant experience (minimum 200 hours) on a project that has received a Smart Growth award.

- Successful completion of professional development trainings in smart growth or elements of smart growth. Trainings must be at least one business day in length.

- Successful completion of a university course or curriculum in smart growth.

- Accreditation as AICP, AIA, PE, or ASLA.

- Authorship and publication of a peer-reviewed article or book on smart growth.

- Attendance at three New Partners for Smart Growth conferences in the past five years.

Alternatively, individuals will be considered eligible to meet the requirement if they have the following qualification:

- Cumulative experience of at least 2,000 hours within the past five years as a principal planner or designer of plans for projects built and/or plans officially adopted by local agencies that are demonstrably smart growth in character. Such character must be documented in a technical report and include, at a minimum, descriptions of regional location, use mix, density, and multimodal transportation facilities.

For the New Urbanism compliance path, individuals must possess at least three of the following qualifications:

- Significant experience (minimum 200 hours) on a project that has received a Congress for the New Urbanism Charter award.

- Successful completion of trainings in New Urbanism or elements of New Urbanism. Trainings must be at least one business day in length.

- Successful completion of a university course or curriculum in New Urbanism.

- Passing grade on an exam on New Urbanism.

- Accreditation as AICP, AIA, PE, or ASLA.

- Authorship and publication of a peer-reviewed article or book on New Urbanism.

- Attendance at three Congresses for the New Urbanism in the past five years.

Alternatively, individuals will be considered eligible to meet the requirement if they have the following qualification:

- Cumulative experience of at least 2,000 hours within the past five years as a principal planner or designer of plans for projects built and/or plans officially adopted by local agencies that are demonstrably New Urbanist in character. Such character must be documented in a technical report and include, at a minimum, descriptions of community- and pedestrian-oriented design, use mix, density, and multimodal transportation facilities.

5. Timeline and Team

This credit should be prioritized at the earliest stage of project startup. A LEED Accredited Professional should be a principal member of the project team, or a professional credentialed in smart growth or New Urbanism should be a principal member of the design team.

6. Calculations

There are no calculations for this credit.

7. Documentation Guidance

As a first step in preparing to complete the LEED-ND documentation requirements, work through the following measure. Refer to GBCI's website for the complete descriptions of all required documentation.

- Obtain confirmation from team members who are LEED APs or professionals credentialed in smart growth or New Urbanism.

	IDP
ND	Credit 2

8. Resources

Websites

Green Building Certification Institute

www.gbci.org

GBCI administers the LEED Professional Accreditation program to ensure objective management of the credential and manages exam development, registration, and delivery. GBCI was established as a separately incorporated entity with the support of USGBC. See the GBCI website for more information on workshops, testing locations, fees, and topics covered on the accreditation exam.

REGIONAL PRIORITY CREDIT

	ND
Credit	RP Credit 1
Points	1-4 point

Intent

To encourage strategies that address geographically specific environmental, social equity, and public health priorities.

Requirements

Earn up to four of the six Regional Priority credits. These credits have been identified by subject matter experts representing the U.S. Green Building Council (regional councils and chapters), the Congress for the New Urbanism (chapters and membership in regions without chapters), and Smart Growth America (members of Smart Growth America's State and Local Caucus or their designees) as having additional regional importance for the project's location. A database of Regional Priority credits and their geographic applicability will be available on the USGBC website, www.usgbc.org.

One point is awarded for each Regional Priority credit earned, up to a maximum of 4. Non-U.S. projects are not eligible for Regional Priority credits.

	RP
ND	Credit 1

Because some environmental and social issues are unique to a region, USGBC regional councils and chapters, working with CNU chapter members and Smart Growth America's State and Local Caucus representatives, have identified six priority credits for each geographic zone within their regions. To encourage focus on these regional priorities, a project that earns one of these credits (at the specified threshold level, if listed) automatically earns 1 RP point in addition to any points awarded for that credit. Up to 4 extra points can be earned in this way.

1. Benefits and Issues to Consider

Refer to the Benefits and Issues section under each Regional Priority credit.

2. Related Credits

For a list of credits identified as regional priorities for the project's geographic zone, visit the Regional Priority database, at www.usgbc.org.

3. Summary of Referenced Standards

Refer to the standards for a particular credit eligible for Regional Priority.

4. Implementation

Refer to the Implementation section under a particular credit eligible for Regional Priority.

5. Timeline and Team

Identify Regional Priority credits early in the project timeline.

6. Calculations

Refer to the Calculations section under a particular credit eligible for Regional Priority.

7. Documentation Guidance

See the Documentation Guidance section under a particular credit eligible for Regional Priority and refer to www.gbci.org for complete descriptions of all required documentation.

8. Examples

Refer to the Examples section under a particular credit eligible for Regional Priority.

9. Regional Variations

Refer to the Regional Variations section under a particular credit eligible for Regional Priority.

10. Resources

Refer to the Resources section under a particular credit eligible for Regional Priority.

11. Definitions

Refer to the Definitions sections under a particular credit eligible for Regional Priority.

APPENDIX. DIVERSE USES

Food Retail

Supermarket
Other food store with produce

Community-Serving Retail

Clothing store or department store selling clothes
Convenience store
Farmer's market
Hardware store
Pharmacy
Other retail

Services

Bank
Gym, health club, exercise studio
Hair care
Laundry, dry cleaner
Restaurant, café, diner (excluding establishments with only drive-throughs)

Civic and Community Facilities

Adult or senior care (licensed)
Child care (licensed)
Community or recreation center
Cultural arts facility (museum, performing arts)
Educational facility (including K–12 school, university, adult education center, vocational school, community college)
Family entertainment venue (theater, sports)
Government office that serves public on-site
Place of worship
Medical clinic or office that treats patients
Police or fire station
Post office
Public library
Public park
Social services center

Adapted from Criterion Planners, INDEX neighborhood completeness indicator, 2005.

Key Definitions

adjacent site a site having at least 25% of its boundary bordering parcels that are each at least 75% *previously developed*. A *street* or other right-of-way does not constitute previously developed land; instead, it is the status of the property on the other side of the street or right-of-way that matters. Any fraction of the boundary that borders waterfront other than a stream is excluded from the calculation. A site is still considered adjacent if the 25% adjacent portion of its boundary is separated from previously developed parcels by undeveloped, permanently protected land averaging no more than 400 feet in width and no more than 500 feet in any one place. The undeveloped land must be permanently preserved as natural area, riparian corridor, *park*, greenway, agricultural land, or designated *cultural landscape*. Permanent pedestrian paths connecting the project through the protected parcels to the bordering site may be counted to meet the requirement of SLL Prerequisite 1, Option 2 (that the *project* be connected to the adjacent parcel by a through-street or nonmotorized right-of-way every 600 feet on average, provided the path or paths traverse the undeveloped land at no more than a 10% grade for walking by persons of all ages and physical abilities).

Adjacent project site based on minimum 25% of perimeter adjacent to previously developed parcels, including allowance for permanently protected land between project boundary and previously developed parcels

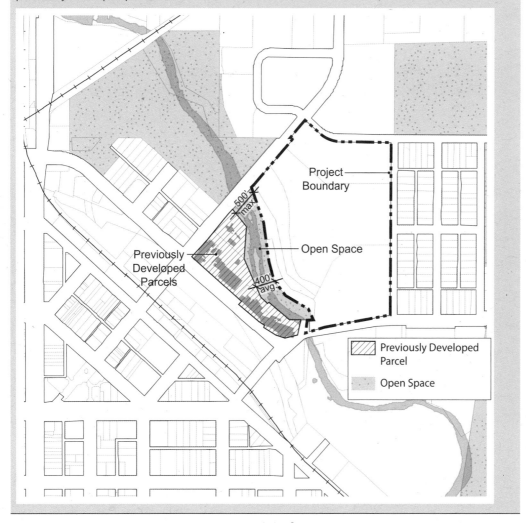

buildable land the portion of the site where construction can occur, including land voluntarily set aside and not constructed upon. When used in *density* calculations, buildable land excludes public rights-of-way and land excluded from development by codified law or LEED for Neighborhood Development prerequisites. An *applicant* may exclude additional land not exceeding 15% of the buildable land base defined above, provided the following conditions are present:

a. The land is protected from residential and nonresidential construction by easement, deed restriction, or other enforceable legal instrument.

AND

b. Either 25% or more of the boundary of each contiguous parcel proposed for exclusion borders a *water body* or areas outside the *project boundary* that are protected by codified law; or ownership of, or management authority over, the exclusion area is transferred to a public entity.

connectivity the number of publicly accessible *street* intersections per square mile, including intersections of streets with dedicated *alleys* and transit rights-of-way, and intersections of streets with nonmotorized rights-of-way (up to 20% of total intersections). If one must both enter and exit an area through the same intersection, such an intersection and any intersections beyond that point are not counted; intersections leading only to *culs-de-sac* are also not counted. The calculation of square mileage excludes *water bodies, parks* larger than 1/2-acre, public facility campuses, airports, rail yards, slopes over 15%, and areas nonbuildable under codified law or the rating system. Street rights-of-way may not be excluded.

infill site a site that meets any of the following four conditions:

a. At least 75% of its boundary borders parcels that individually are at least 50% *previously developed*, and that in aggregate are at least 75% previously developed.

b. The site, in combination with bordering parcels, forms an aggregate parcel whose boundary is 75% bounded by parcels that individually are at least 50% previously developed, and that in aggregate are at least 75% previously developed.

c. At least 75% of the land area, exclusive of rights-of-way, within a 1/2-mile distance from the *project boundary* is previously developed.

d. The lands within a 1/2-mile distance from the project boundary have a *preproject connectivity* of at least 140 intersections per square mile.

A *street* or other right-of-way does not constitute previously developed land; it is the status of property on the other side or right-of-way of the street that matters. For conditions (a) and (b) above, any fraction of the perimeter that borders waterfront other than a stream is excluded from the calculation.

(a). Infill project site based on minimum 75% of perimeter adjacent to previously developed parcels

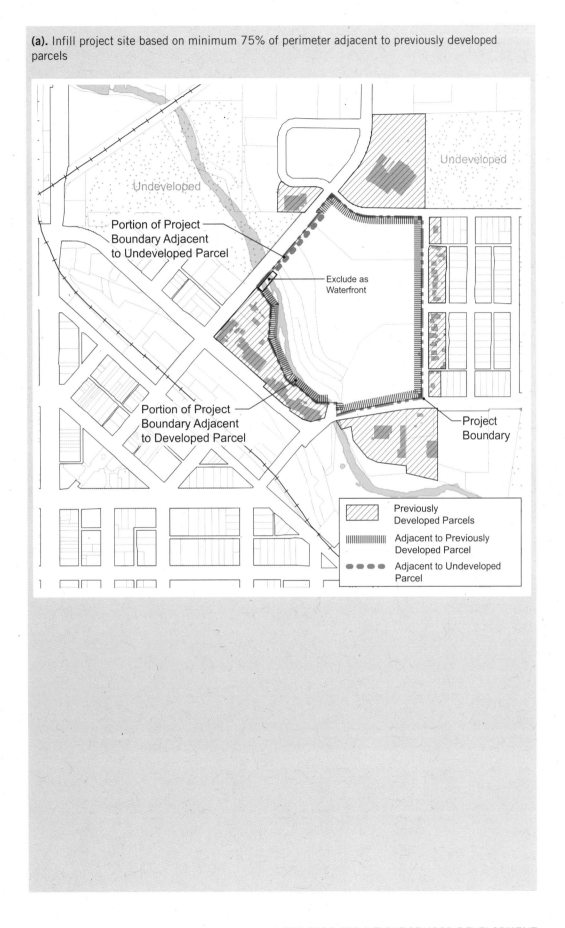

(b). Infill project site based on minimum 75% adjacent to previously developed parcels using project boundary and selected bordering parcels

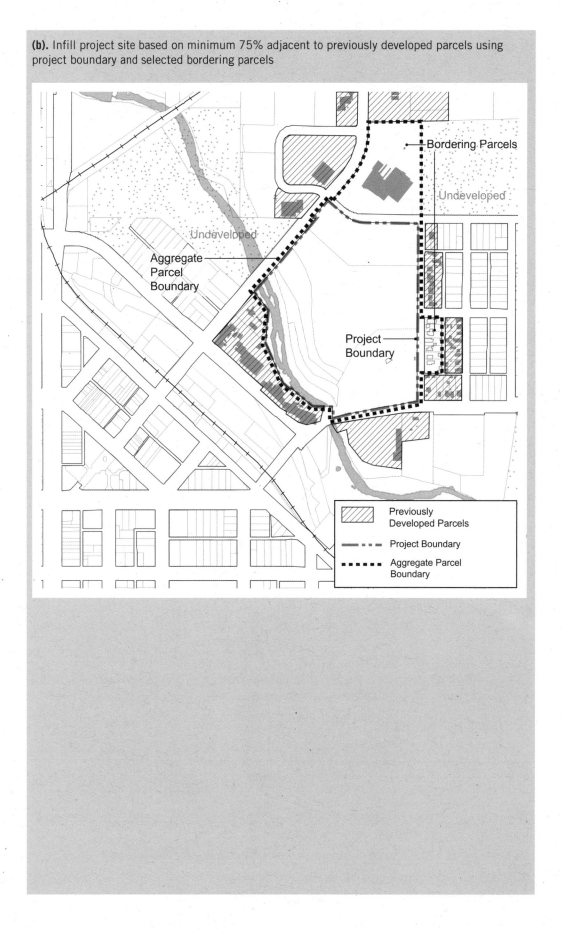

(c). Infill project site based on minimum 75% of land area within 1/2-mile of project boundary being previously developed

1/2 Mile Radius

Project Boundary

Previously Developed Parcels

(Min. 75% of land area within 1/2 mile of project site)

(d). Infill project site based on minimum 140 intersections/sq.mi. within 1/2-mile of project boundary

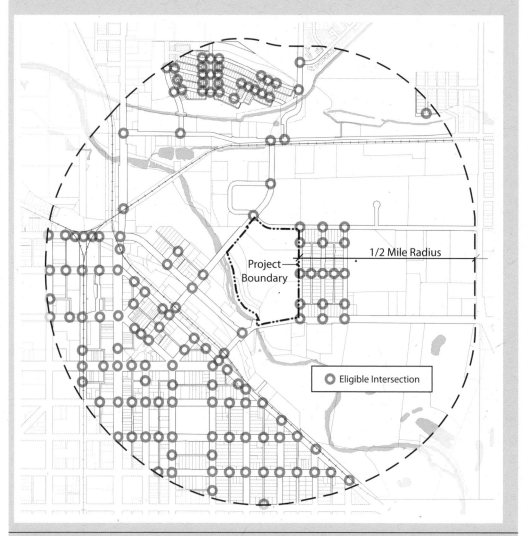

previously developed altered by paving, construction, and/or land use that would typically have required regulatory permitting to have been initiated (alterations may exist now or in the past). Previously developed land includes a platted lot on which a building was constructed if the lot is no more than 1 acre; previous development on lots larger than 1 acre is defined as the *development footprint* and land alterations associated with the footprint. Land that is not previously developed and altered landscapes resulting from current or historical clearing or filling, agricultural or forestry use, or preserved natural area use are considered undeveloped land. The date of previous development permit issuance constitutes the date of previous development, but permit issuance in itself does not constitute previous development.

accessory dwelling unit a subordinate *dwelling unit* that is attached to a principal building or contained in a separate structure on the same property as the principal unit.

adapted (or introduced) plant a species that reliably grows well in a given habitat with minimal attention from humans in the form of winter protection, pest protection, water irrigation, or fertilization once its root systems are established in the soil. Adapted plants are low maintenance but not invasive.

alley a publicly accessible right-of-way, generally located midblock, that can accommodate slow-speed motor vehicles, as well as bicycles and pedestrians. An alley provides access to the side or rear of abutting properties for loading, parking, and other service functions, minimizing the need for these functions to be located along streets. It may be publicly dedicated or privately owned and deeded in perpetuity for general public use.

applicant the entity that prepares the LEED-ND *project* submission and is responsible for project implementation. An applicant may be the *developer* or another cooperating entity.

area median income the median income of a county as determined by the U.S. Department of Housing and Urban Development.

bicycle network a continuous network consisting of any combination of physically designated in-*street* bicycle lanes at least 5 feet wide, off-street bicycle paths or trails at least 8 feet wide for a two-way path and at least 5 feet wide for a one-way path, and/or streets designed for a target speed of 25 miles per hour or slower.

block land bounded by the *project boundary*, transportation or utility rights-of-way that may be publicly dedicated or privately owned and deeded in perpetuity for general public use, waterfront, and/or comparable land division features.

brownfield real property, the expansion, redevelopment, or reuse of which may be complicated by the presence or possible presence of a hazardous substance, pollutant, or contaminate.

build-out the time at which all *habitable buildings* on the *project* are complete and ready for occupancy.

bus rapid transit an enhanced bus system that operates on exclusive bus lanes or other transit rights-of-way; it is designed to combine the flexibility of buses with the efficiency of rail.

community-supported agriculture (CSA) a farm operation for which a community of individuals pledges support so that the farmland becomes, either legally or informally, the community's farm. The growers and consumers provide mutual support, sharing the risks and benefits of food production. Consumers receive portions of the farm's harvest throughout the growing season.

construction impact zone the *project's development footprint* plus the areas around the improvement where construction crews, equipment, and/or materials are staged and moved during construction.

covenants, conditions, and restrictions limitations that may be placed on a property and its use and are made a condition of holding title or lease.

cul-de-sac a *street* segment that terminates without intersecting another street segment.

cultural landscape an officially designated geographic area that includes both cultural and natural resources associated with a historic event, activity, or person or that exhibits other significant cultural or aesthetic values.

GLOSSARY

density the amount of building structures constructed on the *project site*, measured for residential buildings as *dwelling units* per acre of *buildable land* available for residential uses, and for non-residential buildings as the *floor-area ratio* of buildable land area available for nonresidential uses. In both cases, structured parking is excluded.

developer a public and/or private entity that controls a majority of the *project's buildable land* and is committed to making a majority of the investments required for the project implementation described in the LEED-ND submission.

development footprint the total land area of a *project* site covered by buildings, *streets*, parking areas, and other typically impermeable surfaces constructed as part of the project.

dwelling unit living quarters intended for long-term occupancy that provide facilities for cooking, sleeping, and sanitation. This does not include hotel rooms.

employment center a nonresidential area of at least 5 acres with a job density of at least 50 employees per net acre.

existing present on the date of submission of LEED-ND certification documents; similarly, an element or condition that **exists** is present on the date that LEED-ND certification documents are submitted.

floor-area ratio (FAR) the *density* of nonresidential land use, exclusive of parking, measured as the total nonresidential building floor area divided by the total *buildable land* area available for nonresidential structures. For example, on a site with 10,000 square feet of buildable land area, an FAR of 1.0 would be 10,000 square feet of building floor area. On the same site, an FAR of 1.5 would be 15,000 square feet of built floor area; an FAR of 2.0 would be 20,000 built square feet and an FAR of 0.5 would be 5,000 built square feet.

functional entry a building opening designed to be used by pedestrians and open during regular business hours. This does not include any door exclusively designated as an emergency exit, or a garage door not designed as a pedestrian entrance.

graywater untreated wastewater that has not come into contact with toilet waste. Graywater includes used water from bathtubs, showers, bathroom washbasins, and water from clothes washers and laundry tubs. It does not include wastewater from kitchen sinks or dishwashers, unless a graywater definition established by the authority having jurisdiction in the area has precedence.

habitable building a structure intended for living, working, or other types of occupancy. Habitable structures do not include stand-alone garages and utility structures such as pump stations.

heat island thermal gradient differences between developed and undeveloped areas.

historic building a building or structure listed or determined to be eligible as a historic building or structure or as a contributing building or structure in a designated historic district, due to its historic, architectural, engineering, archeological, or cultural significance. The building or structure must be designated as historic by a local historic preservation review board or similar body, be listed in a state register of historic places, be listed in the National Register of Historic Places, or have been determined eligible for listing in the National Register.

historic district a group of buildings, structures, objects, and sites, of varying sizes, that have been designated as historically and architecturally significant and categorized as either contributing or noncontributing.

Home Energy Rating System (HERS) index a scoring system established by the Residential Energy Services Network (RESNET) in which a home built to the specifications of the HERS Reference Home (based on the 2006 International Energy Conservation Code) scores 100, and a net zero energy home scores 0. The lower a home's HERS Index, the more energy efficient it is.

invasive plant either an indigenous or nonindigenous species or strain that is characteristically adaptable, aggressive, has a high reproductive capacity, and tends to overrun the ecosystems it inhabits.

metropolitan (metro) and **micropolitan (micro) statistical area** a geographic entity defined by the U.S. Office of Management and Budget for use by federal statistical agencies in collecting, tabulating, and publishing federal statistics. A metro area contains a core urban area with a population of 50,000 or more, and a micro area contains an urban core with a population between 10,000 and 50,000. Each metro or micro area consists of one or more counties and includes the counties containing the core urban area, as well as any adjacent counties that have a high degree of social and economic integration (as measured by commuting to work) with the urban core. "Core-based statistical area" (CBSA) encompasses both metro and micro areas.

multiunit residential consisting of four or more residential units sharing a common entry.

native (or indigenous) plant a plant species that did or would have occurred on the site or within the subject county prior to the widespread land alterations that accompanied European settlement. Cultivars of native plants may be considered native plants.

park a publicly accessible area that is permanently maintained in a seminatural condition for human recreation and relaxation; it has soil, grass, water, flora, and/or recreation improvements.

paseo a publicly accessible pedestrian path, at least 4 feet wide and no more than 12 feet wide, that provides shortcuts between buildings and through the block, connecting *street* frontages to rear parking areas, midblock courtyards, *alleys*, or other streets. A paseo may be roofed for up to 50% of its length and may be privately owned or publicly dedicated.

planned diverse use a shop, service, or facility outside the *project boundary* that has received a building permit and is under construction at the time of the first certificate of occupancy is issued for any building in the LEED-ND *project*.

planned occupancy the highest estimate of building occupants based on planned use(s) and industry standards for square foot requirements per employee. The minimum planned occupancy for *multiunit residential* buildings is 1 person for a studio unit, 1.5 persons for a one-bedroom unit, and 1.25 persons per bedroom for a two- bedroom or larger unit.

plaza a publicly accessible gathering space that is integrated into the street network and allows vehicular, bicycle, and/or pedestrian travel. A plaza is generally paved, is spatially defined by building fronts paralleling at least two-thirds of its perimeter, and may be privately owned or publicly dedicated.

postconsumer generated by households or commercial, industrial, or institutional facilities in their role as end-users of a product, which can no longer be used for its intended purpose.

potable water water that meets or exceeds EPA's drinking water quality standards and is approved for human consumption by the state or local authorities having jurisdiction; it may be supplied from wells or municipal water systems.

preconsumer diverted from the waste stream during the manufacturing process. It does not include the reutilization of materials such as rework, regrind or scrap generated in a process and capable of being reclaimed within the same process that generated it.

GLOSSARY

predevelopment before any development occurred on the site. Predevelopment conditions describe the natural conditions of the site prior to any human alteration, such as development of roads or buildings.

previously developed site a site that, *preproject*, consisted of at least 75% *previously developed* land.

preproject before the LEED-ND *project* was initiated, but not necessarily before any development or disturbance took place. Preproject conditions describe the state of the project site on the date the *developer* acquired rights to a majority of its *buildable land* through purchase or option to purchase.

prime soil earth with chemical, hydrographic, and topological properties that make it especially suited to the production of crops, as defined by the U.S. Natural Resources Conservation Service.

project the land, water, and construction that constitutes the project application. A project *applicant* does not have to own or control all land or water within a *project boundary*, but all the area within the project boundary must comply with prerequisites and attempted credits.

project boundary the platted property line of the *project* defining land and water within it. Projects located on publicly owned campuses that do not have internal property lines must delineate a sphere-of-influence line to be used instead. *Project site* is equivalent to the land and water inside the project boundary. The project must not contain noncontiguous parcels, but parcels can be separated by public rights-of-way. Projects may also have enclaves of nonproject properties that are not subject to the rating system, but such enclaves cannot exceed 2% of the total project area and cannot be described as certified.

school a kindergarten, elementary, or secondary institution for the academic instruction of children.

single-family residential any residential unit other than *multiunit residential*, including single, duplex, triplex, row house, townhouse and semiattached residential building types.

street a dedicated right-of-way that can accommodate one or more modes of travel, excluding *alleys* and *paseos*. A street is suitable for primary entrances and provides access to the front and/or sides of buildings and lots. A street may be privately owned as long as it is deeded in perpetuity for general public use. A street must be an addressable thoroughfare (for mail purposes) under the standards of the applicable regulating authority.

square (also **green**) a publicly accessible open area for gatherings that is wholly or partially bounded by segments of the *street* network. A square can be landscaped or landscaped and paved, is spatially defined by building fronts paralleling at least 45% of its perimeter, and may be privately owned or publicly dedicated.

unique soil earth with chemical, hydrographic, and topological properties that make it especially suited to specific crops, as defined by the U.S. Natural Resources Conservation Service.

walk distance the distance that a pedestrian must travel between origins and destinations without obstruction, in a safe and comfortable environment on a continuous network of sidewalks, all-weather-surface footpaths, crosswalks, *woonerfs*, or equivalent pedestrian facilities.

water body the surface water of a stream (first-order and higher, including intermittent streams), arroyo, river, canal, lake, estuary, bay, or ocean, excluding irrigation ditches

water and wastewater infrastructure publicly owned water and wastewater infrastructure; this excludes septic and mound wastewater treatment systems.

wetland an area that is inundated or saturated by surface or ground water at a frequency and duration sufficient to support, and that under normal circumstances do support, a prevalence of vegetation typically adapted for life in saturated soil conditions. Wetlands generally include swamps, marshes, bogs, and similar areas, but exclude irrigation ditches unless delineated as part of an adjacent wetland.

woonerf a *street*, also known as a home zone, shared zone, or living street, where pedestrians have priority over vehicles and the posted speed limit is no greater than 10 miles per hour. Physical elements within the roadway, such as shared surfaces, plantings, street furniture, parking, and play areas, slow traffic and invite pedestrians to use the entire right-of-way.

vehicle miles traveled (VMT) the number of miles driven by motorists in a specified time period, such as a day or a year, in absolute or per capita terms.